FLOORS: SELECTION AND MAINTENANCE

BERNARD BERKELEY

LTP Publications • No. 13

FLOORS: SELECTION AND MAINTENANCE

BERNARD BERKELEY

Library Technology Program
American Library Association
Chicago

Library of Congress Catalog Card Number 68-23014
Copyright © 1968 by the American Library Association
Manufactured in the United States of America

PREFACE

Librarians have shown unusually keen interest in all aspects of building design and construction, not the least of which is flooring. Because they are often called upon to make decisions regarding the choice and subsequent care of flooring materials, many librarians believe that they should be well informed on the subject.

The need for a book on floors, organized and written especially with librarians in mind, prompted the Library Technology Program to arrange with Foster D. Snell, Inc., a subsidiary of Booz, Allen & Hamilton Inc., for the preparation of a manual on the selection and maintenance of floors. Bernard Berkeley, in his capacity as a Research Director at Foster D. Snell, was commissioned to write the manual.

The result of this undertaking is the present volume. It is intended to be useful not only to librarians, for whom it was originally conceived, but to anyone interested in floors for institutional, commercial, and even industrial use.

The Library Technology Program and the author are grateful to the many organizations—public and private—that cooperated in the preparation of this book. Without their help, the treatment of this subject could not have been as inclusive, thorough, and up to date as it is.

Some of the material included in this book is based on two publications of the American Hotel & Motel Association, *Care, Cleaning and Selection of Floors and Resilient Floor Coverings,* by Bernard Berkeley and Cyril S. Kimball and *The Selection and Maintenance of Commercial Carpet,* by Bernard Berkeley.

The present book was edited and prepared for publication by Edward Johnson and Richard Luce, members of the staff of the Library Technology Program.

The preparation and publication of this manual were made possible by a grant from the Council on Library Resources, Inc.

FORREST F. CARHART, JR., *Director*
Library Technology Program

CONTENTS

TABLES

ix

1 SELECTION CRITERIA

INTRODUCTION

Selection of floors in the construction of new buildings or in the renovation of existing buildings can be made from a great variety of materials. This book presents descriptions and discussions of almost every type of floor that reasonably could be installed. They may be divided into five general categories: resilient floor coverings, carpet, masonry, wood, and a group called "formed-in-place floors," which are poured in a liquid state to create a seamless monolithic topping.

The resilient floor covering group includes linoleum, rubber, asphalt, cork, homogeneous and laminated vinyl, and vinyl asbestos. Most of these are produced in both sheet and tile form.

Carpet can be categorized according to the fiber used, i.e., wool, nylon, acrylic, antron nylon, and a number of other new synthetic fibers such as those based on polypropylene.

Among the masonry floors are ceramic tile, marble, terrazzo, slate tile, concrete, magnesite, and brick.

Wood floors, for institutional and commercial installations, are now limited almost entirely to hardwoods—usually oak or maple. They can be subcategorized into strip and block varieties.

The fifth group, formed-in-place floors, includes one long-term member —mastic, a seamless flooring surface based on an asphalt binder—and a group of more recently developed resinous toppings based on combinations of certain chemicals such as the epoxies, polyesters, polyurethanes, and silicones.

This section is a discussion of the factors to be considered in the selection of floors. Additional information regarding these factors in relation to a basic floor category is given in subsequent chapters.

There are various points of view on the subject of choosing a floor material for a particular situation. Individual approaches emphasize those factors most important to their proponents. Included among the special interest groups that have an influential voice in floor selections are: architects, builders, designers, contractors, flooring experts, administrators, regulatory agencies, management, trade associations, flooring manufacturers, chemical producers, business managers, and maintenance supervisors.

The most active organizations are those with proprietary interests in flooring materials—the flooring manufacturers, the trade associations, and

1

the chemical specialty suppliers. Through their efforts, a great deal of detailed information on specific materials has been made available to the public. However, there are two rather serious shortcomings associated with much of this material. First, it is likely to reflect self-interest and bias. Second, even if the information is objective, it is likely to be too narrow in scope to be of value to anyone seeking comparative data on a wide variety of floors. However, in spite of its shortcomings, much of this data has been brought together in the preparation of this book, and some of it is presented or cited in the text.

Before moving into the discussion of specific selection criteria, an important point must be made regarding libraries and floor coverings. Libraries are not unique as public buildings; the criteria to be used in selecting floors for libraries are essentially those that must be considered in selecting floors for any public building. Emphasis on particular criteria may vary from one library to another, but all factors discussed in this chapter should be taken into account along with the advice and assistance of flooring experts. Whatever criteria are settled upon as being primary for a particular library building, it should be remembered that more than one type of floor may satisfy the principal requirements, and that the final choice may depend heavily on secondary criteria and personal preferences. It is also important to remember that no single type of floor can possibly meet all conditions of service and that making a selection requires that some compromises be made.

This point was well expressed several years ago when Jack E. Gaston of the Armstrong Cork Company addressed a Building Research Institute conference:

"Ideally . . . the perfect flooring material would be very inexpensive, almost impossible to indent permanently, soft and resilient underfoot, completely resistant to moisture, alkalies, acids, stains, oils, or any other chemical. It would possess a surface so microscopically free of pores that it would be difficult for dirt to be retained, yet open enough so that vapor from a cheaper water-type adhesive could readily pass through the flooring; thick enough to hide irregularities in the sub-strata, yet thin enough to cover many, many square feet per carton or roll; glossy enough for the housewife, yet flat enough to hide traffic marks.

"The ideal floor would never soil or have to be cleaned or waxed. It would be installed in all instances with a single, low cost, water-base adhesive that would be fluid enough to maneuver the flooring in place; then the bond would immediately revert to a completely permanent, insoluble, vaporproof layer that would never loosen until the precise moment when it was desired to change to another style or pattern. Whereupon, presto, the entire floor would strip easily and cleanly down to the bare

Bangkok Industries, Inc.

Teak parquet floor in a basketweave pattern.

underlayment. One final requirement—it would be available in every size, every color, and every pattern that could be conceived by the most imaginative architect that ever lived.

"Lacking this perfect flooring system, the manufacturers, architects, building contractors, and building owners have had to compromise . . . . Where cost is a primary consideration, low-cost materials are available. Where resistance to indentation is the paramount issue, another product is offered. Where moisture problems exist, there are special systems to help solve them. Color, style, patterns, size, gloss—to the extent possible within the boundaries of current technology and raw material availability —can be supplied by the . . . flooring industry in any combination of properties at a cost established by the complexity of the combination desired. It simply isn't possible at the present, however, to provide all the virtues we indicated would be desirable in the perfect flooring nor, for that matter, to combine practically all the best features into one product and keep the price down among the lowest.

"If nothing else is derived from this conference, I hope all of you will leave here with the understanding that the very complexity brought about by the multiplicity of flooring materials and installation systems available to you is an attempt on the part of the manufacturers to provide you with products designed to meet a variety of requirements in the most economical way. If you list your flooring requirements on the basis of what you would *like* to have, you will find your specifications probably call for the theoretical 'ideal' material, but if you will keep your requirements down to the level of what you *must* have, you will probably find an available system that will serve your every purpose in a truly satisfactory manner at the minimum cost."

SUBFLOORS

A subfloor is an unfinished floor laid as a base for a finished floor. A subfloor may be further defined as a supporting floor which has been architecturally designed to carry a load. Wood and concrete are the two principal materials used for the construction of subfloors. All subfloors should be structurally solid, level, smooth, clean, and resistant to the transmission of moisture. Structural firmness is important to prevent movement which could cause cracking or buckling of the finished floor. Smoothness is essential because it is necessary to guard against reflections of surface irregularities of the subfloor or underlayment occurring in the finished floor.

U. S. Forest Products Laboratory

Dampproofing membrane being applied prior to laying of hardwood blocks over a concrete slab on-grade. The procedure includes two layers of 15-lb. asphalt-impregnated felt laid in an asphalt mastic. The mastic is first trowled over the concrete and followed by felt, another mastic layer, and then the final felt.

Moisture resistance is very important because, if the floor does not resist the transmission of moisture, severe damage to the floor covering and the adhesive used for its installation can occur.

The great majority of contemporary floor installations are made over concrete as a subfloor, although floor coverings are frequently installed over wood as well as many other substrates, e.g., ceramic tile.

The properties of concrete make it a very satisfactory and economical material for floor construction, since it can be easily placed and finished, is structurally strong, fire-resistant, termite-proof and universally available. Concrete floors may be installed below-grade and at times in direct contact with water, as in basement construction. They may be on-grade, as in slab-on-ground construction, or they may be entirely above ground. However, the fact that concrete contains water and that under certain conditions some water will pass through it poses a problem that can only be partially alleviated by observing the fundamental rules of making good concrete.

The requirements for wood subfloors include good stiffness, adequate nail holding power, and surface characteristics that facilitate the application of a finished floor. Wood subflooring may be of one-inch board or plywood. The layer between the subfloor and the finished floor may consist of building paper, asphaltic felt, asbestos paper, or gypsum board. Some form of layer should always be used and, if the cost will permit, the increase in fire resistance and sound-deadening properties due to a layer of heavy asbestos paper or gypsum board will warrant the additional expenditures.

Details of the preparation and installation of subfloors are discussed in the Chapters devoted to particular types of floors, especially Chapters 3 and 7.

GRADE LEVELS

One of the most important considerations in selecting flooring is the location of the subfloor in relation to ground level, i.e., grade.

It is sufficient for purposes of this discussion to describe the location of a floor as being below-grade, on-grade, or above-grade. The term "suspended" is synonomous with "above-grade."

Below-grade

Any floor in direct contact with the earth and below the surrounding ground level is classed as a below-grade floor. A typical example is a concrete basement floor. Because moisture passes readily through concrete, there is a strong possibility that ground moisture containing alkaline salts will work its way up to the floor surface. The presence of the alkaline moisture can have a destructive effect on the adhesive bond used with some floor coverings, unless special care is taken to use waterproof and alkali-resistant adhesives. The latest building techniques make use of waterproof membranes, usually a six-mil thickness of polyethylene film, over the base before the concrete subfloor is applied. Such membranes are also used in on-grade construction.

The presence of moisture and alkaline salts in below-grade areas also creates a potential decay situation for carpet, wood, and some resilient floor materials—those based on wood and wood products, such as cork, linoleum, and paper-backed sheet goods.

Types of resilient tile floors which are suitable for installation on below-grade subfloors are asphalt, vinyl asbestos, rubber, and homogeneous vinyl. Some forms of sheet vinyl flooring, which have special water and alkaline-resistant backing materials, are also acceptable for use below-grade.

On-grade

In the construction of buildings with no basements, the subfloor usually consists of a concrete slab installed on the ground over a well-drained gravel base. This type of subfloor is called "on-grade." Although the problem with moisture is not as severe in this case as it is with below-grade floors, it is still a possible hazard.

In addition to those floor coverings mentioned above as suitable for below-grade floors, two more—cork tile and backed vinyl tile—can also be installed on-grade. The American Plywood Association has reported that on-grade concrete floors can be successfully converted for use with all forms of floor coverings. The technique employs a layer of polystyrene or polyurethane foamed plastic cemented to the concrete. Then plywood underlayment is bonded directly to the plastic. Any type of floor covering can be used on the plywood surface.

Above-grade

Floors which are suspended over at least 18 inches of well-ventilated air space are called "above-grade." Even though the location of such floors may be at, or below, the level of the ground, they are not in contact with the earth and are considered to be in the same class as floors which are one story or more above ground level. Because moisture is not a problem with such floors, all types of floor coverings can be used.

COSTS

The total cost of a floor includes initial cost—materials and installation—and maintenance. Installation cost is normally included in the purchase price. For budget purposes, annual costs depend upon initial cost, projected maintenance expenses, and service life.

Initial cost

The initial cost varies according to type and quality of materials and geographic location. As an example of this with respect to type of material, marble is more expensive than most other types of flooring. To illustrate cost differences arising from levels of quality, the price of good quality wool carpet ranges from $11.50 to $20.00 per square yard. Geographic location affects initial cost. Prices of material vary across the country; there are differences in local labor rates, and shipping costs vary according to distances covered and mode of transportation.

In addition to these factors, initial costs can vary because of differences in the size of installation, discounts obtained on flooring materials, and the kind of appearance desired. With respect to the last, certain public areas and some private offices may require a floor covering of high quality and special design effects to convey an appearance of luxury and prestige. The cost of such a floor covering can be very high. On the other hand, in working areas and locations not ordinarily seen by the public, less expensive flooring can be used.

Azrock Floor Products Division, Uvalde Rock Asphalt Company

Vinyl asbestos tile floor.

Because of these variables, substantial differences will be found in flooring cost estimates. As a consequence, it is not practical here to give precise installed costs for particular types of floors. However, the reader can get an idea of approximate costs by using the typical price ranges given in Table 1. These have been compiled from various sources and provide figures for almost all of the floor coverings discussed in this book.

Maintenance cost

The cost of maintenance includes three elements—labor, equipment, and supplies. In determining maintenance costs, the number of times each maintenance operation is performed is of prime importance. This frequency is a function of three basic variables: amount of traffic, level of appearance desired, and type of area to be cleaned. Amount of traffic and appearance level are readily understood. "Type of area," as used here, refers to the configuration, the relative openness, and the condition of the floor, e.g., unobstructed areas, small or semi-private rooms, and high spillage areas such as workrooms and washrooms.

The difficulties of presenting maintenance cost figures in a general way can be understood when one considers the problem of identifying a "typical" level of traffic, a "representative" type of area to be cleaned, or a "standard-ized" level of appearance to be attained. The maintenance cost figures shown in Table 2 for two types of floor coverings are based on studies conducted by four different organizations. To our knowledge, no detailed, impartial studies of costs of maintaining the wide variety of floor materials discussed in this book have ever been made.

Labor. This is the major cost factor in any floor maintenance program. Labor costs can be determined as follows: The time required to perform each maintenance operation on a 1,000 square foot area of floor is mea-sured. The time rate is then multiplied by the frequency per year the opera-tion is performed, to find total time for the operation. The total time is translated into a cost figure through multiplication by labor cost per hour. Typical maintenance operations for a resilient floor that might be measured for an analysis of maintenance costs are: sweeping, mopping, scrubbing, waxing, polishing, and stripping.

Equipment. The cost of equipment includes the initial price and the cost of repair and service. When spread over the life of the machines, the cost of equipment is very low in comparison with other maintenance costs. The annual cost of one machine is equivalent to the initial cost divided by the years of anticipated service life plus annual repair and service expenses. The amount of equipment required for a maintenance operation depends on the size of the area to be served, the time required to perform the opera-tion, and the frequency with which it is carried out. Examples of equipment

TABLE 1
Costs of Floor Materials
(Ranges of Approximate Costs, Installed)

RESILIENT
(per sq. ft.)

Linoleum	$ .35	to	$ .90
Rubber tile	.50	to	1.20
Asphalt tile	.30	to	.50
Cork tile	.70	to	1.60
Vinyl cork tile	.50	to	2.00
Homogeneous vinyl tile	.80	to	1.00
Backed vinyl tile	.70	to	1.50
Vinyl asbestos tile	.25	to	1.00

CARPET
(per sq. yd.)

Wool	$11.50	to	$20.00
Nylon	8.00	to	14.50
Acrylic	10.50	to	16.00
Antron nylon	9.50	to	15.50
Polypropylene	6.00	to	8.00

MASONRY
(per sq. ft.)

Ceramic tile	$1.25	to	$ 2.25
Marble	3.50	to	10.00
Terrazzo	1.25	to	3.75
Slate	3.00	to	4.00
Concrete	.60	to	1.00
Magnesite	1.10	to	1.65
Brick	1.00	to	3.50

WOOD
(per sq. ft.)

Oak (strip)	$ .45	to	$1.25
Maple (strip)	.45	to	1.25
Block	.65	to	1.35
Parquet (block)	.55	to	2.50

FORMED-IN-PLACE
(per sq. ft.)

Mastic	$ .50	to	$ .75
Epoxy	.75	to	1.75
Polyester	1.50	to	2.25
Polyurethane	.75	to	1.60
Silicone	1.00	to	3.50
Polychloroprene	.80	to	1.10

that might be used in a carpet maintenance program are vacuum cleaners, carpet sweepers, shampoo machines, and pile lifters.

Supplies. These include expendable equipment and supplies, that is, those items that are not repaired but replaced when worn out, damaged, or used up. In the case of equipment, the item is not repairable or it is not worth repairing, e.g., a mop handle. In the case of supplies, the item is consumed and must be replenished, e.g., polish. The measurement of actual usage of supplies and resultant cost is usually difficult because of the loose control over such items and variations in their use by different personnel. The annual cost of such expendable equipment and supplies is very small in comparison to labor costs.

Portland Cement Association

Terrazzo with black matrix, large marble chips,
and thick brass strips.

Service life

Service life may be defined as the length of time a floor covering will be acceptable for use. Service life has two aspects—physical and appearance durability. Physical durability refers to the length of time the floor surface will endure. Appearance durability means the length of time the floor surface will retain a presentable appearance.

The person responsible for selecting floor coverings must decide whether for certain areas the continuing good appearance of the floor will take precedence over its physical durability. The appearance of the floor will usually be more important in the public areas, whereas the emphasis may be upon physical durability in those work areas used almost exclusively by employees.

Physical and appearance durability, in turn, depend upon three factors. First is the inherent ability of floor coverings to resist wear, damage, or attack by abrasion, indentation, impact, moisture, chemicals (solvents, acids, alkalies), soiling, and staining. Second is the environmental conditions to which the floor material is subjected. Among these are the level of traffic, the nature of the geographic surroundings—including soil conditions, local weather conditions, extremes of temperature and humidity, and what types of activities are carried out in various areas of the institution. Third is the kind of installation and maintenance utilized; improper installation and inadequate maintenance almost inevitably will shorten service life.

All the floors described in this book, if properly installed and well cared for, can be expected to give satisfactory service in a public building for a long time. However, it is possible to state only approximations of the number of years various types of flooring will stand up under use.

Service life of resilient floors, for example, might range from about eight years for an inexpensive grade of linoleum to twenty years for a high-grade homogeneous vinyl. The life of carpet also depends largely on what one can afford to pay: Carpet at $10.00 to $12.00 per yard will probably last about 10 to 12 years, while carpet at $20.00 to $25.00 per yard will very likely last twice as long.

Some masonry floorings, such as ceramic tile, can be expected to last almost indefinitely, if given reasonably good maintenance. Terrazzo gives good service for 30 years and longer. Wood floors, if carefully installed and cared for, can be expected to give good service for 15 to 25 years, after which they can be completely refinished and used for another 15 years or more. Although the manufacturers are optimistic about the durability of the new varieties of formed-in-place floor products, these have not been available and in use long enough to provide estimates of service life based on experience.

Tile Council of America, Inc.

Special design effect is achieved with unusual
shape of quarry tile.

Annual cost

A realistic estimate of service life of a floor material makes it possible
to calculate annual costs. This is done by dividing the initial cost by years
of service life and adding annual maintenance costs. Calculations of annual
cost for carpet and resilient flooring are illustrated in Table 2.

SAFETY

The three primary considerations in floor selection with respect to
safety are resistance to contamination, relative susceptibility to fire, and
slip resistance.

A floor surface should not retain or harbor harmful micro-organisms
or serve as a repository for organic debris which might decay or provide
food for vermin. Ideally, the floor should be capable of being completely
cleaned and disinfected. These points are particularly stressed for any area
where food may be present or where special sanitation procedures are
required.

Floors especially resistant to contamination are seamless, non-absorptive materials such as epoxy, polyester, and polyurethane. Terrazzo, ceramic
mosaic tile and quarry tile installed with special grouts and cements
are also widely used. Sheet resilient surfaces are generally acceptable because they can be installed with a minimum number of seams.

TABLE 2
ANNUAL COST OF FLOORING — RESILIENT AND CARPET

Reporting agency	American Carpet Institute		Armstrong		Bell		Wharton	
Type of floor	Resil.	Carpet	Resil.	Carpet	Resil.	Carpet	Resil.	Carpet
Estimated service life (years)	18	12	20.5	9.9	19	12	19	10
Initial materials cost (installed per sq. ft.)	$ .55	$ 1.20	$ .42	$ 1.53	$ .38	$ 1.50	$ .51	$ 1.44
Annual materials cost (installed per 1,000 sq. ft.)	30.60	100.00	20.63	154.24	19.63	125.00	23.60	139.00
Annual labor cost (per 1,000 sq. ft.)	230.97	70.10	109.00	230.00	88.72	115.13	105.79	142.19
Annual equipment cost (per 1,000 sq. ft.)	9.65	6.98	6.67	10.24	3.06	6.11	4.58	10.98
Annual supplies cost (per 1,000 sq. ft.)	49.67	5.33	12.33	7.76	12.23	5.66	37.55	17.62
Total annual cost (per 1,000 sq. ft.)	320.89	182.41	148.63	402.24	123.64	251.90	171.52	309.79
Total annual cost (per sq. ft.)	.32	.18	.15	.40	.12	.25	.17	.31

Sources: (1) American Carpet Institute, Inc., *Cutting Costs with Carpet* (New York: The Institute), 1962. (2) Armstrong Cork Company, *A Fresh Look at Flooring Costs* (Lancaster, Pennsylvania: Armstrong Cork Company), undated. (3) Ewing, Jack, "Carpet versus Resilient Flooring," *Skyscraper Management* (January, 1965), pp. 13 +. (4) Parks, George M., *The Economics of Carpeting and Resilient Flooring* (Philadelphia: The Wharton School of Finance and Commerce, Industrial Research Unit, University of Pennsylvania), Copyright—The Trustees of the University of Pennsylvania, 1966.

The fire hazard is directly related to (1) the flammability of the floor material and (2) its susceptibility to damage through contact with burning objects such as cigarettes or matches. In the former category, floor materials such as wood, asphalt, carpet, cork, and linoleum will burn. Vinyl products, though organic in nature, are classed as non-flammable. All the masonry floors are true inorganics and do not support combustion.

Tests for resistance to burning objects give different reactions with each floor. However, the usual result is not serious—a slight burn, char mark, or melted zone. Even in the case of carpets, which are perhaps the most sensitive to hot coals, the fibers tend either to melt under the heat, as is the case with nylon, acrylic, or polypropylene, or to burn for a short distance leaving an ashy residue.

The slip resistance of a floor covering depends largely on its surface characteristics—how rough or smooth the material is. While most flooring materials are reasonably slip-resistant, there are exceptions with highly polished surfaces such as marble, terrazzo, and ceramic tile. In the case of resilient and wood floors, the slip resistance depends also upon the properties of the polish or final finish used to preserve the surface. A non-slip polish or final finish may be desirable under certain circumstances. For areas that require very high slip resistance such as ramps or stairs, floor materials incorporating special abrasive grits should be selected. There are terrazzos, resilient tiles, and epoxy coatings that are widely used for just this purpose. Areas that can be slippery—especially under wet conditions —can be substantially improved by the application of abrasive-coated plastic tapes cemented to the area in question. Because most surfaces are considerably more hazardous when wet, it is a common practice to close off these areas until such time as the floors are completely dry.

DIMENSIONAL STABILITY

Dimensional stability refers to the property of a floor material to resist shrinkage or expansion. Two major causes of dimensional instability are extremes in temperature and moisture. A variety of deleterious effects may result from these conditions, such as buckling, cracking, and the opening of seams. If these effects are severe, the floor may require extensive repairs or replacement.

An obvious example of this problem is the tendency of wood flooring to shrink and swell as its moisture content changes. If the moisture content becomes too low, the wood will shrink and cracks will develop between the boards. If it becomes too high, the wood will expand and buckling will occur. Proper selection, seasoning, and installation of wood flooring can minimize and control the problem.

The same problem exists with resilient tile and carpeting. Here again, good quality materials, correct installation methods, and proper maintenance are required to ensure continuing dimensional stability.

LIGHT REFLECTANCE

There are two factors affecting light reflectance to be considered in selecting a floor. These are the *color* and *texture* of the flooring material. Light colors and smooth surfaces reflect more light than dark colors and rough surfaces. Therefore, the amount of light present in an area is directly related to the reflectance properties of the floor material.

A recent study of lighting in the school environment indicates that light reflectivity deserves greater emphasis than it has been given in the past. The *American Standard Guide for School Lighting* (American Standards Association, 1962) states that the "goal . . . must be to allow students

Space Planning Services, A Division of Carson Pirie Scott & Co.

Loop-pile, wool carpet in executive office.

and instructors to see comfortably and efficiently and without undue distraction. It follows then that an adequate level of illumination for efficient performance of visual tasks is necessary, and the quality of lighting should help to maintain a comfortable and pleasing environment."

The *American Standard Guide for School Lighting* goes on to suggest that ". . . it is important to select suitable reflectances for the room surfaces." For example, the brightness of the floor should range from 30 to 50 percent of the brightness of the visual task, i.e., the reading or writing surface. *Recommended Practice for Library Lighting* (Illuminating Engineering Society, 1949), presently under revision, gives a comparable range for floors of 30 to 40 (± 10) percent.

In a paper titled "Principles of Illumination for Libraries," by Brock Arms, in *The Library Environment: Aspects of Interior Planning* (American Library Association, 1965), the statement is made that, "Some materials and colors absorb light, reflecting so little of it that if they are adjacent to materials which reflect the majority of the light a disturbing brightness contrast will result. For study conditions where reading tasks require a long attention span, it is desirable to use only materials and colors within the field of vision which reflect percentages of light within the allowable brightness contrast ratio of 1 to 10. This does not mean that all colors and tones in a library should be bland. It does mean that within an area used for intense study or concentration they should not produce great contrast."

ACOUSTIC PROPERTIES

Floors account for a large proportion of the total interior surface of an enclosed area. Floors, therefore, play an important part in the acoustic properties of such areas. Most of the impact noise in rooms and corridors is caused by objects coming in contact with the floor, and the level of sound produced by such impact is directly related to the hardness of the floor surface.

Azrock Floor Products Division, Uvalde Rock Asphalt Company

Resilient tile floor coverings offer manifold
design possibilities.

The ability of different floor coverings to absorb impact sounds from pedestrian traffic or falling objects is a measure of their relative quietness and is an important factor in the selection of floors for many areas.

Acoustically, carpet ranks highest in the ability to absorb sound. Of the several resilient floor coverings, cork tile has the best sound-absorbing properties. The remaining resilient surfaces can be rated as "low noise producers" in comparison with wood and masonry. The absorption of noise by wood and masonry floor surfaces is negligible.

INDENTATION RESISTANCE

The ability of the different types of floor covering materials to withstand concentrated loads varies markedly. The problem of indentation of the floor surface in certain types of floors can be serious. Unless precautions are taken, resilient floor coverings, wood floors, and carpet tend to be especially susceptible to marring or damage from indentation by concentrated loads such as may be caused by the legs of furniture. This type of damage is much less likely to occur in the case of masonry floors.

The ability of a floor material to resist indentation depends on the composition of the material, the area of contact, the force applied, and the duration of contact. A general rule for preventing indentation is to distribute the weight of the furniture over a large area thereby reducing the weight per square inch to a safe limit. Distribution of weight can be accomplished through the use of furniture rests, cups, glides, and casters. Recommendations for guards suitable for particular floor coverings should be obtained from the flooring manufacturers or floor contractors.

Cups are recommended for the legs of heavy furniture that is not frequently moved. These are made of a composition material in neutral colors and are designed to prevent the legs of furniture from cutting into the floor. They are manufactured with square openings 1½ to 2⅝ inches and with round openings 1⅜ and 1⅝ inches in diameter.

Glides are recommended for chairs, cabinets, and other lightweight pieces of furniture that may be moved frequently. The glides should have a smooth, flat base with rounded edges, and a mechanism for maintaining flat contact with the floor. With heavier pieces of furniture, larger-size glides should be used. They can be obtained in diameters from 1 to 2½ inches. Small metal domes frequently supplied on the bottom of furniture legs should be replaced with flat glides.

Furniture intended to be moved frequently, such as book trucks, desk chairs, and stools, should be equipped with casters. Such casters should have large-diameter wheels (2 inches or more) with ball-bearing swivels, and wide, rubber-composition treads. Small-diameter, narrow, hard-wheeled casters, particularly those with a crowned head and without ball-bearing swivels, can cause a great deal of damage to most flooring materials.

A special problem of indentation damage arises from the impact of women's stiletto heels on floor surfaces, especially wood and resilient. The concentrated load of these pointed heels may reach more than 10,000 pounds per square inch. The resultant pock marks present an irregular and unsightly appearance and make it difficult to maintain a clean surface.

For minimizing the unsightly appearance of indentation marks in resilient floors, light-colored and multi-colored floorings should be selected rather than dark, plain surfaces. Patterns should be used which are grained or mottled to simulate marble, terrazzo, or mosaic effects. These effects tend to camouflage indentations because of their designs and patterns. Tiles such as homogeneous vinyl that have a "memory," i.e., that readily return to their original shape, should be chosen in preference to coverings that do not recover their shape so readily. Also preferred are textured and embossed surfaces, which tend to conceal markings. The use of matte-finish tiles and low-gloss polish can help to reduce the shadow effects caused by indentation.

It has been suggested that indentation damage to resilient tile can be minimized by installing the tile directly over a rigid underlayment that has as little cushioning as possible. This method of installation will permit the tile more readily to recover its original shape. Four things are to be avoided during installation: the use of soft underlayment, the use of felt lining, the improper spreading of adhesive, and the inadequate rolling of the finished floor.

Once a floor has become seriously damaged by indentation, the condition is difficult to correct. One can replace the floor or grind it down below the level of the indentation marks. It should be pointed out that refinishing techniques can be applied not only to hard-surfaced floors but to some resilient floors, i.e., those that are homogeneous.

DESIGN

Design, which includes color, texture, and pattern, influences visual responses. From the decorative point of view, color helps set the tone for the entire area. Basically, there are seven color groups: blues, greens, golds, reds, greys, beiges, and browns. Within each color family there are many variations from light to dark, solid colors, or subtle mixtures of hue. It is important with some types of floors, particularly carpets, to select the color with some consideration of the type of pedestrian soil or traffic to which the floor is likely to be subjected. For example, if light colors are desired in a heavy traffic area where soiling might be a problem, a two-tone mixture of one color or a patterned style might be selected. These designs are practical since they do not show soil so readily. If it is known that the type of soil in the surrounding environment will be light-colored, then it would be well to avoid dark colors since by contrast the soil will become readily apparent. Likewise, in areas where the soil is apt to be dark, some preference should be given to a dark-colored material.

Certain floor materials tend to be more limited than others in the choice of colors available, for example, wood and cork tile. On the other hand, a wide choice of colors is offered by most of the resilient floor coverings, carpet, marble, terrazzo, formed-in-place materials, and ceramic tile.

Space Planning Services, A Division of Carson Pirie Scott & Co.

Wool area rugs on vinyl asbestos tile.

By texture is meant the character of finish of the floor material, that is, how smooth, rough, hard, soft, coarse, or fine it is. Texture, in addition to its conventional application to carpet, applies to other flooring materials. Unusual examples of variations in texture are the holes occurring naturally in travertine marble and the artificially produced embossing on resilient tile surfaces.

Floor patterns are usually keyed to over-all decor. There are four basic areas in which patterns can be used in a room—on the floor, on the walls, on draperies, and on furniture and upholstery. Because floors and walls are most prominent, it might be suggested that a pattern be used in only one or the other. In general, small rooms require small patterns while larger patterns can be used in large rooms. Very often, patterns are used to define special areas or to achieve spatial effects for waiting areas, walkways, lounges, and entrances.

The major flooring manufacturers have large, capable design staffs whose services are normally available at no extra cost. Also available from each manufacturer are brochures and booklets giving design suggestions for many types of floor areas. Showrooms should be visited and exhibits examined to assist in visualizing the total effect of different designs.

UNDERFOOT COMFORT

The quality of underfoot comfort is a measure of resiliency, i.e., the capacity of a floor covering to absorb the impact associated with walking. Selecting one of the more resilient floor materials for areas in which considerable walking and standing are required can reduce fatigue. Carpet and cork floors offer the greatest underfoot comfort, whereas the masonry surfaces rate lowest in this respect.

Various types of floor coverings arranged in order from most to least comfortable are shown in Table 3.

TABLE 3
COMFORT RATINGS FOR FLOOR SURFACES

Surface	Relative Comfort Rating
Carpet	Excellent
Cork	Very good
Linoleum	Good
Rubber	Good
Homogeneous vinyl	Good
Vinyl cork	Good to fair
Backed vinyl	Fair
Vinyl asbestos	Fair to poor
Asphalt	Poor
Wood	Poor
Terrazzo	Very poor
Concrete	Very poor

THERMAL CONDUCTIVITY

The rate of heat transfer through a floor material may be significant in certain situations. For example, in on-grade installations, where heat loss may have serious effects on user comfort and fuel consumption, one would select a material that insulates well. On the other hand, for installations over floor radiant-heating systems, one would want to choose a floor covering that readily conducts heat into the room.

Thermal conductivity refers to the capability of conducting heat. Technically, "thermal conductivity" is defined as: the quantity of heat (expressed in Btu's) that passes in unit time (hour) through a unit area (square foot) of flooring material whose thickness is unity (1 inch) when its opposite faces differ in temperature by one degree (°F.).

The amount of heat transferred through floor materials is governed by their thermal conductivity. The "K-90" factor is a term used to describe thermal conductivity (Btu/Hr./Sq.Ft./°F.) for a 1-inch thickness of flooring material (excluding lining felt) at a 90° F. mean temperature. For calculation of the amount of heat flowing through a floor material, the K-90 factor for thermal conductivity is divided by the thickness of the material.

TABLE 4

K-90 FACTORS FOR TYPICAL FLOORING MATERIALS

Floor Material	Btu/Hr./Sq.Ft./°F./1" @ 90° F.
Concrete	11.4-16.4 (depending on mix)
Marble	5.1-23.8 (depending on shade and grade)
Asphalt	5.0
Vinyl asbestos	4.8
Rubber	3.7
Linoleum	1.6
Backed vinyl (mineral backing)	1.4
Wood (oak)	1.2
Wood (maple)	1.1
Homogeneous vinyl	1.1
Vinyl cork	0.62
Cork	0.53

2 MAINTENANCE

INTRODUCTION

Floor maintenance is a part of general institutional sanitation. In this context, sanitation may be defined as maintenance which is organized, supervised, and carried out to provide attractive, comfortable, healthy, and safe surroundings and to expedite the productive function. Proper floor maintenance serves the additional purpose of protecting the floor surface, thereby increasing its useful life and preserving its appearance.

Floors receive an estimated 90 percent more wear than any other part of the building and account for about 40 percent of the over-all cost of building operations. For this reason, proper maintenance of floor coverings is one of the most important aspects of good building operation. Improper maintenance inevitably mars appearance and substantially increases maintenance costs. Maintenance must be protective and preventive, rather than curative.

Floor maintenance requires more consideration and effort than other types of maintenance. The constant wear due to traffic—especially noticeable when some areas are affected more than others—and the accumulation of dirt and soil transferred from shoes and deposited from the air are factors that increase the floor maintenance problem.

The difficulty encountered in maintaining floor surfaces is governed to a large extent by the nature and the age of the accumulated dirt and soil. For example, dry dust is readily removed by sweeping, mopping, or by vacuuming. However, when the dust absorbs moisture or mixes with wet or oily contaminations, it will become bonded to the floor surface making removal much more difficult. The longer a bonded soil remains undisturbed, the firmer the bond between the soil and the surface becomes, and further soil accumulation tends to build up more heavily. The use of modern floor finishes prevents the soil from bonding to the floor surface, relieving much of the difficulty of soil removal, and thereby reducing the cost of floor maintenance.

Untreated floors are somewhat porous and may have surface irregularities; many types are softer than the soil that accumulates on them. Foot traffic grinds the soil into the pores and irregularities, and the abrasive action tends to scratch and wear the surface. Sweeping and dry-mopping do not readily remove this ground-in soil. It is generally necessary to scrub with a suitable cleaning solution to effect removal. The scratches and other effects of wear are not removed, however, and the wet-cleaning results in an appreciable absorption of solution by the untreated floor. The use of penetrating sealers and surface finishes helps to protect the floor from abrasion and absorption of solutions. The finish and appearance of a polished floor will be affected by the soil and attrition, but the finish can be readily removed and replaced while the floor itself remains essentially unaffected.

3M Company

The kinds of soiling predominantly found on floors are air-borne, siliceous and carbonaceous dust, tracked-in dirt, spilled materials, heel burns, and scuff marks. The natural dust or soil that settles on the floor from the atmosphere will vary in composition according to the area. Analytical data on the composition of soil deposits in different cities have revealed that, in general, the deposits are made up of carbon, silica, iron oxide, grease, and salts. Deposits of siliceous particles of soil greatly increase the likelihood of wear on the surface or finish of floors. Heel burns are discoloring traffic marks that probably consist of rubber and carbon particles. Scuff marks are non-discoloring traffic marks that appear as smears on the floor surface or floor coating.

How quickly and severely any floor surface becomes soiled depends upon the type of activity in the building area, the volume of traffic that passes over the floor, and the finish applied to the floor surface. For example, with regard to floor finishes, it is to be expected that the softer wax films will pick up dirt and heel marks rather easily. Hard, non-resilient films will show scratches, but will resist the embedment of soil accumulations.

Because of the wide variety of flooring materials and soil conditions, it is important to select a suitable cleaning compound and to employ the proper maintenance methods and equipment. Maintenance practices vary for different kinds of floors; methods, supplies, and equipment that are highly effective for one type of floor may be less effective, or even detrimental, to another. Floors can be ruined by improper maintenance.

CLEANING COMPOUNDS

Some understanding of the principles of cleansing power associated with various types of cleaning compounds and of the differences among these products is useful in setting up a suitable floor maintenance program.

The general principles of cleansing action (i.e., detergency) apply here in the sense that soil particles are removed from the floor as a consequence of the physical action of scrubbing combined with the wetting, penetrating, and displacing power of the cleaning solution, and the suspending action of the surfactants (surface-acting agents) used. Solvent action may also play a part in the cleansing process, e.g., when such water-soluble solvents as glycols and pine oil are utilized.

Thus, the principles involved in the functioning of cleaning compounds are: (1) detergency via surface activity, (2) saponification of soil and polishes through added alkalinity, (3) mild solvent action by means of specific chemicals.

Soap-base compounds

Soaps used for cleaning purposes are alkali salts of fatty acids. In practical terms, the fatty acids are mixtures of a homologous series varying in molecular weight. They consist largely of stearic, a saturated acid; oleic, an unsaturated acid; and, in a separate category, tall oil fatty acids. Stearic acid is a solid at ordinary temperatures; oleic and tall oil fatty acids are liquid at ordinary temperatures. Solid soap-base compounds are largely composed of the sodium salts of stearic and other saturated fatty acids but do contain some oleic and other liquid fatty acids. Liquid soap-base compounds are largely composed of potassium salts of liquid fatty acids including tall oil fatty acids. These liquid soap-base compounds may contain ammonia soap and/or amine soaps.

In addition to soap, these soap-base compounds usually contain alkaline-salt builders and alkaline sequestering agents which improve detergency. Sodium or potassium polyphosphates, combined with silicates and carbonates or borates, are the commonly employed builders (substances added to increase cleansing action). The use of alkaline salts as builders for soap-base compounds should not be viewed with disfavor, even though excessive use of highly alkaline salts is frowned upon by the manufacturers of floor coverings and is prohibited in many specifications. These builders can, and do, serve a useful purpose as long as a proper balance is maintained.

From the standpoint of practical maintenance of floor surfaces, the following points should be kept in mind when choosing soap-base compounds: (1) The solid varieties of soap-base compounds contain sodium soap, which is less soluble in cold or lukewarm water than potassium soap. For this reason, compounds containing sodium soap are not as easily rinsed or removed from the flooring surface as are compounds containing potassium soaps. (2) Because the liquid soap-base compounds contain potash soap, they are readily soluble in cold water. They usually contain other chemicals, such as cyclohexanol, alcohol, pine oil, glycols, and ammonia, which are intended to exert solvent action on oil and grease, resinous soils, black heel marks, and wax deposits.

Alkaline-salt compounds

These products, the least expensive of the floor cleaning compounds, are composed of one or more alkaline salts, including trisodium phosphate, tripolyphosphate, sodium carbonate (soda ash), sodium silicate, and borax. They may or may not contain some proportion of powdered soap-base compound or synthetic detergent. The proportion of soap-base compound or synthetic detergent present in the mixture is the factor that distinguishes the alkaline-salt compound from a built, heavy-duty synthetic detergent. The former contains a relatively small proportion of soap-base compound or synthetic detergent. The latter usually contains a larger percentage of soap-base compound or synthetic detergent.

Alkaline-salt compounds may be used in one of two ways—solely as a cleaning agent in the wash water, or as a builder for soap-base compounds or synthetic detergents. In the latter case, a relatively small amount of soap-base compound or synthetic detergent is added to the wash water along with the primary alkaline-salt compound.

These compounds have a definite place in the maintenance of floors, but they can cause damage to floors and floor coverings and, therefore, should be selected and used with care. The factors to be considered for proper and safe use of alkaline-salt compounds are (1) the pH (the degree of alkalinity) of the cleaning solution prepared with this compound, (2) the concentration employed, (3) the frequency of use, (4) the type and condition of floor surface, and (5) the nature of the soil to be removed. Alkaline-salt compounds having a pH value higher than 11.5 should be avoided. The minimum concentration required for the particular cleaning job at hand should be employed. For example, the removal of grease or oil from a concrete floor will require a higher concentration than is needed for the cleaning of a terrazzo surface or for removing old floor-polish films. (The procedure for removing floor polishes is commonly called "stripping.")

In general, alkaline-salt compounds should not be used regularly to clean linoleum, asphalt tile, vinyl asbestos tile, or rubber tile. Where floor coverings have become porous ("washed out") due to attrition and loss of binder at the surface, this type of compound should not be used. These alkaline-salt compounds are best suited for heavy-duty cleaning, such as the removal of stains, stubborn soil deposits, and oil and grease accumulations.

Synthetic detergents

Cleaning compounds containing synthetic surface-active agents are similar to soap-base compounds in that they contain alkaline salts as builders. They are sold in solid, powdered, granulated, and liquid form. In other respects, they are dissimilar to soap-base compounds. These compounds are known as synthetic detergents, commonly called "syndets" in the trade.

Synthetic detergents are highly effective floor cleaning compounds; they are not affected by hard water, as are soap-base compounds. They have very good wetting, dispersing, and emulsifying action, and are free-rinsing. In general, from the standpoint of performance and safety, these cleaning compounds are preferred for use on all types of floors and floor coverings.

Granulated synthetic detergents suitable for heavy-duty floor cleaning are sold as packaged products and in bulk form. Liquid synthetic detergents formulated specifically for industrial and institutional maintenance are generally not similar to the liquid household detergents. Liquid synthetic detergents are usually well suited for the purpose of cleaning floors and potentially less apt to cause deterioration of floors and floor coverings than granulated and powdered synthetic detergents, granulated soap-base compounds, and alkaline-salt compounds.

Some liquid soap-base compounds are composed of mixtures of potash soaps and synthetic detergents. Except in hard water-areas, they perform efficiently and can be considered equivalent to liquid synthetic detergents.

"Biodegradable" is a term that has been applied recently to synthetic detergents that readily decompose in the presence of bacteria in sewage plants, septic tanks, and natural waters. Since there are, as yet, no generally accepted, quantitative yardsticks for biodegradability, synthetic detergents are commonly classified as "soft" or "hard." Although these terms are not technically descriptive, they are convenient to use. Biodegradable (soft) detergents readily decompose by biochemical means, whereas non-biodegradable (hard) detergents resist bacterial decomposition.

Abrasive compounds

Cleaning compounds containing abrasives have their place in institutional maintenance, but their proper use is more limited than is understood by the average maintenance worker. (Abrasive compounds suitable for household use are often called "household cleansers" or "scouring powders.") It must be emphasized that abrasive compounds should be used only very occasionally, where nothing else will do the job, as in the case of spotting or staining.

These compounds are basically composed of either synthetic detergents or soap-base compounds (the latter are becoming outmoded). Both also contain alkaline salts, such as alkaline phosphates; carbonate and silicate; and an inorganic insoluble abrasive, e.g., ground feldspar, ground silica, finely divided pumice, and volcanic ash. During the past few years, the use of bleaching agents—which liberate oxygen or chlorine—has become so popular that it is difficult to find abrasive compounds without bleaching agents in them. While these bleaching agents may be effective on porcelain and glazed ceramic surfaces, they are not very effective and, in fact, are undesirable for use on most floor surfaces.

Abrasive compounds exert a mechanical action, i.e., a scouring effect, on soil deposits and, therefore, are fast-acting and efficient. The very nature of the action is potentially damaging to floor surfaces, and perhaps of even greater importance is the fact that it is almost impossible completely to remove residual deposits of the abrasive material. Therefore, even after the most thorough rinsing, the residue will continue to exert attrition on that surface.

Scientific studies have proved satisfactorily that resilient floor coverings, linoleum in particular, can be badly deteriorated and the wear layer penetrated in a relatively short period by the repeated use of abrasive compounds. Therefore, except for those circumstances where there is no alternative, such as the removal of stubborn stains, spots, and soil accumulations which are water insoluble, it is recommended that the use of abrasive compounds on resilient floor coverings be avoided.

Abrasive compounds should not be used on hardwood floors. Other abrasive materials, such as steel wool and nylon pads, are as effective, if not more so, than abrasive compounds, and they are much less damaging to wood floors.

Abrasive compounds are not desirable, hence not recommended, for regular use on masonry floors. Here again, it is practically impossible to remove all residual deposits of the abrasive which exacerbate wear of the surface. Abrasive residues, especially the heavier and larger particles, can also cause scratching.

Special-purpose compounds

Cleaning compounds containing germicidal agents have become popular in the past few years, probably as a direct result of the public awareness of staphylococcus infections in hospitals and other institutions. Cleaning compounds claiming anti-bacterial properties are controlled by the regulations of the Federal Insecticide, Fungicide and Rodenticide Act, administered by the U.S. Department of Agriculture. Many states have corresponding laws which control such poisonous products. These products must be labeled in accordance with strict regulations that require substantiation of claims of anti-bacterial effectiveness. The label must include an ingredient statement showing the active anti-bacterial agents as well as specific instructions relative to the use-dilution at which the product will exhibit the claimed anti-bacterial effects.

Since we are primarily concerned with the selection and maintenance of floors, it is beyond the scope of this manual to provide detailed discussion of cleaning compounds containing germicidal agents. From the standpoint of effectiveness of cleaning compounds, these germicidal products may not differ materially in composition or performance from other cleaning compounds for which no anti-bacterial claims are made. The germicidal features should, therefore, be regarded as plus values, and the selection made on a basis of cost, desirability, need, and a comparison with other methods of obtaining equivalent anti-bacterial effects. It should be remembered that an inefficient, poorly performing floor cleaning compound, which may have excellent anti-bacterial properties, cannot be justified, especially at an increased cost. The same anti-bacterial effects can be obtained by other means, such as adding a disinfectant to the floor cleaning solution or using rinse water containing a germicidal agent.

Floor-polish removing compounds (strippers) have become popular in recent years. The majority of these products intended for institutional use are dual-purpose, that is, they serve as polish removers at a high concentration and as floor cleaning compounds at a low concentration. While individual brands will vary in effectiveness, the reputable floor-polish removers are more effective than the conventional cleaning compounds, because they are formulated for the purpose of removing coatings of floor polish, with general-purpose cleaning deemed secondary. Many of these polish removing compounds contain ammonia or organic amines which act as re-emulsifying agents for dried floor-polish films. Cleaners containing ammonia are usually quite effective in removal of these dried floor-polish films. There are objections to the odor of ammonia. Ammonia is an alkaline detergent, but it is a volatile substance and, therefore, does not leave residual alkaline deposits on the floor. To a large extent, solutions of soap-base compounds or synthetic detergents can be made into effective floor-polish strippers by the addition of aqueous ammonia to the solution.

Floor bleaching compounds, designed for use on wood floors, contain chemicals which release oxygen or chlorine in solution. These products are suggested for the stripping of worn shellac or varnish films from floor surfaces, particularly hardwood floors. The products are strongly alkaline and potentially damaging to wood and other floor coverings. They should be used with much caution and with particular attention to specific directions for use. It is suggested that the use of bleaching compounds be limited to spot and stain removal where other means of removal are ineffective.

METHODS AND EQUIPMENT

Sweeping and dry-mopping

Of all floor maintenance operations, sweeping is the most commonly performed; it is almost always a necessary preliminary to other cleaning operations.

Daily sweeping is recommended for the removal of loose dirt and grit, which, if not removed, may become embedded in the flooring.

Sweeping every day will reduce the frequency of wet-cleaning and scrubbing and will help to preserve the life of the floor covering. Sweeping can be accomplished by using brooms, brushes, cloths, mops, and vacuum sweepers. The choice of equipment will, to some extent, depend on the type of floor covering and the nature of the dirt to be removed.

While proper attention to efficient sweeping will cut down the frequency of wet-cleaning, it is not intended to be a substitute for washing and scrubbing. Thus, when adherent soil and stains become apparent, sweeping is no longer effective and washing is needed.

General/Boushelle Corporation

Team of commercial maintenance specialists
dust-mopping asphalt tile floor.

Mops and cloths. Mops used for sweeping are constructed of strands of cotton yarn, which may vary in length, attached to a canvas sleeve designed to slip over a mop frame attached to a handle. Mop handles are usually about 5 feet long. The mop frames, which are usually constructed of metal rods or heavy wire, come in variable sizes for attaching mops from 12 to 60 inches in length and 3 to 6 inches in width. Mops can be purchased in untreated form or rented, chemically treated, from rental-service laundries.

Chemically treated dust cloths for use on floors can be mounted on specially designed wood frames equipped with a long handle. An advantage in using the treated cloths is that they are easier to change when they become soiled than mops are.

An important development in sanitary maintenance during the past ten years has been a scientific approach to sweeping by the use of chemically treated cotton mops and cloths. Through the combined efforts of leaders in the field of sanitary maintenance administration and engineering and suppliers of equipment and maintenance chemicals, systems for floor maintenance have been developed that (1) reduce labor costs, (2) are more effective and more sanitary, and (3) improve the day-to-day appearance of the floors. Generally speaking, the preferred and recommended method of sweeping is by the use of chemically treated sweeping tools.

The user has three choices in obtaining chemically treated mops or cloths. First, he can purchase the necessary chemical-treatment compounds from reliable suppliers of chemical specialty products and apply them to his own mops or cloths. Proper use of these treated sweeping tools requires that they be washed and re-treated frequently. Therefore, unless suitable laundry facilities are available, this choice is foreclosed. Also, while chemical treatment is desirable, the improper application of the treating compounds can cause floor maintenance problems (dulling and more rapid re-soiling) and actual damage to some floor coverings (staining, softening, and swelling). It is recommended that users do not treat their own mops or cloths unless they have the proper equipment and well trained personnel to supervise directly the laundering and re-treatment of these items.

The second choice, available widely throughout the United States in metropolitan areas and becoming increasingly available in smaller communities, is the rental of chemically treated mops and cloths from laundries. There are a variety of widely advertised trademarked brands of treatments and treated mops available through local laundries with franchises for preparation and distribution of the treated mops. Other laundries supply similar treated mops under their own brand names. Purchasers should exercise care and judgment in choosing treated sweeping tools to make certain they are properly prepared. It is important that the mops and cloths do not contain an excess of the treatment component and that, when used on clean and highly polished floors, no dulling deposits remain.

The third choice is to purchase disposable treated cloths made of non-woven cotton and rayon fibers. The use of these lint-free fabrics overcomes the dangers inherent in misapplication of treating compounds by inexperienced personnel and does away with the inconveniences associated with storage, delivery, and pickup of laundry. The disposable treated cloths are available in various sizes, including 12 by 17, 16 by 24, 24 by 18, and 40 by 16 inches. Priced at about 8 to 10 cents per cloth, they are considerably more expensive than a do-it-yourself treatment operation, but compare quite favorably with a laundry rental service. The disposal feature and uniform treatment make these cleaning and sweeping cloths highly desirable for many maintenance situations.

Floor brushes. Brushes consist of bristles set in wooden or plastic blocks and have removable handles that can be adjusted for use in various positions. Bristles are made from horsehair, plastic, tampico, nylon, wire, polystyrene, palmetto, palmyra, and bassine. Each type or combination of bristles has special characteristics which make the brush especially suited to different floor conditions. The blocks into which the bristles are set come in various lengths, ranging from 12 to 48 inches with flat or raised center portions. The bristles are usually trimmed to 2⅜ to 4 inches in length. Handles for the brushes can be obtained up to 10 feet long, although the standard sizes are 54, 60, and 72 inches. V-shaped brushes are manufactured for cleaning baseboards, moldings, and stair risers.

Brooms. Bristles are made of broom corn, natural fibers, or synthetic materials, such as nylon or plastic. The bristles are usually about 10 inches long and are fastened together by a series of stitchings or, more securely, by a metal frame that has been closed by riveting.

Sweeping compounds. In general, sweeping compounds, consisting of impregnated sawdust or other bulky, fibrous material, are not required and should not be used on resilient or hard-surface floor coverings. They may be useful on hardwood floors under some conditions. Compounds containing inorganic matter should be avoided.

Dustpans. Dustpans are made of steel, tin, rubber, or plastic. They come equipped with long or short handles and with or without lids. Selection depends on frequency of use and type of soil to be collected.

Mechanical sweepers. There are three types of sweepers: manually operated, and gasoline- and electric-powered units. In manually operated sweepers, the turning of the wheels revolves the brush. The brush itself is usually about 27 inches wide. Gasoline-powered sweepers are intended for outdoor use or in factories or warehouses having adequate ventilation. Electrical sweepers are battery- or line-operated and use a 36- to 48-inch brush.

Vacuums. Vacuum cleaners are essential in maintenance of carpet; with wand attachments, they are also suitable for use on hard-surface floors. For a discussion of various types of vacuum cleaners, their applications, and attachments, see the discussion on this type of equipment at the end of this chapter.

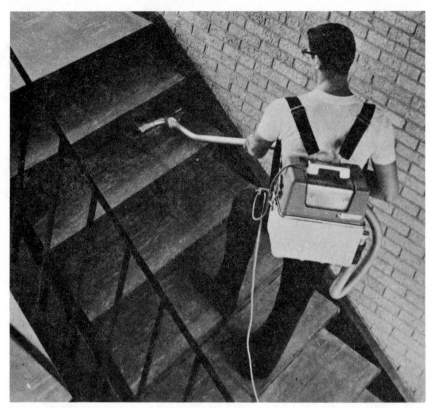

Breuer Electric Mfg. Co.

Portable vacuum cleaner.

Wet-mopping

Mopping, in industrial and institutional maintenance, generally means using water in the operation. As already suggested, dry-mopping, especially with chemically treated mops, is another form of sweeping. There are two categories of wet-mopping, depending on the amount of water coming in contact with the floor surface. Damp-mopping refers to the use of a mop which has been well wrung out to remove all excess moisture leaving only the amount of water retained by the mop yarn. Wet-mopping means the use of sufficient water to "flood," i.e., cover, the floor surface with a layer of water which must subsequently be squeegeed off or picked up by various methods.

Damp-mopping is usually done frequently and in combination with sweeping. The purpose is to remove water-soluble soil deposits and stains that cannot be removed by sweeping, but to avoid removal of the protective coating of floor polish. Frequently, cold water alone is employed, but the use of a minimum amount of neutral synthetic detergent—liquids are preferred—will aid in wetting greasy soils. Avoid excess detergent and vigorous rubbing of the floor surface; the objective is to retain the film of floor polish and allow for re-buffing to bring up the gloss to its original level.

Successful damp-mopping can be achieved only if certain fundamental principles are recognized. Dirt removal, not dirt redistribution, is the primary purpose. Therefore, the mop should be rinsed frequently and the rinse water changed quite often.

It is not good practice to damp-mop hardwood floors regularly. On properly sealed hardwood floors which are maintained with buffable solvent-base floor polishes, damp-mopping with a solution containing a minimum of synthetic detergent may be employed for the removal of water-dispersible soil accumulations or for cleaning up spillages.

Marble, terrazzo, concrete, and other masonry surfaces can be damp-mopped as needed and without limitation.

Damp-mopping should be done as often as is necessary and practical. Generally, it is required at least once a week. To some extent, damp-mopping has been replaced by the use of chemically treated sweeping tools.

Wet-mopping is done as a separate operation, or in conjunction with stripping soiled coatings of floor polish from floors. There are precautions to be observed in wet-mopping. Damage can be caused to floor coverings, particularly resilient tile, by penetration of the cleaning solution through the cracks or spaces between the tiles and into the adhesive cement holding the tiles to the subfloor. Therefore, avoid flooding the floor surface with an excessive amount of cleaning solution and allowing the cleaning solution to remain on the surface more than a few minutes. These precautions are of particular importance on any newly installed resilient floor. Lifting, cupping, and curling of tile can result from "wash out" of adhesive. Where waterproof cement has been used to bond the tile to the subfloor, as is recommended for below-grade installations, this type of adhesive failure is rare.

Rubber, homogeneous vinyl, and vinyl asbestos tile are less sensitive to deterioration by absorption of moisture than are linoleum, cork, and asphalt tile floor coverings. Maintenance workers often do not understand that frequent and continued exposure to water of unprotected surfaces of linoleum and asphalt tile will cause these floor coverings to wear more rapidly. Water has a softening action on these surfaces and, to a lesser extent, on vinyl asbestos tile. If these coverings are frequently softened and kept from drying out completely by repeated contact with excessive amounts of water, indentation marks, scratching, and gouging will result, along with more abrasive wear and ingraining of dirt. The effect is more pronounced when highly alkaline cleaning solutions are employed.

In the stripping of soiled coatings of floor polish from resilient floor coverings, it is necessary to allow a soaking period to remove the coating effectively without using excessive scrubbing or scouring action. This is permissible because stripping is not generally required more often than once a month and the trend in industrial maintenance, by employment of improved systems, is to lengthen the period between strippings to eight to ten weeks or more.

Hardwood floors should never be wet-mopped or scrubbed; water will cause raising of the grain, warping, and swelling. Chapter 6, "Wood Floors," contains a discussion of recommended methods of cleaning.

Masonry floorings can be wet-mopped without restriction, provided the proper cleaning solutions are used and the procedures suggested in the separate sections dealing with particular types of masonry floors are followed (see Chapter 5).

For satisfactory results in wet-mopping, it is necessary to use mops of good quality and of sufficient body and absorbency. The precise concentration of cleaning solution recommended by the manufacturer should be employed. For acceptable products, this will mean that sufficient cleaning compound, but not an excess, is used. In the case of some alkaline-salt mixtures, using excess compound may damage the floor. The mop should be lightly pressed out, retaining as much solution as it will hold without dripping a stream. The solution should be applied over an area of about 10 square feet, covering all portions of the surface. The soil should be loosened by rubbing the mop back and forth. Then the floor should be squeegeed and the soiled solution taken up with a well-wrung-out mop.

The cleaning solution should be changed at frequent intervals. The necessity for this will depend upon the amount of soil on the floor. The tendency to continue using the same cleaning solution until it gets thick should be avoided.

The final, and perhaps most important step, is rinsing the floor. This should be done immediately following the squeegee operation, using clear water and a clean mop. The mop used for applying the cleaning solution should not be used for rinsing. The rinsing mop should be wrung out enough for it to pick up any residual film of soiled cleaning solution. The mop should be dipped frequently in the rinse water, which should be changed often.

Most cleaned floors are coated with a polish to protect them against ingraining of dirt, to improve the gloss, and to extend their life.

Damp cloths. Frequently overlooked by maintenance men is the use of moist cloths in conjunction with a sweeping tool. Such cloths are available in sheet form for broom attachment, or in sack form with a taped center hole which fits over the brush handle, permitting the cloth to be tucked under the brush. The soiled cloths are laundered and re-used on a regular basis. Dampened cloths are completely safe for all types of floors, except wood and cork, and offer the extra benefit of removing light, water-soluble soils.

Wet mops. Mops consist of long strands of twisted cotton yarn or cellulose attached to a handle. Cotton mops are classified by weight, ranging from 12 to 48 ounces. Cellulose mops, being more absorbent than cotton yarn, are made to weigh from 8 to 32 ounces. The strands of a mop are usually 16 to 21 inches long. A typical cotton yarn mop will hold three times its weight in water, and a cellulose mop will hold somewhat more. Bleached cotton yarn is generally more absorbent than unbleached. Bleaching, however, could result in lower yarn strength. Therefore, good mop yarn should be a balance between absorbency and strength in order to obtain maximum service life and optimum usefulness. Other contributing factors to strand strength are the degree and permanency of twist. Strands that become untwisted and separated are more likely to break than full-twisted strands. Mops should be well rinsed and hung to dry to prevent souring, mildew, and attack by residual chemicals.

Mop buckets. Buckets are generally made of galvanized iron. Capacities range from 3 to 45 gallons; the larger sizes are mounted on casters for easy handling. Small sizes may also be fitted with casters, if desired. Mop bucket assemblies consist of two buckets on a dolly. One bucket is for the cleaning solution and the other for the rinse water.

Wringers. There are two general types of wringers in use. The roller type functions like an old-fashioned clothes wringer. The rollers can be spread to allow for insertion of the mop. Foot pressure brings the rollers together while the mop is being pulled up between them. The other type of wringer is a "squeezer." This consists of four perforated metal sections, fitted together like a triangular crate. One of these sections is on a hinge, so it can push forward to compress or "squeeze" the wet mop.

Sponge mops and squeegees. Sponge mops consist of a cellulose sponge mounted on a hinged, perforated metal plate. When the sponge becomes saturated with liquid, it can be hand-wrung by bending the plates from the hinge and applying pressure. These mops are used chiefly for water pickup in a mopping operation. Typical lengths range from 10 to 36 inches.

Floor squeegees are excellent companion tools for use in wet-mopping and scrubbing operations. Made of flexible neoprene, the blades are available in 18- and 24-inch lengths with handles in standard sizes, i.e., 54 and 60 inches.

Scrubbing

Scrubbing is an effective means of removing embedded soil, gross accumulations of greasy, resinous, and water-insoluble soil, and old floor polish. Scrubbing can be accomplished by hand, using either a mop or a scrubbing brush, or by a power-driven machine. Many types of machines are available, but it should be remembered that the weight of the machine and friction generated thereby are important factors in the effectiveness of such scrubbing equipment.

One method of scrubbing, which is best adapted to dense and smooth surface floor coverings, is to use the heel of a mop in the scrubbing operation. For example, a floor area between 200 and 400 square feet would first be wet with cleaning solution. The operation of wetting an area this size permits sufficient time for the cleaner to contact the dirt. The floor is then mop-scrubbed, followed by wet-pickup and rinse operations.

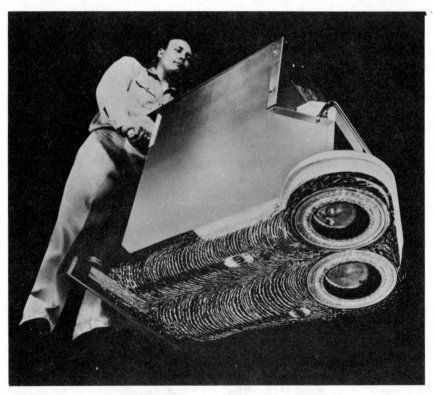

American-Lincoln Corporation

Floor scrubbing machine in operation.

3M Company

Cleaning baseboards with special brush on floor machine.

A heavy machine with a 14- or 16-inch brush is ideal for scrubbing, because it has the necessary weight to penetrate crevices and pores and to strip coatings of floor polish. (See section on "Powered Maintenance Equipment," page 49.) The cleaning solution should be applied to the floor, and a soaking period of at least 2 or 3 minutes should follow. The soaking should loosen the dirt particles and re-emulsify the polish coatings. Next, the floor should be scrubbed and the dirty solution removed. Rinsing and final removal of water must be thorough to avoid damage to the floor. A vacuum water-pickup machine is useful in removing scrub water and rinse water.

Many attachments are available for scrubbing jobs. Brushes for use on fabrics and other fine materials are manufactured, and each has its advantages. For difficult stains, fine steel-wool brushes are made. Silicon carbide disks are desirable for heavy-duty applications. Nylon-web disks, while expensive, do a completely satisfactory job and can be rinsed out and used again.

Authoritative studies of floor maintenance procedures have led to the use of scrubbing teams on large-size floors. This enables one man to scrub while one or two other men spread the cleaning solution and pick it up from the scrubbed areas. Moreover, greater efficiency has been found, where women are employed, in the use of lighter-weight scrubbing machines.

Most scrubbed floors are finished by application of a polish to obtain a lustrous appearance, preserve the floor, and lengthen the time interval between cleanings.

Polishing

It has been proved that polishing of all resilient floor coverings is advantageous and desirable. Also, in the case of industrial and institutional maintenance, it has been shown that the use of floor polish can reduce the cost of maintenance by lowering the labor cost because less time is required to keep up the appearance. Therefore, the regular maintenance of all resilient floor coverings by polishing is recommended.

Hardwood floors have long been maintained with floor waxes. A well-sealed hardwood floor, when properly maintained with a good solvent-base buffable wax, is rich-looking and attractive. Water-base emulsion waxes should not be used on wood floors.

There are severe limitations to the use of floor polishes on masonry floors (see Chapter 5).

Before a fresh coat of floor polish is applied, the floor itself should be prepared by removing all dirt and residual film of old floor polish. This means that the floor surface should be swept, mopped or scrubbed, rinsed and allowed to dry. If polish is applied over a layer of dirt, rubber heel marks, or stains, the soil will be sealed in, thus making subsequent removal all the more difficult.

Certain developments in the floor polish industry during the past 15 years may have caused confusion as to what a floor polish actually is. To reduce such confusion, brought about by use of the terms "waxless floor polish," "bright-dry wax," "resin finishes," "floor dressing," and other labels, the term "floor polish" will be used here. By this is meant any composition or product intended for use as a temporary and removable coating on a floor surface to protect it, make maintenance easier, and improve the appearance of the floor. From the standpoint of composition, a variety of floor polishes are available. For the practical consideration of the consumer, however, these can be reduced to two principal categories, namely, buffable—those that can be buffed to increase their gloss, and non-buffable—those that are not appreciably improved in gloss by buffing. Compromises between the two are possible.

It is the consensus in the sanitary maintenance field that there is a place for both buffable and non-buffable floor polishes. Generally, the buffable types are needed for areas opening directly off the street, or where a good deal of siliceous dirt is tracked in on shoes. Expressed another way, high-quality buffable waxes will withstand more severe traffic conditions with less maintenance and replacement than the majority of non-buffable products.

In areas of less severe traffic, the non-buffable polishes enjoy a wide acceptance, because they require less maintenance effort. They are not buffed after sweeping with chemically treated mops and, hence, there is a saving in cost of maintenance. Because they are customarily used on areas of lighter traffic and because they produce tough films, they may require less frequent stripping and replacement that, again, makes for economy in maintenance.

Regarding safety or potential accident hazard, it is impossible to make recommendations that will govern all conditions and circumstances. Anti-slip buffable and non-buffable polishes are available and are specified by certain large consumers of institutional floor polish.

The purchaser of floor-polishing materials should be alerted to the potential fire hazard of some of these products. The possibility of fire exists during the application of solvent-base polishes and while they are drying. The degree of hazard is in direct relation to the "flash point" of the product being used, i.e., its level of flammability. "Flash point" is defined as "the lowest temperature at which a material will evolve sufficient vapor to form a flammable mixture with air."

This hazard does not exist in the case of water-base emulsion polishes. With respect to the solvent-base polishes, it would be wise for the purchaser to choose a product having a relatively high flash point. In general, the person selecting a floor polish should ask the supplier about the relative flammability of the product.

When certain factors make the use of a product with a low flash point particularly desirable, the user should take special precautions to avoid fire, such as applying the material in a well-ventilated room, being careful about matches, cigarettes, electrical sparks, and other sources of ignition.

Buffable polishes. When exposure to traffic mars the appearance of a buffable finish, it can be damp-mopped and buffed many times with little loss of original gloss. This capacity for being repeatedly buffed, as needed, greatly extends the interval between necessary re-coatings. Buffable floor polishes are available in three general types—liquid-emulsion, solvent-base, and paste-emulsion.

Liquid-emulsion polishes produce a gloss upon drying, but a higher gloss is obtained by buffing. The polish film, which is rich in wax content, is usually soft and, therefore, susceptible to scuffing, marring, and heel marking. Heel marks and scuff marks may be removed from the dried film by damp-mopping, or sweeping with chemically treated mops, and re-buffing to restore original gloss. After buffing, liquid-emulsion polishes are generally more resistant to water spotting.

Buffable liquid-emulsion polishes are composed of waxes, resins (synthetic and natural), emulsifying agents, and water. They may contain polymers, leveling agents, anti-slip agents (e.g., collodial silica) and plasticizing agents. The degree to which a polish film is buffable depends upon the proportion of waxes, or other materials having wax-like properties, which are present.

Solvent-base polishes are available as liquids and pastes. Except for solids content, the liquids and pastes are similar. Solvent-base polishes should not be used on some types of resilient floor coverings—specifically asphalt, rubber, and homogeneous and backed vinyl—because the hydro-carbon solvents soften or dissolve some constituents of these floor coverings. Solvent-base floor polishes should be used on wood and cork and may be used on linoleum and vinyl asbestos. The choice between liquids and pastes is more a matter of convenience than a fundamental difference in behavior or properties. Generally, a heavier coating is laid down by application of a paste, and, in limited cases, this may be advantageous—for example, when being applied to a somewhat porous wood or cork floor. However, liquids are more easily applied and, in addition, serve as effective cleaning agents.

Solvent-base polishes must be buffed to produce a gloss. Electrically powered, heavy, buffing machines achieve the best results. Multiple-brush machines help to eliminate swirl marks, the appearance of which some people find unsatisfactory but others consider the distinctive sign of a well polished floor.

Paste-emulsion polishes are a combination of water-emulsion, bright-drying polishes, and solvent-base polishes. The polishes contain water, but they also contain solvent. They were designed primarily for use on asphalt tile, vinyl asbestos tile, and rubber tile. Water is the external phase of the emulsion. In theory, the water is supposed to wet the surface upon application of polish, thereby inhibiting the penetration and absorption of hydro-carbon solvents by the floor covering. However, as a matter of practice, the pre-application of two or three thin coats of an acceptable water-base emulsion polish that does not contain solvent is advised to seal the surface after it has been stripped.

There are a variety of these paste-emulsion products sold under different brand names; some are designated as "maintenance compounds," and "cleaning and polishing systems"; others are labeled simply as "emulsion-paste waxes." All of these products are composed of substantial amounts of waxes, and several contain acrylic polymers or polystyrene. They also contain surface-active ingredients which act as emulsifying agents and, when applied with mechanical action, function as cleaning agents.

The claim is made that these floor polishes eliminate the need for wet-cleaning, scrubbing, and stripping. Although such polishes are recommended by the manufacturers for use on all types of floors, application is subject to the limitations mentioned previously relating to the use of polish on masonry floors.

The standard procedure calls for spreading the paste emulsion on a very fine steel-wool pad or a non-woven nylon pad, placing the treated pad under the brush or holder of a heavy, powered polishing machine, and then running the machine back and forth over a limited area of floor surface. The dirt on the floor is loosened by the combined action of the emulsifying agents and the mechanical abrasion of the pad. In theory, the soil is transferred to the pad; the emulsion breaks down and releases the waxes and other polishing agents, which are buffed by the continuous action and produce a gloss. The contact of hydrocarbon solvent with the floor surface is kept at a minimum, and no damage is caused to floor coverings ordinarily affected by solvents.

The limitations and drawbacks connected with the use of paste-emulsion polishes are: (1) The pads become fouled with floor soil and require frequent changing on heavily soiled floors; (2) The cleaning action is not as efficient as wet-cleaning, and, for best results, scrubbing must be done periodically; (3) The expense for pads or the cost of washing the pads (in the case of non-woven nylon pads) may equal or exceed any savings in labor costs for wet-cleaning; (4) The polish film is less durable than other types.

The advantages of the paste-emulsion polishes are that they work fast and may reduce labor costs, and they can be employed without closing off to the public the floor area which is being cleaned and polished.

Non-buffable polishes. A non-buffable finish will hold its initial good appearance for a long period of time with an absolute minimum of interim maintenance. But, as the finish wears, its appearance level drops faster than that of a buffable polish. This means that the time period between stripping and refinishing a non-buffable polish is normally shorter than when a buffable polish is used.

At one time, it could be stated that there was only one type of industrial or institutional non-buffable floor polish—namely, water-base emulsion. This is no longer the case since the introduction of a solvent-soluble polymer, which is readily re-dissolved by subsequent application of the solvent system. While these solvent-polymer systems are currently limited to wood floors, they have made an impact on the market. They dry to a bright, glossy finish, yet can be easily maintained by the one-step cleaning process associated with the paste-emulsion polishes.

The typical non-buffable polishes differ in composition from the buffable water-base emulsion polishes, mainly in the proportions of waxes or wax-like materials incorporated. Generally, these polishes contain a substantially higher proportion of emulsion polymers, such as the acrylics and polystyrenes. Thus, the dried polish film is usually harder and less tacky than a film of buffable-type polish.

Although the non-buffable polishes, under certain conditions, require less stripping and can be maintained at lower labor costs, they have some disadvantages. Generally, they tend to become scratched instead of showing scuff marks. Much greater care is required for their application, since "skips" (areas not coated) will show up readily as "holidays," easily picking up dirt and becoming unsightly blotches. Buffable polishes tend to spread or transfer to the uncoated areas during buffing. The non-buffable polishes may become brittle and begin to powder or show traffic-lane wear under conditions of low temperature and humidity. They also may be more difficult to remove by the usual stripping procedures. This disadvantage was more important when the non-buffable polymer-type products first came on the market. Substantial improvement in removability has since been made.

New types of polish. During the last few years, floor-polish manufacturers have introduced new types of water-base polymers that have greatly expanded the choice of products available for maintenance. Some of these new products consist of polymer systems, which are highly resistant to alkaline cleaning compounds. Their ability to withstand such strong cleaning agents makes it possible to remove effectively more types of soil and restore the original level of cleanliness without loss of gloss. The performance of such polymer systems on floors is otherwise comparable to other non-buffable polishes, since they can be given intermittent maintenance by broom or treated sweeping tool. They differ from the usual product in the methods used for their removal. One of these types may be stripped by using a mildly acid solution, supplied by the manufacturer. Some floor surfaces are adversely affected by acids. Therefore, before selecting this type of polish, it is important to know whether the acidic cleaning agent will damage the floor in question.

A second type of polish, resistant to alkaline cleaning compounds, also requires a special kind of polish remover containing water-soluble solvents to accomplish complete stripping from the floor. Using abrasive pads during the stripping operation greatly facilitates the removal of the polish.

A third type of polish, resistant to alkaline cleaning compounds, which is used in the household field, but may be offered for institutional use, requires treatment with ammonia solutions to effect complete removal.

Of the three types described here, the first has been on the market for the longest period. So far, it has met with varied success. The other two polishes have not been available long enough to be fully evaluated in maintenance work.

A completely different approach in water-based polishes is presented with the wash-and-wax products. These materials combine cleaning and polishing in one step. Although they are basically combinations of polymers and synthetic detergents, their formulation requires skill on the part of the manufacturer to achieve the proper blend of properties, while maintaining adequate shelf stability. To date, the use of wash-and-wax products is limited to household operations.

Polish specifications. There is a great temptation on the part of many users of floor polishes to write purchasing descriptions that are a conglomeration of every specification in the field. This is done in the mistaken beliefs that all specifications are compatible and that a polish must contain certain ingredients in order to be acceptable. While materials such as carnauba wax, polystyrene, and acrylic copolymers are used to make outstanding products, it does not follow that their presence in a polish guarantees superior performance. Frequently, purchase descriptions are written with little regard to whether the required ingredients can be accurately determined by analysis. There have also been instances where the chemical structure of the specified raw materials is incorrectly stated.

The user must decide which of the many maintenance systems is best suited for his particular situation. Once this has been determined, a specification can be prepared. It should contain at least four basic elements. First, performance without regard to composition should be specified. For example, the purchaser may want to specify a polish that will dry to a hard, bright finish without buffing for particular building areas. For other areas, he may want to specify a buffable polish that is slip-resistant.

The second element of a good specification is the inclusion of adequate tests for deleterious action by the polish on specific flooring materials. For example, in the manufacture of polishes for use on rubber flooring, certain ingredients must be avoided, because they are known to have a harmful effect on rubber.

The third element of a good specification has to do with inspection tests designed to assure the user that he is consistently getting the product he originally selected. These could be tests for non-volatile matter, benzene solubles, alcohol solubles, pH, ash content, and so forth. Fourth, agreement between buyer and seller is necessary to establish the acceptable degree of variation for each of these appraisal points.

Accessory equipment

Work carts. Because custodial staffs are required to perform many cleaning functions besides floor care, it is becoming increasingly popular to invest in mobile carts to carry a variety of tools including mops, brushes, pails, cleaning compounds, dust pans, wiping cloths, and so forth. Easily loaded and pushed, these tool caddies reduce the number of trips to supply closets and increase the efficiency of personnel.

Mats. Floor mats play an important part in floor care because they prevent dirt from being tracked into buildings, protect floors from damage, and provide safe areas for work and walking.

Mats are available for all types of exterior and interior floors and are manufactured in many shapes and from many materials. They are made of rubber, vinyl, steel, wood, cocoa, nylon, cotton, carpeting, abrasive-coated fibers, and sponge. In many cases, mats are available with sponge backings to improve foot comfort.

Solid varieties of rubber and vinyl have deeply embossed and corrugated surfaces to trap dirt, water, and snow. Surface effects also include rib constructions in many choices of design.

Perforated mats are sold with holes of many geometric shapes to serve the same general purposes as their solid counterparts.

Link mats are among the older types of matting; the links are held by metal reinforcing springs. The open construction of such mats permits rapid drainage while serving as foot scrapers to clean shoes. Surface materials used in link mats include rubber, vinyl, metal, and wood.

The natural-fiber cocoa mats are the oldest forms of floor mats. They are sold in thicknesses of 1½ and 1¾ inches, in widths ranging from 14 to 72 inches, and in any length. In runner forms, their ends are finished with metal, rubber, or fabric webbing.

Combination carpet-rubber mats have nylon or viscose surfaces for absorbency and rubber backings to prevent slipping, bunching-up, or curling. The carpet is easily cleaned if proper cleaning compounds are used. Special carpet runners made of nylon-wool blends with latex backings are also available for building entrances.

Flexible wooden mats with or without rubber cushion bases are sold in widths up to 72 inches and in any length. They form durable platforms for work areas.

The newest type of floor mat is treated, deep-cotton-pile carpet with heavy non-skid backing. Developed as an outgrowth of chemically treated dust cloths, such "walk-off" mats are used especially in entranceways to pick up and retain dust, grime, dirt, grit, and salt. Their use can result in substantial savings in maintenance costs incurred by scrubbing, polishing, and vacuuming. These mats are usually available from the same type of laundry service that handles chemically treated cloths and mops.

WORKROOMS AND STORAGE

A properly organized supply closet of adequate size can appreciably reduce maintenance costs. It should be an integral part of a workroom, which, in the preferred situation, is a space set aside for use by maintenance personnel and for storage of maintenance equipment. If such a room is not available, the supply closet could be located in a washroom or locker room. If space limitations prohibit this, the closet should be located near such a room. This arrangement improves efficiency, because supplies and cleaning facilities are readily accessible.

Supply closets should be well ventilated, with odors exhausted mechanically to avoid contamination of the workroom air. Proper heating and ventilation will prevent polishes and sealers from spoiling.

Shelves for orderly and separate storage of mop wringers, buckets, sponges, mops, brushes, towels, tissue, and other supplies should be in the well-planned closet. Pole racks for mops and brooms are also essential. The service sink should have a hot- and cold-water mixing faucet, and the sink rim should be protected from chipping with a stainless steel cover.

There should be enough shelving to store all supplies so that floor space is not used for storage and thereby obstructed. Equipment and supplies left exposed are unsightly and facilitate pilferage, waste, and spoilage. Closets should be kept locked.

Materials packaged in small containers should be distributed in those containers; bulk items such as cleaning compounds, disinfectants, floor polishes, etc., should be distributed in gallon plastic jugs. Each jug should be marked with a product label or with paint designating the type of product, its use, and the correct dilution.

Non-porous flooring materials are best for workrooms because they are easy to maintain. Floors in this category would include concrete, terrazzo, and ceramic tile. Where floors are pitted or porous, re-surfacing with a variety of materials can correct the condition. It is possible today to re-surface floors with colored cement mixes that eliminate the need for periodic painting. The application of floor sealers will make this type of surface non-porous and permit quick hosing-down and mopping. Hosing-down is restricted, of course, to those rooms having floor drains.

Wall surfaces should be impervious to moisture, dirt, and odors. Such non-porous surfaces are easy to keep clean. Walls and ceilings should be checked for their cleanliness and evidence of good housekeeping, as well as for their basic condition. Unwashed walls are depressing and tend to reduce light efficiency. Walls should be covered where they join the floor to eliminate corners where dirt can accumulate and to facilitate cleaning. Walls behind washbasins should be protected with splashboards, if the wall surface cannot withstand frequent scrubbing. The entire workroom can be dadoed or wainscoted with a material such as porcelainized steel tile to a height of 80 inches from the floor.

SAFETY PRECAUTIONS

Most floor materials are reasonably slip-resistant, but there are exceptions. Smoothly finished, unpolished surfaces such as marble, terrazzo, and ceramic tile can be very slippery, especially when wet.

For new installations, special slip-resistant surfaces should be specified on all ramps and stairs. Where terrazzo is to be used, abrasive materials such as silicon carbide and aluminum oxide can be added to the topping. Abrasive inserts are also used with marble, terrazzo, and metal stairways to improve traction. Special resilient tiles are available with abrasive fillers to reduce slipperiness.

Existing floors can be covered with strips of abrasive tapes having pressure-sensitive adhesive backings. These materials are sold in widths up to 36 inches and in rolls up to 60 feet long. Such non-skid safety strippings can be applied directly to smooth, clean, dry surfaces by peeling off the protective backing and pressing the adhesive surface onto the floor. A special grade of tape with a separate liquid adhesive is also sold for use on rough surfaces such as concrete floors and areas where dust and moisture cannot be completely eliminated.

For routine finishing and maintenance, a special precaution should be noted. The degree of friction in the surface coating—varnish, lacquer, polish, etc.—should not vary within a particular area or between adjacent areas. That is, the relative resistance to slipperiness should be as consistent as possible. A person walking across a floor should not suddenly find himself on a much more slippery surface without warning. Conversely, the hazard of slipping and falling is increased if a person unexpectedly moves from a smooth, slippery surface to a rougher one. Therefore, the use of finishing and polishing materials with different frictional qualities should be avoided within one floor area or on adjacent areas.

Floors should be kept in good repair. Cracks, dents, ridges, and holes should be corrected as they appear, and tiles with raised edges replaced immediately. Wrinkled carpets require re-stretching; loose seams and tears should be sewn or cemented into place or both. Worn areas in marble and terrazzo, especially on stairways, should be replaced or re-surfaced. Loose, springy, wood boards should be fastened securely or replaced.

Spilled oil or grease should be removed from the floor as quickly as possible. Oil should be removed with rags or absorbed with dry sweeping compounds. Grease should be scraped up and the soiled area cleaned, rinsed thoroughly, and dried.

Spilled or tracked-in liquids should be wiped up as soon as possible. Entrances should be covered with floor mats during wet weather, and runners laid out in areas leading from outside doors.

Hard surfaces can become dangerously slippery if cleaning solutions are allowed to dry without adequate rinsing. The area should be thoroughly rinsed to remove residual cleaning materials and then mop-dried or wet-vacuumed to pick up all liquids.

Floors should be kept free of loose foreign objects—paper, pins, clips, pencils, etc.—by sweeping or vacuuming regularly.

While cleaning or other treatment of floors is going on, the area should be barricaded with readily visible ropes and stanchion barriers. Warning signs reading "No Passing," "Wet Floors," and so forth can be provided at the main approaches to areas being cleaned or treated. Stairways should be blocked off at both top and bottom; doorways should be blocked off on both sides.

If an area of a floor has become hazardous because of spillage or damage, a warning sign should be posted until the condition has been corrected.

POWERED MAINTENANCE EQUIPMENT

Proper floor maintenance requires a variety of powered equipment in addition to hand tools. The choice and amount of equipment to be acquired depend on the types of floors to be maintained, the extent of floor space, the size of the work force, and the working time available.

Powered floor maintenance equipment includes three general classes of machines, all of which are used in a variety of ways for cleaning and polishing floor surfaces: (1) Basic machines composed essentially of a frame mounted on wheels with a motor—usually gear-driven—which rotates a mechanism to which brushes are attached; (2) Combination scrubber-vacuum machines that apply a cleaning solution, scrub the floor, vacuum up the dirty solution, and leave the floor squeegee-dry in one continuous operation; (3) Vacuum cleaners, both wet and dry, with various accessories. This section describes and discusses such powered maintenance equipment.

Basic machines

The forerunner of the contemporary floor machine was designed and developed by Walter Scott Finnell and marketed in 1903. The basic principle was to create friction by brush action on the floor surface. There has been no fundamental change in the original principle, but over the years there have been improvements and refinements.

The original machine consisted of a frame supporting two wheels which, when moved along the floor, turned a beveled gear which in turn rotated a ring to which brushes were attached. A simple mop-type handle allowed the operator to work in an upright position. Three years later, an electric motor was used to power the unit and a new industry came into being.

Divided-weight machines. The early electrically powered units were divided-weight machines, that is, the weight of the motor—which was horizontally mounted—was carried by the revolving brush at one end and a pair of fixed wheels at the other end. In the modern version, power is transmitted to the brush through a worm-gear drive in a position directly over the brush. Because the wheels remain on the floor during operation, the brush weight on the floor consists of the combined weight of the brush and gear box plus a portion of the motor weight. The advantages of the divided-weight machine are: (1) Operating the machine is easy and does not require previous experience. This advantage is especially useful in situations where there is frequent change of machine operators. (2) The low silhouette permits access under low fixtures. (3) The low brush weight is desirable for rug scrubbing.

Concentrated-weight machines. After 1913, competition became sharper and machine styles began to change. Gear-case designs were shortened so that the motor assembly could be located on top of the brush covers, and the transporting wheels were made adjustable to an "up" position so that the full weight of the machine was on the operating brush. This concentrated-weight machine, commonly called "swing-type" or "weight-on-brush-type," has dominated the market since it was found to be more efficient and faster in operation. However, its operation requires more skill than the divided-weight machine and, because of its concentrated weight, it can damage floors in the hands of an untrained operator. These machines are moved by tilting the machine during operation to change its center of gravity.

Twin-brush machines. A third type of machine is the twin-brush (or multiple-brush) machine. The chief advantages of these units are their stability and extreme ease of use which are achieved by two counter-rotating brushes. These advantages explain their ready acceptance in household applications. Such machines were popular for a time as mainte-

Finnell Division,
Masury-Young Company

Divided-weight machine.

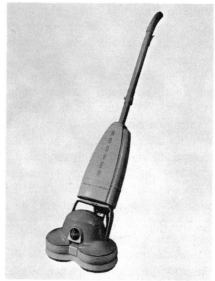

The Hoover Company

Twin-brush machine.

Nobles Engineering &
Manufacturing Company

Concentrated-weight machine.

S. C. Lawlor Co.

Combination scrubber-vacuum.

nance equipment in areas containing sensitive instruments, such as control rooms of telephone companies, but their industrial and institutional use has declined almost completely in favor of the concentrated-weight machines.

The principle of counter-rotation has achieved acceptance in the combination scrubber-vacuum machines. These consist of a motor-driven assembly, a cleaning solution tank from which the solution is dispensed through the brushes, a vacuum with self-adjusting squeegees for picking up dirty cleaning solution, and a dirty-water tank. (The battery-operated versions of these combination units are described in more detail later.)

Machine refinements. There have been a number of general improvements in floor machines over the years. Although no single machine combines all the latest refinements, all manufacturers have adopted most of the innovations.

Although most machines today are completely gear-driven, dispensing with chains and belts, one model still relies on a chain drive, and another has a toothed, neoprene, nylon-faced pulley drive. In the past, belts and chains were used for gear reduction primarily because they were quieter in operation; this is less true today. In addition, gear trains have been lowered in height so that the floor machine can be produced with a much lower silhouette. Low machines are not only better balanced than the earlier high ones, but can be used under low furniture or projections.

One machine is equipped with a stainless steel base, instead of the usual aluminum base. Less metal is used in the "skirt" of the base and the skirt is flatter and lower than those on some of the other machines. It is said to reach as far as 6½ inches under projections with a height as low as 3¼ inches. It is also claimed that the stainless steel base is not affected by strong cleaning agents. Another machine achieves a low profile by use of a gear box that rotates with the brush. It glides under a 3½ inch overhang. As with many other units, a foot pedal regulates the angle of the handle.

Although several new machines still utilize the hinged-wheel carriage, which can be raised for operation and lowered for transportation, machines are now being made with a stationary carriage, the wheels being large enough and so attached that the machine is simply tilted back for moving it about.

Another manufacturer claims "concentrated action" for his machine. He demonstrates its steadiness in operation by setting a glass of water on the motor. The manufacturer also claims that, because of the concentrated power, the motor cannot overheat. All the machine's weight is balanced along the center of gravity running in a straight line through motor, gears, and brush to the floor surface.

An offset motor design is offered by another manufacturer who claims that only two gears are required rather than five to eight gears for center-mounted machines. The simplified gear design enables the manufacturer to guarantee the gears against breakage for the life of the floor machine.

A planetary-type gear unit, with oversize ball bearings and hardened alloy steel and meehanite gears, is claimed by a manufacturer to increase durability and decrease noise. The gear unit is said to be very quiet in operation and is guaranteed for three years. The manufacturer claims that the specially designed ⅓ h.p. motor has 30 percent more power without an increase in the weight.

Another manufacturer has adapted his machine for interchange of motors, providing a choice of power to fit the job, obviating the need for two machines. Three-component precision gears form a direct drive from motor to brush. These machines are available in chromed steel, polished aluminum, and fused ceramic finish.

Explosion-proof floor machines are available that combine safety with efficiency when cleaning and polishing in the presence of combustible gases, liquids, and dust. The motor is completely enclosed, as are all other electrical components, such as switch and safety box.

A baseboard scrubber that is claimed to reduce manual labor substantially is a recent innovation in floor maintenance equipment. This floor machine features a nylon abrasive drum, 10 inches in diameter, impregnated with silicon carbide. The drum height comes in two sizes for 4-inch and 6-inch baseboards. The machine moves along, stripping dirt and wax from any baseboard, and at the same time serving as an edger on the floor next to the baseboard. It is fitted with a 1½-gallon solution tank similar to those used on conventional floor machines. The unit can be converted quickly to a 12-inch floor scrubber and polisher.

Handles and switches. Handles have been designed for quick and easy adjustment on most machines. In some cases, handles are hinged at the base of the machine so they can be swung up or down. The angle of the handle is usually regulated by a foot pedal that also locks the handle in position. A few machines have the handle in a sleeve so it can be lowered or raised to adjust to the height of the operator. Almost all handles are designed to permit vertical storage of the machine. In some cases, the handle can be completely removed. At least one manufacturer uses a handle of a tapered rectangular steel design that is claimed to be stronger than conventional tubular handles. Handle switches, formerly on only one side of the handle bars, are now available for either hand. The level principle is still used with most switches, although at least one machine uses the motor bike handle switch control. The handle grip is twisted forward or backward to operate the switch.

Brushes and pads. As in the case of the machines themselves, increasing use and competition have stimulated improvements in practically all attachments and accessories for the floor machine. Conventional brushes are made better, and the advent of synthetic buffing and scrubbing pads has increased the uses and efficiency of the machines. For example, steel wool is excellent for scouring all floors except terrazzo, marble, and oak. It is objectionable for use on these floors because fragments of steel wool left on the floor rust and cause stains which are difficult to remove. Pads of synthetic material that does not rust have solved this problem.

An important development in floor machine brushes appears to be an accordion-pleated ring of synthetic materials, ½ inch high and 2 inches wide, attached to the outer edge of the brush block. It is claimed that this type of brush will not flatten out or warp as brushes with bristles often do.

Another new kind of brush is a combination of nylon abrasive with conventional bristles set into a standard wooden base with a 5-inch bore.

Advance Floor Machine Company

Foot lever facilitates handle adjustment.

The combinations include a bassine/fill-nylon abrasive for scrubbing and stripping and a union mix or palmetto/fill-nylon abrasive for buffing operations.

A recent interim federal specification[1] describes thick nylon floor pads ($\frac{5}{8}$ to $\frac{7}{8}$ inch thick), thin nylon floor pads ($\frac{3}{16}$ to $\frac{3}{8}$ inch thick), and thick curled-hair floor pads ($\frac{5}{8}$ to $1\frac{1}{4}$ inch thick). The federal government uses all three types of pads, which are available for polishing (fine), buffing (medium), and scrubbing (coarse).

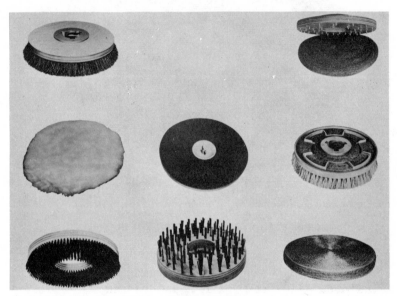

Clarke Floor Machine Division, Studebaker Corporation

Typical brushes and pads used with floor machines.

The thick nylon pads are made of spirally wound ribbons of interlocking nylon fibers bonded into a ring-shaped disk; the thin nylon pads are made of nylon webbing bonded or interlocked into a solid disk.

The thick floor pads, known commercially as "curled-hair pads," are made of a mixture of animal hair and hog bristles.

Polishing pads are manufactured without any abrasive; buffing and scouring pads are impregnated with a scouring agent in the form of a natural or synthetic abrasive, selected for particle size and hardness.

[1]"Interim Federal Specification 00-P-0046: Pads, Floors (Floor Polishing, Buffing, and Scrubbing and Pads, Driving and Pad Holders)," Washington: General Services Administration, Federal Supply Service, July 15, 1963.

The thin floor pads are used with a driving pad placed between the standard wood block and the floor pad. The driving pad is made of sponge rubber on one side and a driving face of rubber with small nubs or projections on the other side.

Nobles Engineering & Manufacturing Company

Combination nylon-abrasive and bristle brush.

Steel wool is still widely accepted by machine users. It is available in several grades—00 (finest), 0, 1, 2, and 3 (coarsest)—and a variety of shapes and sizes. Steel wool is manufactured to fit most conventional machines in pad form (either plain or, for additional strength, braided or welded), and in roll form for those who wish to fabricate their own pads. Several methods exist for attaching steel-wool pads to the machine. Sharp spikes, dull protrusions in the form of plugs or rods, plastic devices, and finger-like tools are used. The solid-disk, steel-wool floor pad is easily used by resting the floor machine with brush on the pad, relying on the brush bristles to hold the pad in place.

The coarsest steel-wool grades, #2 and #3, are used for removal of polish in conjunction with a stripping solution of sufficient strength to soften the polish. On coming in contact with the softened polish, the steel-wool pad shaves its way through and under it, lifting it from the floor. A considerable portion of the polish is absorbed by the body of the pad while the remainder on the floor is left to be picked up by a wet vacuum or mop.

A popular use of the finest grades of steel wool (#0 and #00) is for buffing polished surfaces to remove traffic grime and grit while simultaneously leveling the polish over the surface.

A separate class of floor abradant pad is an open-mesh cloth disk treated with silicon carbide. The disk is available in grit sizes ranging from 80 to 400 and in diameters from 10 to 24 inches. With this new cloth (according to the manufacturer), it is possible to restore floors that have been badly dented by women's spike heels. This method is advised only in

3M Company

Adjusting pad during floor maintenance operation.

cases where dents in the floor are so deep that replacement of the floor is being considered.

One manufacturer offers two different-size brushes with his equipment and has designed the top of the motor housing to carry the extra brush.

Operational efficiency. If properly cared for, the typical floor machine is capable of performing usefully for ten to fifteen years. However, because the purpose of the floor machine is purely utilitarian, its use may become so routine that a gradual decline in its efficiency may escape notice. As the machine gets old, more time is likely to be required to obtain desired results, and even those results may become less satisfactory. Labor is the most costly factor in building maintenance, and getting the most out of the labor expended depends on the tools the worker must use. By comparing an old machine with a new one, one may be convinced that the old machine is no longer doing an adequate job and should be replaced.

When considering the efficient use of floor machines, the question should be asked whether one is expecting too much of a single machine. How much time is lost moving a floor machine from one area of a large building to another? If the work load is divided between two or more machines, time may be saved and the efficiency of the operation may be improved.

Finally, what size of floor machine is needed for the job it is expected to do? Table 5 relates machine size to floor area and motor size. Machine size is expressed as the brush spread under the weight of the machine.

TABLE 5

FLOOR MACHINE SIZE

Floor Area (Square Feet)	Machine Size (Brush Spread in Inches)	Typical Motor Size (Horsepower)
Up to 2,000	12	⅓
" " 3,500	13	⅓
" " 5,000	14	½
" " 7,000	15	½
" " 9,000	16	½
" " 11,000	17	¾
" " 13,000	18	¾
" " 17,000	19	1
" " 20,000	20	1
" " 24,000	22	1
Over 24,000	23	1½
" 24,000	25	2

Specifications. A number of features and their specifications should be checked prior to selecting a floor machine. To assist the purchaser, a summary of the various machine characteristics is given in Table 6.

Combination scrubber-vacuum machines

Battery-powered, combination equipment automatically applies a cleaning solution, scrubs the floor, vacuums up the dirty solution, and leaves the floor squeegee-dry in one continuous operation. With varying degrees of ease (depending on the make and model), the same equipment can be converted to perform polishing and dry-vacuuming on a continuous basis. For automatically accomplishing these operations, the unit consists of the following elements: (1) motor-driven scrubbing brush or brushes; (2) tank for cleaning solution; (3) squeegee vacuum-powered by separate motor; (4) recovery tank for dirty solution; (5) batteries to provide power for the d.c. motors; (6) battery charger, wall-mounted or unit-attached; (7) motive power supplied by the rotating brush(es) or by gear arrangement to the wheels; (8) controls for speed, brush pressure, solution feed rate, squeegee pressure, and motor switches.

TABLE 6
TYPICAL CHARACTERISTICS OF FLOOR MACHINES

Feature	Specification
Brush spread	Ranges from 12 to 25 inches.
Voltage	Available in 115 v., 120 v., and 230 v.
Motor size	Varies from ⅓ to 2 h.p.
Motor temperature rise	40° to 60° C.
Motor type	Repulsion-induction, capacitor type.
Motor speed	About 1,725 rpm.
Brush speed	160 to 175 rpm for hard surfaces; 200 rpm for carpets.
Weight	61 to 185 lbs.
Cable length	40 ft. or more.
Cable size	Depending on motor, 12 to 16 gauge.
Switch	Momentary contact safety switch should be rated for starting current. Should be accessible to either hand.
Brush housing	Most are polished aluminum casting with reinforced ribbing on underside. Stainless steel available in some models.
Wheels	Should be large (4 inches or more) and non-marking; optional as to whether fixed or adjustable.
Gear unit	Various types: pulley, Watson-Flag type (3-planetary gear unit), double compound helical gear drive.
Starting current	8 to 13.5 amp. at 115 v., depending on motor.
Running current	42 to 80 amp. at 115 v., depending on motor.
Solution tank	Should be corrosion resistant. Volume varies up to 3½ gal.
Bumpers	Should encircle base and top of motor.
Contour	Lowest skirt clearance is 3¼ inches for recess reach of 2 to 6¼ inches, depending on model. Skirt clearance varies depending on model. Many machines have no skirt.
Handle	Generally one-piece construction of round tubular steel. Other designs call for two tubes, round or square. Should be fully adjustable to any lock-in position.
Brushes	Should have available assortment of brushes and attachments, i.e., polishing, buffing, scrubbing, dry-scrubbing for concrete, drive pad for abrasive pads, and steel-wool pad holder.

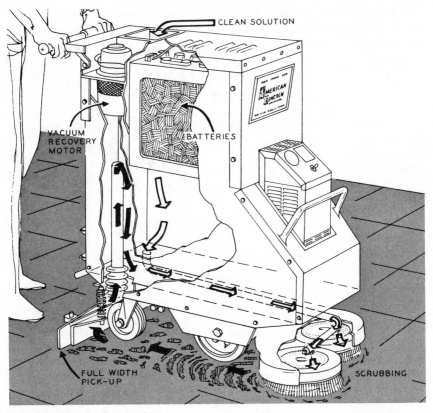

CLEAN SOLUTION

VACUUM
RECOVERY
MOTOR

BATTERIES

FULL WIDTH
PICK-UP

SCRUBBING

American-Lincoln Corporation

Cutaway drawing of combination scrubber-vacuum in operation.

Battery-powered equipment is to be preferred over the conventional type that is plugged into an electrical outlet. The trailing cord is a nuisance to the operator; he has less mobility; and the area he can cover before he must disconnect and move the cord to a new outlet is limited. An added advantage of a battery-powered machine is that the operator can move it under power to a storage space.

There is no question that the use of battery-powered, combination scrubber-vacuum equipment offers tremendous labor-saving advantages over the operation of single-disk, floor-scrubbing machines and separate wet-vacuum pickup units. The possible savings in time are illustrated in Table 7. These figures represent average cleaning time. Layout, obstacles, level of sanitation desired, the availability of facilities to fill and drain the machines, and so forth, will affect cleaning time.

Prerequisites for use. The buyer must be able to justify the cost of the combination equipment in any of three ways—by reducing his maintenance staff, by making more economical use of the time available for maintenance, and by providing better floor maintenance service. However, before purchasing such equipment, several in-use factors must be taken into consideration:

(1) Sufficient floor area is essential to warrant fully automatic equipment. A minimum of 10,000 square feet of scrubbable space is estimated to be required. Even a small, fully automatic unit is potentially capable of covering 10,000 square feet in as little as 1½ hours, depending on the floor layout.

(2) Most of the area should be open or free of fixed obstructions. An important factor in the operation of the equipment is its rapid forward

TABLE 7

Estimated Cleaning Time For One Man

Floor Area (Square Feet)	Deck Scrub-brush and Mop (Hours)	Floor Scrubbing Machine (16″) and Wet-Vacuum Pickup (13″) (Hours)
2,000	8	3
2,500	7	3.5
5,000	13	6
10,000	24	11.5
15,000	37	17
25,000	61	28
50,000	118	55
100,000	232	108
120,000	480	182
150,000	600	233

Floor Area (Square Feet)	Combination Scrubber-Vacuum (Brush Spread in Inches)				
	18	19	21	26	30
2,000	9.2 min.	—	—	—	—
2,500	—	15 min.	—	—	—
5,000	—	28 min.	24 min.	—	—
10,000	46.0 min.	50 min.	44 min.	—	—
15,000	—	—	62 min.	50 min.	33 min.
25,000	—	—	—	1⅓ hr.	1.0 hr.
50,000	—	—	2.9 hr.	2⅓ hr.	2.0 hr.
100,000	—	—	—	5½ hr.	4.0 hr.
120,000	—	—	—	—	4.4 hr.
150,000	—	—	—	—	—

Source: American-Lincoln Corp.

motion. Ideally, it should be possible to keep the unit moving forward at full speed for long stretches of floor. Frequent interruptions to clear a path and having to slow down to avoid fixed objects impose heavy penalties on the time-saving advantages of the equipment.

(3) Aisles and doors should be wide enough to accommodate passage of the equipment. Most machines are at least one inch wider than their rated scrub path. The smaller 18- to 26-inch units do not ordinarily present passage problems. The use of larger and wider pieces of equipment, how-

Advance Floor Machine Company   *Advance Floor Machine Company*

Changing brushes and squeegee tools on combination
scrubber-vacuum machines.

ever, requires careful study of the physical layout to determine how freely the machines will be able to operate. Attention should be given to turning points, blind passageways, supporting columns in aisles, and access to clean-out stations and supply and storage centers.

(4) The floor should be suitable for heavy equipment. The floor or floor covering should be capable of sustaining loads of about 400 pounds for the small units and 1,000 pounds for the 26- and 30-inch pieces of equipment.

(5) Adequate storage space for equipment must be available. It is advisable to provide a permanent storage area for the equipment to secure it against accidental or mischievous damage. Proximity to a water tap, floor drain, and an electric outlet is also recommended, and some provision must be made for storing replacement parts with the unit.

(6) To be of greatest value, the equipment must be able to reach easily all scrubbable areas on the same floor. Steps, steep ramps, and raised or sunken areas of the same floor can be serious obstacles to the movement of the equipment. In multi-story buildings there must be elevators large enough to accommodate the weight and size of the machines.

Selection criteria. In general, it is best to choose the largest possible size of unit that can pass through the narrowest aisle, door, or passageway. However, other considerations may dictate the final choice. For example, if most of the area to be cleaned consists of uniform aisles, the unit should be selected on the basis of minimum number of passes required to scrub with about a 1- to 2-inch overlap in the scrub paths. However, if the major portion of the floor area is wide and unobstructed, the best choice would be a larger unit, even though the scrubbing overlap in aisles might be as much as 6 to 10 inches.

The following general guide for the selection of machine size (Table 8) is based solely on scrubbable area without consideration of the width of aisles and passageways.

TABLE 8
AREA TO BE CLEANED RELATED TO MACHINE SIZE

Area To Be Cleaned (Square Feet)	Scrub Path of Combination Scrubber-Vacuum (Inches)
10,000 to 20,000	18 to 20
20,000 to 50,000	24 to 26
Over 50,000	30 to 32

Fundamentally, all the scrubber-vacuums are similar, although some models emphasize certain features believed by the manufacturer to make his unit superior to that of his competition. From the standpoint of the prospective purchaser, the following list, in question form, may give some idea of various characteristics that may make a difference to him in the selection of these machines and to his maintenance personnel in its use.

(1) Does the manufacturer provide good service?

(2) Is installation included in the purchase price?

(3) Does the manufacturer offer an adequate training program for maintenance personnel?

(4) What are the guarantees and warranties? Consider:
    a. Material and workmanship
    b. Batteries
    c. Battery charger
    d. Exclusions

(5) What is the nature of the frame construction, i.e., welded steel, bolted aluminum, etc.?

(6) Is the model under consideration twin-brush or single-brush?

(7) Can the machine be converted to floor-polishing and dry-vacuuming?

(8) What is the construction of the brush or brushes?

(9) Do the model numbers indicate the true scrub path?

(10) What is the brush force, in pounds?

(11) What is the brush speed?

(12) What is the traverse speed (feet/minute)?

(13) Is there a "dead-man" control?

(14) What are the specifications for the drive motor, e.g., power, voltage, revolutions per minute, etc.?

(15) What type of traverse drive does the machine have—two-wheel, brush?

(16) What type of clutch is used?

(17) What are the specifications for the vacuum motor?

(18) Does the machine have a protective shut-off float?

(19) What type of battery does the machine use?

(20) What is the available energy (in watt-hours)?

(21) What is the operating time of the batteries?

(22) What type of charger is used?

(23) What type of squeegee is used?

(24) What are the capacities of solution and recovery tanks?

(25) How are the solution and vacuum tanks constructed, e.g., steel coated with epoxy or vitreous porcelain?

(26) Does the machine have valve drains?

(27) Does it have a clean-out door?

(28) How much does the machine weigh?

(29) What are its dimensions?

(30) What is its list price?

Vacuums

Wet-dry vacuums. The portable wet- and dry-pickup vacuum is one of the most useful tools ever engineered for making cleaning easier. The most popular model consists of an upright tank mounted on a frame with large fixed wheels in the back and a caster in the front. A transport handle in the back allows the unit to be wheeled easily from place to place including up and down stairs and ramps. Smaller models, mounted solely on casters, are also available.

In ordinary use, the vacuum unit is pulled by its hose, which is usually 10 feet long, and the machine trails the operator as he carries

Clarke Floor Machine Division, Studebaker Corporation

Wet-dry vacuum.

out the vacuuming operation. Accessory floor squeegee tools are sold for use on large floor areas. These can be attached to the tank with a short hose. This feature enables the operator to push and direct the equipment with the carriage handle. Standard equipment for most units is an automatic float shut-off device to protect the motor during wet pickup. For conversion to a dry-vacuum operation, the motor is lifted from the top of the tank and a separator filter is installed. Many commercial units have an optional method of collecting dry dirt in a disposable paper bag placed inside the tank rather than simply collecting it in the tank. Models with outside filter bags are also available for longer operations. Generally, these are less popular than machines with internal filters.

Dry vacuums. The biggest use for dry vacuums is in carpeted areas where frequent vacuuming and the need for brushing calls for special equipment. The upright type of vacuum with an external filter bag is probably familiar to everyone. This machine incorporates a rotating brush head that loosens embedded dirt and dust enabling the vacuum effectively to remove them from the pile.

The upright vacuum cleaner has been developed in a special version that is used as a combination pile brush and vacuum. In one manufacturer's machine, there is a spirally wound solid brush that is gear-driven

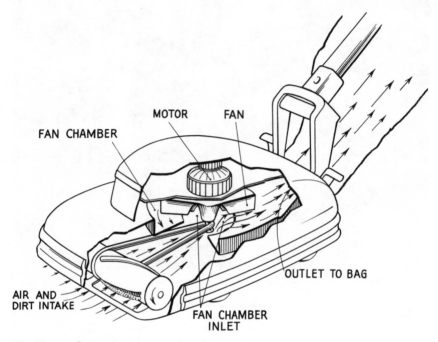

The Hoover Company

Cutaway drawing of upright dry vacuum in operation.

to ensure continuous brushing action. Pile brushes are finding more and more use for pre-shampooing and post-shampooing work as well as for routine carpet care.

Horizontal tank-type vacuums are available for institutional use, and there are lightweight "stick-type" cleaners that are as portable as brooms. The latter are frequently used as accessory equipment for spot-cleaning on stairs, upholstery, and floors.

A relatively new class of portable dry-vacuum cleaners is fast becoming popular because it is lightweight and ruggedly constructed, does all the ordinary maintenance jobs, and is as convenient to use as a household vacuum. This machine can be strapped to the operator's back, thereby making certain cleaning operations easier. The equipment is capable of performing all the normal vacuuming chores; it is usually designed for use with a 1½-inch (inside diameter) hose and floor tools of commercial type and size. The vacuum can also be used as a wheeled unit by attaching an accessory dolly.

Multi-Clean Products, Inc.

Explosion-proof floor machine.

Tanks. The tanks are generally round in shape, although one manufacturer uses square tanks claiming greater volume capacity without requiring more storage space. Tanks are available in a variety of sizes which are measured in terms of gallons for wet-pickup recovery and in terms of bushels for dry pickup. Since the inlet hose connection is below the top of the tank, the amount of recoverable volume is always less than the tank size. Sizes range from 2 to 55 gallons; capacities in the 10- to 16-gallon range are most popular. The tanks are generally constructed from stainless steel or baked enameled steel and, in many instances, can be obtained with a "dump valve" as an accessory feature. This is a simple spigot-type valve set in the extreme lower rim section of the container. It is very helpful to have a floor drain available. Small units in the 5-gallon range are constructed of fiber glass reinforced plastic. Also available are steel tanks lined with plastisol, epoxies, resins, etc., which are claimed to be corrosion-proof.

Filters. Some manufacturers offer vacuum cleaners featuring special filters and filter assemblies that are claimed to be suited for areas requiring extreme cleanliness. Examples of "sensitive" areas are hospitals, computer

TABLE 9
VACUUM CLEANER CHARACTERISTICS

Feature	Expressed In or As
Tank size	Gallons
Recovery capacity, wet	Gallons
Recovery capacity, dry	Bushels or cubic inches
Tank construction	Gauge and type of metal
Outside finish	Varies widely
Inside finish	Should be corrosion resistant
Motor	
Type	Bypass, non-bypass, universal
Use	Constant or intermittent
Voltage	115 v., 120 v., or 220 v.
a.c. frequency and phase	60 cycles, single-phase
Bearing	Ball-bearing
Speed	rpm.
Temperature rise	°C.
Filter design	Internal or external
Filter area	Square inches
Hose connection diameter	Inches
Air exhaust	Concentrated, diffuse, upward, angled
Guarantee	Usually one year, minimum
Mounting	Fixed wheels, casters, dolly
Electric cable length	30 feet, minimum
Dimensions	Height, width, weight

rooms, and clean rooms, i.e., areas where contaminants and the amount of dust must be kept below a stated minimum. One unit uses a special filter made of polyurethane, a foam-like material, treated with a germicidal agent. Another manufacturer has designed his equipment with three pre-filters on the suction side of the machine and an "absolute" final filter on the vacuum side. All air used by the machine in cleaning and motor cooling passes through the absolute final filter, providing control of both cleaning dust and carbon dust particles produced by the wear of motor brushes. Other special filtering devices are offered which are claimed to provide 99.97 percent retention of micro-organisms and particles as small as 0.3 micron.

Attachments. The availability of a wide variety of tools and attachments makes vacuum cleaners suitable for many uses besides floor cleaning. Indeed, there is a tool for removing dust from almost every hard or soft surface; the reader should consult individual manufacturers for specific recommendations. A partial list of tools and attachments follows:

Hoses (vinyl, neoprene, flexible metal, cloth-covered rubber)
Hose adapters and connectors
Wands (double curved, swiveled, straight extensions)
Floor tools (fiber-shod, felt-shod, fabric-shod, steel-shod, bristle-shod)
Squeegees for wet pickup
Wall and overhead fixture tools
Tuft, crevice, and radiator tools
Bin, shelf, and upholstery tools
Blower nozzles
Furnace and boiler-tube cleaning tools
Filter bags
Carry baskets for tools
Handles for transport

3

RESILIENT
FLOOR COVERINGS

DESCRIPTION

The term "resilient" is used here to refer to a number of smooth-surfaced floor coverings which are similar in respect to their manufacture, installation, and general physical characteristics. Carpet, which is obviously a form of resilient floor covering, although in another sense of the term, is discussed in Chapter 4.

Considered in this chapter are linoleum, rubber, cork, asphalt, and a group of smooth-surfaced floor coverings derived from vinyl chloride resins. After 1920, there was a great increase in the use of most of these materials, and in the 1960's, the extensive use of concrete subflooring in institutional and commercial as well as residential structures had further expanded the market.

Basically, resilience is a measure of the ability of a material to recover or return to its original shape after an external load has been removed. Vinyl asbestos, for example, is more resilient than asphalt, which has almost no recovery when subjected to heavy loads. However, vinyl asbestos is less resilient than vinyl, linoleum, rubber, and cork.

In general, these floor coverings are manufactured by mixing a plastic material with fillers and pigments to create a plastic mix that is rolled into sheets and then calendered (flattened and smoothed between rollers) to the desired thickness. If a backing material is used, the plastic sheet is calendered onto the backing. In tile production, the sheets are cut by an extremely accurate cutting machine into squares.

A wide variety of decorative effects can be obtained with this technique, including mottles, jaspé, and spatter patterns. This is accomplished by adding one or more other components of the same general composition as the base material in the form of sheets, chips, or granules. By controlling the extent of mixing, various decorative appearances can be achieved. In some applications, the added color is not mixed in but is pressed into the surface of the sheet.

Resilient floor coverings are sold in several forms. The more flexible materials are available in sheet form in several widths and delivered in rolls. The trend, however, is heavily toward tile, and 9-inch square tile—the standard size—is widely manufactured.

71

These floor coverings are offered in several gauges, i.e., thicknesses, ordinarily ranging from 1/16 to 3/16 inch, although in some cases the material is thicker.

Gauge is closely related to the service life and cost of each type of resilient floor material. At one time, when resilient floor coverings were limited to linoleum and asphalt, gauge was the primary consideration in judging over-all quality. With the introduction of new resilient flooring based on more durable resins, gauge alone is not a sufficient criterion for estimating the service life of the different types. Gauges once believed to be too thin for light-duty institutional and commercial uses are now regarded as satisfactory.

Gauge of resilient flooring materials is expressed in fractional inches, e.g., 1/16, 3/32, 1/8, 5/16, or in decimal inches, e.g., 0.050, 0.0625, 0.0937.

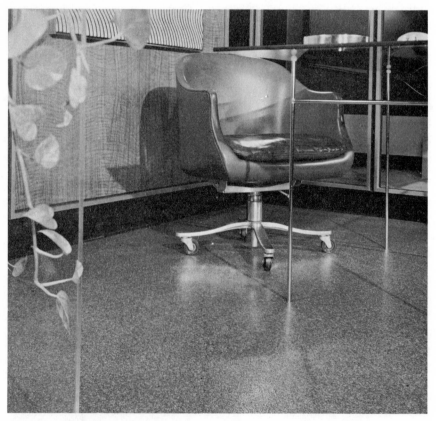

Armstrong Cork Company

Armstrong Cork Company   *Armstrong Cork Company*

Homogeneous resilient flooring with embossed styling (left)
and backed resilient flooring (right).

The thickness of floor materials, in addition to influencing service life and cost, is also a factor in underfoot comfort, quietness, heat transfer, and appearance. Minor irregularities in the subfloor, which might show in the top surface, are better hidden by thicker gauges.

The usual gauge for homogeneous floor materials, such as vinyl, rubber, vinyl asbestos, and asphalt, is ⅛ inch. In contrast, backed floor materials, such as linoleum and vinyl sheet, have thinner wear layers. For vinyl sheet goods, for example, the thinnest wear layer recommended for institutional use is 0.050 inch.

SUBFLOORS

Information on wood and concrete subfloors suitable for use with homogeneous vinyl and rubber resilient flooring has been published by the Rubber Manufacturers Association. This material, because it is generally applicable to all types of resilient floor coverings, has been adapted, along with additional information, for this discussion.

New concrete subfloors

A large proportion of the total area of installed resilient flooring materials is laid over concrete. The properties of concrete make it a quite satisfactory and economical material for floor construction. It can be easily placed and finished; it is structurally strong; it is fire resistant, termite proof, and universally available.

General requirements. Concrete subfloors suitable for installation of resilient floor coverings should be dry, clean, smooth, level, and structurally sound. They should be free from dust, solvents, scaly paint, polish, oil, grease, asphalt, sealing compounds, and other extraneous materials. A loose, sandy, or scaly surface, and evidence of a white, powdery surface indicate an unacceptable floor. Expansion joints, cracks, grooves, and other irregularities should be filled or leveled and the surface of the floor brushed clean. Where patching or leveling are required, the use of a good quality latex underlayment, approved by the resilient flooring manufacturer, is recommended.

Materials and mix. Concrete subfloors should be of a good standard mix, as recommended by the Portland Cement Association, using clean sand and crushed stone. In addition to careful selection of materials and mix proportions, good compaction and finishing procedures and adequate moist curing are necessary to obtain a satisfactory concrete floor. The concrete should contain not less than five sacks of portland cement per cubic yard and the minimum amount of water that will allow proper placement. The water content should not exceed six gallons per sack of cement. Probably the most common fault in concrete work is the use of more water than is required to get good workability.

The aggregate should be sound and well graded. A mix commonly recommended includes one part portland cement to 2¼ parts of fine aggregate to three parts of coarse aggregate. The grading of the aggregate has an important effect on the final concrete product. The shape of the particles and grading determine the void content of the aggregate, and this in turn determines the amount of water needed to produce adequate workability. A well graded aggregate will have a minimum of voids and thus will require a minimum of water and cement to fill the voids and bind the aggregate. Aggregates with high water requirements necessarily require more portland cement to produce a given strength.

The shrinkage of concrete is determined largely by the amount of water in the concrete mix and increases almost directly with the amount of water in the fresh concrete. It is only slightly affected by changes in the cement content. Studies have shown that concretes with lower water-to-cement ratios have less shrinkage than those with higher ratios.

Compaction and troweling. To be suitable for a resilient tile installation, a concrete floor finish must be hard, dense, and smooth. The concrete should be consolidated by vibration or by thorough spading and tamping, after which it is screeded to grade. A vibrating screed that compacts and levels the concrete in one operation is commonly used. Screeding is immediately followed by floating or darbying, a combination leveling and compacting process.

The darby is a specially constructed long float. It has a three-fold purpose: (1) to embed coarse aggregate in preparation for hand floating and troweling, (2) to level the surface and eliminate straight-edge or screed marks, and (3) to achieve additional compaction of the surface.

Mechanical floats permit the use of a much stiffer mixture than can be used when floating is done by hand. They also shorten the total time required for finishing.

Troweling is an extremely important operation; it requires experience and skill for the best results. Troweling should be done after the concrete has hardened sufficiently to prevent drawing moisture and fine materials to the surface. Cement or mixtures of sand and cement should not be spread on the surface to absorb excess water. Rather, the mixing water should be kept to a minimum and troweling delayed until the bleeding water has been re-absorbed by the concrete. Final troweling should be done after the concrete is so hard that no mortar accumulates on the trowel and a ringing sound is produced as the trowel is drawn over the surface. This will polish the surface to a smooth finish.

Curing. The term refers to perfecting green concrete by maintaining proper conditions of moisture and temperature. It has a substantial effect on the strength and impermeability of the final product. Floors that are to be covered should be kept moist for at least three days; floors that are to be exposed require a minimum of five days of moist curing. These periods are applicable to warm weather. If the ambient temperatures are around 40° F., the time allowed for curing should be doubled. There is enough water in a good concrete mix to allow adequate hydration of the cement provided the water is retained in the concrete. Curing can be accomplished by covering the slab floor with wet burlap as soon as this can be done without causing damage to the floor. Moisture-proof paper, polyethylene sheets, or other membranous materials may be used to prevent loss of water from the slab.

Drying. Following curing, concrete slabs should be thoroughly dry before installation of the floor covering. Depending on atmospheric conditions and possible excess water content, the underfloors will require at least six weeks' drying time before they may be regarded as ready for moisture tests. Floors containing lightweight aggregate or excess water may need a much longer drying time; in any case, concrete should not be covered with resilient flooring materials until it is proved to be dry. Because dampness must always be suspected, moisture tests should be made. It is the responsibility of the flooring contractor to determine whether the concrete is sufficiently dry for covering.

Neutralizing. New concrete floors may be neutralized to remove excess alkali. One part of muriatic acid and nine parts of water, or a mixture of one part vinegar in five parts water, make a satisfactory neutralizing solution. During this process, rubber gloves and galoshes and protection for the eyes are recommended. The floor should be flooded with the neutralizing solution and allowed to remain for at least an hour before being rinsed off with clear water. Then the concrete should be allowed to dry thoroughly.

Curing compounds. Concrete curing agents, parting compounds, surface hardeners, **and** the like should not be used on the subfloor unless

Portland Cement Association

1. Spreading concrete mix.

Portland Cement Association

2. Screeding concrete to proper level.

Portland Cement Association

3. Compacting concrete by means of mechanical float.

Portland Cement Association

4. Hand-floating concrete to produce an even, plane surface.

Portland Cement Association

5. Hand-floating and troweling concrete
to produce smooth finish.

Installing concrete subfloor.

specific approval from the resilient flooring manufacturer has been obtained. With the increasing use of curing compounds for concrete floors, architects, engineers, and flooring contractors have been confronted by some serious problems following the installation of resilient floor coverings.

While some of these compounds are entirely satisfactory for use, others may prevent an adequate bond between the tile and the concrete floor; still others may be injurious to the adhesive or the tile itself. Removal of these agents, if necessary, can be extremely difficult. Therefore, it is extremely important to know that suitable compounds are specified and used and that unsuitable compounds are avoided.

For some time, the Asphalt and Vinyl Asbestos Tile Institute has carried on research to solve some of these problems. Following is a guide, adapted for the present purpose from that prepared by the Institute, to assist in the specification of satisfactory products.

The curing compound or parting agent should consist of materials that will not interfere with the installation and performance of resilient flooring. Having served its purpose, it should either remain as a harmless film on the concrete or be easily and economically removed prior to installation of the floor covering.

Among the factors known to have caused difficulties are:

(1) Solvents of low volatility that tend to remain within the concrete over long periods and that can damage the tile or adhesive after installation.

(2) Soft, greasy, or oily compounds that interfere with the adhesive bond to the concrete.

(3) Materials of a saponifiable nature that may soften and interfere with the bond in the presence of alkaline moisture normally present in concrete floors on- and below-grade.

(4) Film formers and those chemicals injurious to or lacking in affinity for the adhesives normally used in the application of resilient floor coverings.

When actual test installations cannot be made, the following tests are helpful but not conclusive in evaluating the acceptability of curing compounds and parting agents prior to installation of resilient floors.

(1) Solvent volatility:
   The solvent should be sufficiently volatile, such that 95 percent will distill below 350° F.
(2) Film hardness and drying time:
   (a) Four grams of the compound should be accurately weighed into a 4-inch diameter, flat-bottomed dish and allowed to dry at 77° F. and at a relative humidity no greater than 65 percent.
   (b) The resultant film should be dry to the touch and should be hard after drying for 24 hours.

(3) Resistance to alkali:

(a) A microscope slide (3 by 1 inch) should be wiped with acetone-soaked tissue. Frosted end slides (write-on type) aid in the identification of samples.

(b) The slide should be dipped three-fourths of its length into the test curing agent. Then the slide should be suspended vertically and allowed to air-dry for 24 hours.

Temperature—77° F. ± 2° F.

R. H. (maximum)—65 percent.

(c) The slide should be immersed to one-half its length in a 5 percent sodium hydroxide solution for 6 hours at 77° F.

(d) The slide is removed, but not rinsed, and examined.

Classification I—Satisfactory: No appreciable effect on the film or bond to the glass slide other than a moderate clouding of the film.

The Institute has found no simple means to detect or test compounds on the floor itself. Therefore, it becomes important to discover what type of compound, if any, was used, and whether it should be removed before resilient flooring is installed.

Some compounds may be readily removed by brushing the floor thoroughly with a powered steel brush. Steel wool should not be used. Surfaces of some floors may require grinding down to remove the compound completely.

The Institute suggests that when specifying curing compounds for any new concrete floor, both the tile manufacturer and the curing compound manufacturer should be consulted to determine the correct type of compound to use for the desired type of floor installation. Finally, the manufacturer's instructions for using the compound should be carefully followed. A final warning: the compound should not be cut with low-volatility solvents such as kerosene or similar materials.

Old concrete subfloors

For best results, old concrete floors should be prepared to conform as closely as possible to new concrete floors. Cracks, expansion joints, and uneven and rough areas require the application of a good-quality rubber latex underlayment to make the surface level. The subfloor must be firm and free from moisture, dirt, dust, solvents, scaly paint, polish, oil, grease, asphalt, sealing compounds, and other extraneous foreign materials. If an old resilient floor surface is to be renovated, the flooring contractor should be consulted regarding the necessity for removal of the old flooring.

Paint should be removed by sanding the floor until it is clean. Coarse No. 4 or No. 5 open-grit sandpaper should be used. A strong solution of trisodium phosphate or lye may be required in difficult cases. If alkaline solutions are used, the floor must be neutralized with acid, as described earlier. Good-quality chlorinated rubber-base paint may be left on suspended, on-grade, or below-grade floors if the paint film is found to be securely bonded to the underfloor. The film integrity of a chlorinated rubber-base paint can be tested by applying to the surface a small quantity of a solution of two tablespoons of lye to a cup of water. (In these procedures, rubber gloves should be used; lye is harmful to the skin.) If, after application of this solution for four hours, the paint has not been removed, it may be left on the floor.

On- and below-grade concrete subfloors

Concrete slabs in contact with the earth at any point, or those without at least 18 inches of cross-ventilated air space beneath, require special attention. Unless such construction incorporates a continuously effective, permanent moisture barrier, usually called a membrane, bonding failures may occur. If a permanent moisture barrier, such as six-mil polyethylene film, is used, it should be sufficiently effective to restrict transmission of moisture through the floor to less than 3 pounds per 1,000 square feet in 24 hours. In this situation, most types of floor coverings recommended for on-grade or below-grade concrete floors—solid vinyl, rubber, asphalt, and vinyl asbestos—may be safely installed with regular suspended-floor adhesives, as specified by the manufacturer. The effectiveness of the moisture barrier should be such that the specification—i.e., a limit of 3 pounds of moisture per 1,000 square feet in 24 hours—must be passed at the time of installation of the flooring and also at any future date. If such a barrier is not used, or if the type used does not meet this specification, the use of on-grade or below-grade adhesives as specified by the manufacturer of the resilient flooring is required. Moreover, in the absence of such a barrier, certain adhesives intended for use with on-grade or below-grade floors may not prevent flooring failures in the presence of hydrostatic pressure (pressure by water).

Efflorescence. There is a certain amount of water present in all concrete slabs built on or below grade.

With most slabs in contact with the ground, moisture constantly rises through the concrete and evaporates from the surface into the air above. If a surface finish is applied, it should be of a type that will not seal the surface of the concrete but will permit it to breathe and give off the moisture.

For this reason, sheet floorings, covering large areas with comparatively few joints, are not generally recommended over slabs in contact with the ground, because the moisture is trapped underneath. Tiles of various types are recommended for these installations. The large number of joints permit the evaporation of a considerable amount of moisture. When these tiles are set in a suitable type of adhesive, a satisfactory job should result.

Sometimes, even the correct tile material laid in a proper adhesive will develop areas in which the edges of the tiles curl up. When these tiles are lifted, generally there will be found a concentration of white powder along the edges. This is called "efflorescence"; it is not uncommon in masonry construction. The white powder is dissolved salts brought up by moisture.

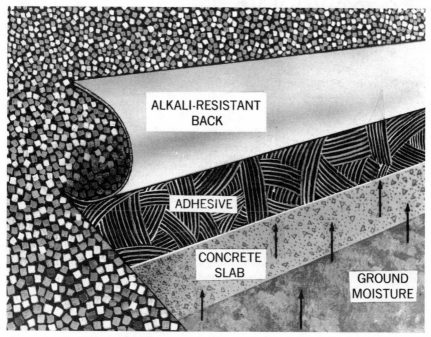

Armstrong Cork Company

Specially treated backings, resistant to alkaline moisture, permit the installation of sheet vinyl floors over on-grade and below-grade concrete subfloors.

The moisture rises through the slab and moves to the joints in the tile where the water evaporates leaving the white powder behind. The build-up of this powder destroys the bond between the tile and the slab, causing the tile to curl up at the edges.

Moisture alone is not the cause of this condition. Efflorescence can occur whenever a suitable combination of high-moisture transmission and excess water-soluble salts are present in the concrete slab. Such variables as moisture in the earth below, the thickness and texture of the cinder fill

used in the subfloor, and the porosity of the concrete slab make it possible for these combinations to vary a great deal. Furthermore, a slab is
seldom poured with one mixing of concrete, so another variable is added.
This combination of circumstances cannot be foreseen by any flooring
contractor. Even if the contractor took up a portion of the slab and had it
analyzed, he would have an analysis of only the immediate area from which
the sample was taken. In such cases, the contractor cannot be held
responsible.

As to countermeasures, one procedure calls for (1) removal of the
tiles, (2) cleaning of tile adhesive from the slab, (3) treatment of the slab
with a 10 percent solution of hydrochloric acid for 12 hours to neutralize
the slab, (4) rinsing with water, (5) allowing the surface to dry, and
(6) laying a new floor. Although this is generally an effective procedure, it
cannot be guaranteed.

This method is often unsuitable because of the damage to baseboards,
wood paneling, or other wall finishes by the acid solution. In addition, both
the owner and the workmen are often hesitant to use an acid of this type.

A second method has been used with moderately good success by
many contractors but, again, cannot be guaranteed. This procedure requires
(1) removing the tiles from the offending area, (2) cleaning up all traces
of white powder with clear water, and (3) removing the old tile adhesive
by scraping and sanding. The area should then be flooded with a solution of white vinegar (4 to 5 percent acetic acid) and water, using a quart
of vinegar in 2 gallons of water. This solution should be allowed to soak
into the slab at least overnight. The slab is then washed again with water.
When it is completely dry, a cut-back primer (prime-coat adhesive thinned
with appropriate solvent) should be applied according to instructions. The
tiles should then be re-laid in a cut-back tile cement.

Either of the two methods can best be carried out at a time when the
weather is dry; good ventilation should be provided.

Wood subfloors

Wood subfloors in contact with the earth, or on concrete in contact
with the earth, are generally not suitable for the installation of resilient floor
coverings. The manufacturer of the particular resilient material under
consideration should be consulted if plans call for installation over wood
subfloors at ground level. On the other hand, *suspended* wood subfloors,
when properly prepared, are suitable for installation of all resilient floors.

General requirements. The wood underfloor must be solid, well nailed
at joists, and free from spring or motion. Any unevenness should be
smoothed out with a sanding machine. The sanding machine should be run
diagonally to or with the grain of the wood, not across the grain. All polish,

grease, dirt, and dust should be carefully removed or the adhesive bond to the resilient covering may be impaired. Any plywood to be used should also be completely sanded.

Double wood subfloors. On suspended double wood floors, loose or broken boards should be re-nailed or replaced and the wood floor sanded to remove any irregularities such as warped or cupped boards. On suspended double wood floors with top boards less than 4 inches wide, 15-pound asphalt-saturated felt paper should be cemented in place using linoleum paste. The felt paper should be laid across the boards, with the edges butted—the felt should not overlap—and the floor rolled with a 150-pound roller from the center to the edges to ensure a good bond and to eliminate air bubbles.

If the double wood floor is in very poor condition, in which sanding will not eliminate the irregularities, or if the top boards are more than 4 inches wide, the installation of fully sanded Douglas fir plywood (DFPA underlayment grade plywood) with a minimum thickness of ¼ inch is required. In areas subjected to surface moisture, DFPA underlayment grade plywood bonded with exterior glue or C-C plugged and sanded exterior grade plywood should be used.

(DFPA certifications are promulgated by the Division For Product Approval of the American Plywood Association, formerly known as the Douglas Fir Plywood Association.)

Underlayment grade ¼-inch hardboard, which meets the Rubber Manufacturers Association Recommended Minimum Quality Level, may be used in place of ¼-inch plywood. Unless otherwise recommended by the resilient flooring manufacturer, the ¼-inch hardboard should be installed with the smooth side up.

The use of particleboard, tempered hardboard, or any boards other than those specified above, require specific approval from the manufacturer of the resilient floor covering. In some cases, proprietary underlays are required, if manufacturers' warranties are to be validated.

The underlayment is installed with cross joints staggered at least 16 inches. The underlayment is fastened to the underfloor, using annular (ring-grooved) or screw nails which will penetrate 1¼ inches into the subfloor. These fasteners should be spaced 6 inches on center throughout the board and spaced 3 inches apart along the edges. The center of the board is nailed first, with the carpenter working out toward the edges to eliminate any irregularities. The underlayment should not be fitted too snugly; space should be left between the boards about the thickness of a dime. Fasteners should be driven flush with the surface or set not more than 1/16 inch below. Any surface roughness, especially at the joints and around nails, should be lightly sanded.

Single wood subfloors. Plywood underlayment board with a minimum thickness of ¼ inch, as previously described, is recommended for installation over single wood subfloors in which the boards are not over 4 inches wide. If the width exceeds 4 inches, ½-inch underlayment grade plywood should be used. The face grain should be perpendicular to the joists. Installation is as described above.

Open wood joist construction. For 16-inch joist spacing (or less), ⅝-inch underlayment grade plywood should be installed. For joist spacing up to 24 inches, ¾-inch plywood should be attached directly to the open wood joists. Blocking or bridging (supports between joists) is required under the plywood along the edges perpendicular to the joists.

The plywood should be nailed with annular (ring-grooved) or screw nails penetrating 1¼ inches into the joists. These fasteners should be spaced 6 inches apart over the joists and 3 inches apart along the edges.

When properly installed over open wood joists spaced 48 inches or less, a combination underfloor and underlayment plywood panel can be used in what is called a "2-4-1" installation. The "2-4-1" tongue-and-groove plywood, which is 1⅛ inches thick, requires no blocking or bridging. The installation uses 2½-inch ringed shank nails or screw-type nails spaced 3 inches on center at all bearings (supporting beams or joists).

ADHESIVES

The steadily increasing use of resilient floor coverings has been paralleled by the growth in the technological development of flooring adhesives. The progressive development and successful invention of better-performing and easier-to-use adhesives have contributed greatly to the growth of the resilient flooring industry and the broadening of the choice for the purchaser among the varieties of these materials.

The expansion in adhesive installation methods has occurred largely because adhesives are practical and economical. Stresses are distributed and absorbed over the entire bonded floor area rather than being concentrated at a few points. Thus, the chances of the flooring tearing or rupturing at fasteners are reduced. Buckling failures or unsightly wrinkles resulting from "growth" are minimized. In addition, some of the newer adhesives and adhesive-integral barrier systems can contribute to the waterproofness and chemical resistance of the floor.

Because of these advantages, an extensive technology has developed over the years in the formulation of adhesives and installation procedures as well as in the performance and service characteristics of various adhesive-flooring systems. This technology has been accumulated by responsible adhesive and flooring materials manufacturers and is available to the purchaser as "recommended practice" for the use of their materials.

In general, no difficulty is experienced in making satisfactory installations with adhesives on subfloors which are dry, even, rigid, and clean. Instructions for the preparation of the surface are usually clearly stated by the manufacturer of the resilient floor covering in question. Regardless of expert workmanship, product, or method, however, a resilient floor will be no smoother than the underfloor. An adhesive bond will be no stronger than the weakest boundary layer. For this reason, all loose dirt, oil, grease, and moisture must be removed. When working on concrete, oily or waxy curing or parting compounds must be avoided. Any curing or parting compounds should be abraded off prior to bonding. The bond between the resilient floor covering and the subfloor can be no stronger than the cohesive strength of the underlay, whether that be mastic, felt, wood, paper, or the interlaminar strength of a composite floor covering.

Where the subfloor is cracked or not firm, one should use a flexible or elastic adhesive. It is always desirable for the elasticity of an adhesive to be lower than that of the materials it holds together. An elastic adhesive can absorb stress, thus preventing or delaying development of flaws in the materials being joined. A brittle adhesive, when flexed repeatedly, will crack and fail. Elastic adhesives, rather than plastic, flexible ones, are preferred, because the latter are subject to the defect of creeping when subjected to continuous low stress.

In general, the elastic adhesives are rubber cement, rubber latex, and the chemical-set adhesives. The plastic adhesives are asphalt, sulfite liquor, and oleoresinous and pressure-sensitive adhesives.

For normal conditions, i.e, dry service on a smooth, rigid subfloor, certain inexpensive adhesives have been installed quite successfully. Normal conditions are usually met with installations on suspended concrete, plywood, and strip-wood. These conditions are also met with installations on old linoleum, mastic underlays, and felt installed over such suspended subfloors. Such inexpensive adhesives include asphalt and coaltar pitch emulsions and cutbacks (solvent-thinned coatings), lignin (sulfite liquor), and oleoresinous pastes. For areas where more severe service is occasionally encountered—such as where water may splash onto the flooring—synthetic rubber latex-base adhesives are the conservative recommendation and represent the next upper grade in the quality of flooring adhesive.

By far the greater proportion of resilient flooring installations are made with two very inexpensive materials—sulfite liquor-based adhesives and asphalt-emulsion adhesives. The sulfite materials tend to resist stains but are affected harmfully by water and alkali substances and may be very brittle. The use of sulfite liquor-based adhesives, therefore, is limited to the best protected, smooth, dry, above-grade applications. The asphaltic adhesives are soft, plastic, and quite water-resistant. They can be recom-

Armstrong Cork Company

1. Repairing damage to existing floor.

Armstrong Cork Company

Installing sheet vinyl
over old resilient floor.

2. Sanding strip where adhesive
will be applied.

Armstrong Cork Company

3. Applying adhesive.

Armstrong Cork Company

4. Sliding new flooring material into place.

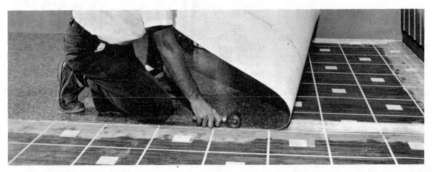

Armstrong Cork Company

5. Forcing adhesive into backing by means of hand roller.

Armstrong Cork Company

6. Hand-rolling along the seam. Excess adhesive is
wiped up with a damp rag.

mended for on- and below-grade use. Problems with these adhesives include potential staining of sensitive tile materials and, when improperly applied, oozing up between the tiles.

Table 10 shows recommendations of adhesives by chemical types for various floor coverings. The chart has been prepared by combining information from several sources. In general, recommendations from different manufacturers overlap and coincide in most important respects. In Table 11, adhesives commonly used for resilient floor installations are classified according to certain performance characteristics.

TABLE 10
RECOMMENDED FLOORING ADHESIVES

	Wood (Suspended)	Concrete (Suspended)	Concrete (On-grade)	Concrete (Below-grade)	Mastic (Under-layment)	Steel, dry, (Non-porous)
Linoleum	S	S	—	—	S,L	L
Rubber	S	S	L*C	C*	L	L,C
Cork	S,L	S,L	L,R	—	S,L	L
Asphalt	A	A	A	A	A	A
Vinyl, coated backing	S	S	L*,C*	—	S,L	L
Vinyl asbestos	A,S	A,S,D	A	A	A,D	A,D
Vinyl, homogeneous	L	L	L,C	C	L	L,C

*Flooring supplier should be consulted.

Key: Adhesives, by chemical type.

    A—Asphaltic   L—Synthetic rubber latex
    C—Chemical set   R—Resinous
    D—Rubber/asphaltic dispersion   S—Sulfite liquor

TABLE 11
PERFORMANCE CHARACTERISTICS OF ADHESIVES FOR RESILIENT FLOORS

Code	Type of Adhesive	Dry Strength	Wet Strength	Tendency to Stain	Alkali Resistance
S	Sulfite liquor	Good	Low	Slight	Low
A	Asphaltic	Good	Good	Yes	Good
D	Rubber/asphaltic dispersion	Good	Fair	Yes	Fair
L	Synthetic latex	Good	Good	No	Good
R	"Alcohol" type (cumar, oleoresinous)	Good	Fair	Slight	Low
C	Latex-hydraulic cement	High	High	No	High
C	Epoxy-polyamide	High	High	No	High

MAINTENANCE

Basic maintenance procedures are the same for all types of resilient flooring. The maintenance materials to be used, however, will differ depending on the type of floor and the amount of traffic it bears. Resilient floors are, by their nature, somewhat porous and tend to be softer than some kinds of dirt. Thus, foot traffic causes an abrasive action that scratches the floor surface and fills the pores and any irregularities with dirt. This dirt is not easily removed by sweeping or dry-brushing operations, because it is ground into the floor rather than remaining on the surface. Generally, wet-cleaning with a suitable cleaning compound is needed. Even so, after the dirt is removed, the scratches and surface irregularities remain.

Regular maintenance of resilient floors calls for the use of a protective finish to fill the irregularities and seal the pores in the surface. This makes cleaning easier, improves the appearance, and prevents the damaging effects of abrasive dirt. The protective finish itself is likely to be affected by the same factors that damage the floor. Therefore, the usual practice is to use protective finishes which can be easily removed and replaced, that is, waxy, resinous, and polymer polishes. In short, basic maintenance procedures for resilient floors can be summed up as "clean, then protect."

For illustrative purposes, consider a resilient floor surface covered with a protective finish, such as that provided by two coats of a water-base emulsion wax. The dirt produced by traffic is ground into the wax rather than the floor itself. The floor is protected against the abrasive action of the dirt, and stains or other damage due to accidental spillage are greatly reduced. Cleaning is easier because the dirt has not been ground into the pores of the resilient surface. Light cleaning will easily remove the dirt together with some of the surface film of wax. If properly applied, the first coat of wax that seals the pores and prevents absorption of liquids, will be affected very little, if at all, by light cleaning operations. Occasionally, it will be necessary to apply an additional top coat of wax in order to restore the surface film to its original thickness. This is the usual commercial maintenance procedure for light and moderate traffic areas. Where traffic is heavy, additional coats of wax are needed to prevent wear-through of the protective finish in traffic lanes.

Through routine maintenance of this type, about 90 percent of the dirt is removed in each cleaning operation. After several cleanings, the residual dirt becomes noticeable; it appears as a general graying in the traffic lanes. In addition to the accumulation of residual dirt, a gradual build-up of wax behind doors, along the edges of corridors, and in light-traffic areas will occur, since it is difficult when restoring the surface film to replace the exact amount of wax or other protective finish that has been removed by wear and cleaning. Sooner or later, depending on the skill of the maintenance personnel, residual dirt and wax build-up detract from the appearance of the floors. When this occurs, a stronger cleaning solution is used to strip the wax and dirt from the floor surface, and the routine maintenance cycle is repeated. Where experienced maintenance personnel are available, stripping is usually required only two or three times per year.

Cleaning materials

Whatever the methods employed for maintenance, the results depend on the suitability, quality, and proper application of the materials used. Using the wrong cleaning compound on a particular type of resilient flooring, for example, can cause serious damage after a few applications. Following are some general rules which can be helpful in choosing and applying the proper floor cleaning material.

(1) Always use a product specifically designed and recommended for the particular resilient floor under consideration. Most cases of severe damage observed by experts in the field have resulted from the use of furniture polish, kitchen cleansers, and so forth, rather than proper floor cleaning materials. Literally hundreds of special cleaning products have been formulated for resilient flooring. They are produced by companies specializing in floor maintenance materials and are available from flooring manufacturers or their dealers. Generally, the products recommended for maintenance of resilient floors are liquid compounds with a soap or synthetic detergent base that are neutral or mildly alkaline in nature. Both the Rubber Manufacturers Association and the Asphalt and Vinyl Asbestos Institute have established standards for products of this type, and most floor cleaning compound manufacturers adhere to the recommendations of these organizations.

(2) Avoid the excessive use of water or cleaning solutions. When too much water is used, especially hot water, it may penetrate between joints or seams to the adhesive and cause a loosening of the adhesive and eventual warping of the flooring. Using too much cleaning solution is not only uneconomical but requires additional rinsing to prevent leaving a residue.

(3) Avoid the use of abrasive agents. Resilient floor surfaces are relatively soft and may be permanently scratched by abrasives if they are used routinely. However, abrasives, if used carefully, may be used for removing deep-seated stains.

(4) Avoid harsh alkaline compounds. Strong alkalies may attack the binder, filler, or color pigments used in the manufacture of resilient flooring causing embrittlement, fading or roughness of the surface.

Floor polishes

The correct choice of a material to provide a protective coating for resilient floors depends on the type of floor and the kind and amount of traffic to which it will be subjected. Following are brief descriptions of the basic types of floor polishes with general comments on their applications:

(1) Liquid water-base emulsion wax. The material is a dispersion of waxes and other modifying materials in water. This is a widely used finish for resilient floors. It is suitable for all types of resilient flooring except natural cork. Products with excellent slip resistance are available. Water-emulsion waxes dry with a gloss which may be improved by buffing with a floor polishing machine. Scuffs and traffic marks may be removed by buffing.

(2) Paste water-base emulsion wax. This is similar to the liquid product described above except that it is produced in paste form. This wax must be polished for luster. It is suitable for use on all types of resilient floors except natural cork. Paste water-base emulsion wax is usually applied with a thin steel-wool pad affixed to a floor polishing machine. The wax is spread by the machine and allowed to dry. It is then polished to a high luster with a second, thicker steel-wool pad. The lubricating effect of the wax prevents the steel-wool pad from scratching the floor surface. When applied in this way, the wax has some cleaning ability and is often used for "one-operation-clean-and-wax" maintenance in areas with light to moderate traffic.

(3) Liquid solvent-base wax. This product is a mixture of waxes and other ingredients in a solvent base. It must be polished for luster. Liquid solvent-base wax should not be used on rubber or asphalt tile but may be used on the other resilient floor varieties. Care should be taken on the thinner-gauge floors because excess solvent may penetrate the seams and cause bleeding of the adhesive.

(4) Paste solvent-base wax. This is similar to liquid solvent-base wax except that it is produced in paste form. It should not be used on asphalt tile or rubber floors but may be used on the other types. Paste solvent-base wax is always recommended for natural and factory-waxed cork floors.

(5) Water-base emulsion resins and polymers. These products are a dispersion of synthetic resins, polymers, and modifying materials in water. They are usually plasticized to impart some buffability. Water-base emulsion resins and polymers may be used on all resilient floors except natural and factory-waxed cork. When these coatings are applied over waxed surfaces, they tend to show poor adhesion and will wear off rapidly. Otherwise, they produce hard, tough coatings with a high luster. Because of their

hardness, they tend to scratch rather than scuff; the scratches are more difficult to buff out than is the case with water-base emulsion waxes. For this reason, water-base emulsion resins and polymers should be avoided in areas subjected to large amounts of sand or gritty soil. Some of these products have excellent resistance to oil and grease, and most of them are better in this respect than the waxes. Their qualities of high scuff resistance and luster make them well suited to prestige floors where appearance is of great importance.

Maintenance systems

During the past fifteen years, a number of floor maintenance systems—incorporating supplies, equipment, and techniques—have been devised by experts in the floor maintenance field to reduce the cost of floor maintenance. Each system is adapted to a particular purpose and is based on new developments in floor polish compositions and in tools and machines for their application. For convenience, we will ascribe titles to the systems, which, while descriptive, are not necessarily in general use.

Chemically treated mop system. (Specific techniques for using chemically treated dust mops and cloths have been discussed in the section on "Sweeping and dry-mopping," pages 30-33.) The system is composed of chemically treated mops and cloths, other elements, including floor polish, and the procedures for scrubbing and stripping the degraded polish film and its replacement.

This system is best suited to the maintenance of asphalt, vinyl asbestos, rubber, vinyl cork, linoleum, backed vinyl, and homogeneous vinyl. Because the system uses non-buffable water-base emulsion polishes, it is not recommended for cork floors. Following are the steps in this system:

(1) The floor should be thoroughly cleaned and all old polish film stripped off at the start of the cycle.

(2) By mopping, apply a thin coat of a water-base emulsion polish. The mop should be clean and well wrung out after immersion in the polish to prevent the application of a too heavy coat. This should be allowed to dry for at least 30 minutes. Then apply a second thin coat. If the floor is porous and the initial coat penetrates the surface, it may be necessary to apply three or more thin coats.

(3) Maintain the floor by daily sweeping with chemically treated mops or cloths.

(4) Periodic light spot-cleaning using a damp mop, wet with clear water and well wrung out, may be required for limited areas.

(5) When there is a noticeable loss of luster, but the appearance

of the floor is otherwise acceptable, a single, light top-coat of non-buffable polish should be applied as in (2) above.

(6) When there is noticeable degradation of appearance—ingrained soil, heel marks, scratching, and marring of the surface—the floor should be stripped as in (1) above and the cycle begun again. It is possible to extend the cycle between strippings to 8 to 10 or more weeks, even under heavy traffic conditions.

(7) To avoid polish build-up and discoloration effects in the re-application of floor polish, do not apply polish to a strip about 6 inches wide next to walls and around non-movable objects.

Damp-mop/buff system. This is not a new system, but it is still well suited to the maintenance of all varieties of resilient floor coverings, except cork.

(1) Clean the floor thoroughly, making sure that all old polish film is stripped off.

(2) By mopping, apply a thin coat of buffable water-base emulsion wax, making sure the mop is well wrung out after immersion in the polish. Allow surface to dry at least 30 minutes, and apply a thin second coat as before. If the floor is porous, three thin coats may be required.

(3) Buff the dried polish film thoroughly, using a heavy, powered buffing machine.

(4) Sweep daily with brushes, brooms, treated mops or cloths.

(5) Once a week, or more frequently if heavy traffic demands it, the floor should be damp-mopped, using clear water or water containing the minimum amount of cleaning compound recommended by the manufacturer. The mop should be well wrung out and rinsed frequently in the cleaning solution.

(6) When the floor has dried, it should be buffed with a heavy, powered buffing machine to remove heel marks and evidence of marring and to restore the gloss.

(7) Continue sweeping on a daily basis.

(8) When there is noticeable degradation of the appearance due to embedded soil and heel marks, the floor should be scrubbed and stripped to remove all the old polish film as in (1) above and the cycle begun again.

(9) When applying additional coats of polish in heavy-traffic areas, it is best to stay about 6 inches away from walls and non-movable objects to prevent polish build-up and consequent discoloration.

Paste-emulsion/buff system. This system has been described under the heading, "Paste water-base emulsion wax," page 91. It consists of only one step—buffing with steel wool or nonwoven nylon pads to which the paste is applied.

The system is best suited to floors that must be maintained during times when they are subject to traffic. No wet-cleaning is required, the floor is ready for traffic immediately after a given area is buffed, and the system is very rapid. Off-street entrance areas requiring frequent maintenance attention are places where this system is especially suitable.

Spray/buff system. This system requires the use of a sprayer attachment on a heavy, powered buffing machine or a buffing machine equipped to deliver a fine spray of water-base emulsion polish to the floor without splashing. The water-base emulsion floor polish is specially formulated to contain synthetic detergents; it usually responds to buffing. This mixture, undiluted with water, is sprayed on the floor, just ahead of the revolving brush, with a non-woven nylon pad covering the brush. The power-driven buffer is drawn back and forth over the floor, and cleaning and polishing are accomplished in one simple operation.

When the solids content of the spray polish is too high, agglomerates of soil and dried polish tend to collect on the non-woven nylon pad and slough off onto the floor. These deposits make it necessary to sweep or vacuum the floor immediately after the cleaning operation. Moreover, the pads become fouled rather quickly and, hence, the cost of pad inventory and washing can be rather high.

A properly formulated product (about 6 percent solids), used with an open-weave nylon pad, will remove an amount of finish solids equal to that being applied. Thus, with a balanced system, it is possible to eliminate for an indefinite period the need for stripping.

The type of spraying apparatus is a matter of choice, although a powered spray applicator using compressed gas is preferred for achieving a fine mist all the time.

This system is ideally suited for spot cleaning or special area cleaning.

It is claimed that regular use of a proper spray/buff program offers savings of 25 percent on floor-care costs over conventional wet-system methods.

(1) Clean floor thoroughly, making sure that all old polish film is stripped off.

(2) If the floor is porous, first apply a water-base floor sealer and undercoat, then two thin coats of a non-buffable water-base polish. See the method of application under "Chemically treated mop system," page 92.)

(3) Maintain the floor by daily sweeping with chemically treated mops or cloths.

(4) For spray-buffing, apply a fine mist ahead of a machine equipped with an open-mesh nylon pad. Using the same motion as for scrubbing, pass the machine over the sprayed area until it is dry (two or three passes). Move forward; spray the next area just ahead of the machine; and pass the machine over the area sprayed until dry. Repeat this process until the entire work area is covered.

(5) Buff to the desired gloss.

(6) Rinse the floor pads thoroughly when the job is completed or if the pad becomes clogged.

Liquid solvent-base/buff system. Floor coverings or surfaces that are solvent-resistant, such as cork, linoleum, and vinyl asbestos, can be maintained with a liquid solvent-base wax in the following manner:

(1) For initial application, two thin coats of wax are recommended. Apply the first coat with a clean cloth or applicator covering only enough area to permit a soaking period of 2 or 3 minutes. Go back over the area and wipe up any excess wax with a wrung-out cloth or applicator.

(2) Allow 15 to 25 minutes drying time, and then buff with a powered machine. Apply a second coat in the same manner, preferably the next day.

(3) Sweep daily with brushes, brooms, treated mops or cloths.

(4) If marks from scuffs, light soil, or heels appear, polish the floor with a clean, steel-wool or non-woven nylon pad.

(5) When polishing alone fails to restore the gloss or clean appearance of one part of the floor, a coat of polish should be applied.

(6) Spread a thin coat of polish over a limited area. Allow to soak for 2 or 3 minutes; then run a polishing machine once over the surface while the wax is still wet. If time permits, allow the floor to dry for 15 to 25 minutes longer, then polish with a clean pad. If the area must be put into service immediately, skip the drying stage and buff until maximum gloss is reached.

(7) For spot-cleaning, apply a heavy coat of solvent-base wax, allow to soak, rub with steel wool, wipe up the excess wax and dirt, and then buff dry.

Liquid solvent-polymer/bright-dry system. The system is intended primarily for wood but can be applied to any floor covering that is naphtha resistant, such as linoleum or cork, in the following manner:

(1) The floor must be stripped of old wax; otherwise the resultant finish will be lusterless. Stripping may be accomplished by the use of naphtha or petroleum solvent. If the old wax coating has not penetrated too deeply or if the build-up is not too great, the surface may be cleaned by multiple applications of the bright-dry solvent-base wax.

(2) For initial applications, two thin coats of wax are recommended. Apply the first coat with a clean cloth or an applicator, covering only enough area to permit a soaking period of 2 or 3 minutes. Go back over the area and wipe up any excess wax with a wrung-out cloth or applicator.

(3) Allow to dry for at least 30 minutes or until the surface is not sticky. If the floor is not glossy enough after the application of the second coat of wax, apply a third coat.

(4) Sweep floors daily with brushes, brooms, or properly treated mops or cloths.

(5) If light-soil or heel marks appear, rub the surface with a cloth or applicator dipped in the solvent-base wax.

(6) Traffic lanes can be touched-up periodically with fresh coats of polish.

(7) The floors may be buffed at regular intervals to maintain a good appearance.

Removing damaged tile

Dry-ice method. A wooden frame is constructed with no top or bottom. The frame should be about 3 inches deep and as long and wide as the area of tile or tiles to be removed, but not more than 21 inches square. Dry ice is placed in the frame in contact with the damaged tiles. The top of the frame is covered with burlap or old carpet which acts as an insulator and directs freezing action to the tiles. The dry ice and insulator are left in place for about 5 minutes. Then the cover, dry ice, and frame are removed, and a wide-blade chisel is used to lift off the tile. The old adhesive should be scraped off the subfloor before the new tile is cemented down.

Heat method. Resilient flooring manufacturers prefer the dry ice method, but heating with a blowtorch, hot water, or electric iron is quicker. If a large number of tiles are to be removed, using a blowtorch is fastest. However, if the blowtorch operator is inexperienced, adjoining tiles can be damaged. Hot water or an electric iron are recommended alternatives to the blowtorch. A flat-bottomed pan the size of the tile to be removed is filled with hot water and placed on the tile. The pan is allowed to stand for 3 to 5 minutes and then is removed. The tile is lifted with a chisel and the subfloor area scraped until it is clean. Or, a tough sheet of paper (not too heavy) is laid over the damaged tile and ironed back and forth for a minute or two with a hot iron. Then the tile is lifted with a suction cup of the type used by plumbers. Wetting the edges of the suction cup will make it more effective. (Rubber and solid vinyl are good insulators; it may take longer to melt their adhesive bonds.) Cork is such an effective insulator that neither the freezing nor heating methods are practical. The material is soft enough, however, to chisel out easily without any preparation.

Refinishing damaged tile

Once a floor has become seriously scarred and pock-marked, there is very little that can be done except to replace the floor or to grind it down below the level of the indentation marks. The technique of ridding resilient flooring of scratches, gouges, and depressions caused by women's

Behr-Manning Division of Norton Co.

Preparing to refinish damaged tile.

spike heels, or other objects with great weight concentrated in a small area, may be likened to the cosmetic surgeon's technique of surgically sand-papering pock-marks or freckles from skin.

One of the polish manufacturers has found that resilient floors can be honed by placing a coarse 100-grit abrasive screen disc under a floor machine. To prevent dust from rising, an industrial vacuum is connected to the housing of the floor machine, and a ⅛-inch-thick rubber skirt is placed around its base. Following sanding with the coarse disc, a finer 150-grit screen is used. The application of two coats of polish after final sanding is said to leave the floor looking like new.

In at least one situation, it has been estimated that the reconditioning process can be accomplished at about one-tenth the cost of replacement. Experience has shown that at least three such reconditioning operations can safely be performed before the floor must be replaced.

Stain removal

A properly maintained resilient floor covering should have sufficient floor polish on the surface to protect it against most water-base stains and many oil- and solvent-base stains. Fresh stains should be wiped or blotted up immediately before they have a chance to dry. Dried stains, usually of doubtful origin, are more difficult to remove and may require more than one treatment, using different stain removers.

A solvent-type cleaning agent (turpentine, naphtha, benzine, dry-cleaning solution) should never be used on asphalt or rubber.

A portable stain-removal kit should be available to the custodial staff. The kit might include the following chemicals and tools:

   (1) Concentrated general-purpose cleaning solution.

   (2) General-purpose cleaning compound, diluted 1 ounce per gallon, in a convenient hand-spray plastic bottle.

   (3) Steel-wool pads of varying coarseness, e.g., No. 0, No. 00.

   (4) Putty knife.

   (5) Turpentine or naphtha.

   (6) Denatured alcohol.

   (7) Acetic acid, 5 percent.

   (8) Ammonia solution, 5 percent.

   (9) Paint remover.

 (10) Hydrogen peroxide, 3 percent.

 (11) Oxalic acid, 10 percent.

 (12) Acetone.

 (13) Glycerine solution, 20 percent.

 (14) Floor polish.

Following is a list of stains and the suggested procedure for removing them from resilient floor coverings:

Acid: Clean with dilute general-purpose cleaning solution. Strong acid stains may require neutralization with ammonia solution. If the surface is etched or color-lightened, burnish with coarse steel wool. Rinse thoroughly with water, dry, and apply polish.

Adhesive, flooring: Rub with No. 00 steel wool dipped in dilute cleaning solution. Some mastic adhesives may respond better to naphtha and steel wool. On asphalt or rubber, use alcohol instead of naphtha.

Alcoholic beverage: Rub with No. 00 steel wool and dilute cleaning solution. Wine stains may require alcohol or hydrogen peroxide.

Alkali: Neutralize with acetic acid solution; rinse thoroughly, dry, and apply polish.

Blood: Rub with cold dilute cleaning solution. Tenacious stains may require No. 00 steel wool and concentrated cleaning solution.

Candle wax: Scrape off with a putty knife. Rub with No. 00 steel wool and naphtha. (Use concentrated cleaning solution on asphalt and rubber.) Wash with dilute cleaning solution; rinse, dry, and apply polish.

Candy: Scrape off with a putty knife. Apply dilute cleaning solution; then rub with fine steel wool.

Carbon paper: Rub with No. 00 steel wool dipped in naphtha. (Use concentrated cleaning solution on asphalt and rubber.) Wash with dilute cleaning solution; rinse, dry, and apply polish.

Chewing gum: Scrape off with a putty knife, if necessary, first freezing with dry ice. Remove residual gum with No. 0 steel wool dipped in naphtha. (Use concentrated cleaning solution on asphalt and rubber.) Wash with dilute cleaning solution; rinse, dry, and apply polish.

Chocolate: Scrape off with a putty knife. Rub with No. 00 steel wool dipped in dilute cleaning solution. Rinse, dry and apply polish.

Cigarette burn: Rub with coarse, then mild, steel wool dipped in dilute cleaning solution. Rinse, dry and apply polish. Slight indentations may require patching. See page 103.

Coffee: Wash with dilute cleaning solution. A build-up of residue may require the use of mild steel wool. If the stain is old, place over it an absorbent cloth saturated with a glycerin solution. Let stand for about a half-hour. Then re-clean with dilute cleaning solution. A deep stain may require the use of hydrogen peroxide.

Crayon: Scrape off with a putty knife. Rub residual mark with No. 00 steel wool dipped in naphtha. (Use concentrated cleaning solution on asphalt and rubber.) Wash with dilute cleaning solution; rinse, dry, and apply polish.

Detergent: See "Alkali."

Dishwashing compound: See "Alkali."

Drain cleaner: See "Alkali."

Fruit juice: Use dilute cleaning solution. Persistent stains may require hydrogen peroxide.

Grass stain: See "Coffee."

Ink, ball point: Clean with naphtha and/or alcohol. (On asphalt and rubber, rub with No. 00 steel wool dipped in concentrated alcohol.) Rinse, dry, and apply polish.

Ink, washable: Use dilute cleaning solution. If ink has soaked into the floor, apply an alcohol-soaked blotter for several minutes followed by an ammonia-soaked blotter for several minutes. Wash with dilute cleaning solution; rinse, dry, and apply polish.

Iodine: Clean with alcohol or an ammonia-saturated cloth. Deep stains may require longer contact with ammonia-saturated cotton. Rinse with dilute cleaning solution, then clear water; dry, and apply polish.

Lipstick: Scrape with a putty knife. Rub the residual stain with No. 00 steel wool dipped in concentrated cleaning solution. Deep stains may require the use of hydrogen peroxide followed by dilute cleaning solution. Rinse, dry, and apply polish.

Lye: See "Alkali."

Nail polish: Clean with acetone. (Use alcohol and steel wool on asphalt and rubber.) Wash, rinse, dry, and apply polish.

Oil and grease: Use dilute cleaning solution; rinse and dry.

Paint: Use paint remover sparingly. (Do not use solvent on asphalt and rubber; rub with No. 0 steel wool.) Apply dilute cleaning solution; rinse, dry, and apply polish.

Pencil: Use dilute cleaning solution; rinse and dry.

Plaster: Scrape off with a putty knife. Clean with No. 00 steel wool dipped in cleaning solution. Tenacious plaster may require treatment with acetic acid solution. If the surface is roughened, burnish with steel wool; wash, rinse, dry, and apply polish.

Black rubber: Rub with No. 0 steel wool dipped in concentrated cleaning solution or naphtha. (Do not use naphtha on asphalt and rubber.) Apply dilute cleaning solution; rinse, dry, and apply polish.

Rust: Use oxalic acid solution; rinse thoroughly, dry, and apply polish.

Shellac: Clean with alcohol. Apply dilute cleaning solution; rinse, dry, and apply polish.

Shoe polish: Rub with No. 00 steel wool and concentrated cleaning solution. Some polish may need naphtha. (Do not use naphtha on asphalt or rubber.) Apply dilute cleaning solution; rinse, dry, and apply polish.

Solvent: Solvents may roughen floor surface or cause color mixing. Burnish damaged area with an abrasive pad or coarse steel wool. Wash, rinse, dry, and apply polish.

Tar: See "Chewing gum."

Toilet bowl cleaner: See "Acid."

Tobacco: Apply dilute cleaning solution. On porous floors, use lemon juice and water or equal parts of alcohol and glycerin. It may be necessary to bleach the stain with hydrogen peroxide or a liquid bleach.

Urine: Apply dilute cleaning solution. If stain is old, use oxalic acid solution followed by cleaning solution. Rinse, dry, and apply polish.

Varnish: See "Paint."

Wine: See "Alcoholic beverage."

TABLE 12
COMMON MAINTENANCE PROBLEMS—RESILIENT FLOORS

Problem	Cause	Remedy	Prevention
Loose tiles.	Tiles unsuitable for grade level.	Replace tiles.	See discussion on grade levels. Review manufacturer's recommendations.
	Alkaline moisture and efflorescence on concrete subfloor. White powder should be evident.	Remove tiles; neutralize floor with acid; use waterproof adhesive.	See discussion on subfloors. Select the proper tile and adhesive.
	Residual concrete curing or parting compounds.	Remove tiles; grind or power-brush surface.	See discussion on curing compounds.
	Wrong adhesive or improper installation.	Subfloor may have to be replaced or re-prepared; use proper adhesive.	Check manufacturer's recommendations.
	Excessive water.	Remove tiles; allow subfloor to dry completely; re-cement tiles.	Review sections on maintenance. Never flood with water.
	Use of harmful cleaning compounds or polish removers.	Re-cement tiles.	Use safe and effective cleaning compounds. Check warranties, experience of others, manufacturer's claims.

Problem	Cause	Remedy	Prevention
Cracked or broken tiles.	Subfloor too springy.	May require new subfloor; use more flexible floor covering; consider sheet goods or carpet.	See discussion on subfloors; check with flooring contractor or supplier.
	Subfloor not level.	May require re-preparation of surface (grinding or patching of low spots; use of plywood underlayment).	Examine subfloor before installation of tile; see discussion on subfloors.
	Use of harmful cleaning solutions or improper maintenance techniques may have made tiles brittle.	Entire floor may have to be replaced. Use proper cleaning solutions and maintenance methods.	Use suitable products. See sections on maintenance.
Pitting, softening, bleeding, roughness of asphalt and rubber tiles.	Inferior floor material.	Entire floor may have to be replaced.	Use reliable flooring contractor and tile manufacturer; review warranties, claims.
	Exposure to oils, grease, or solvents.	If damage is moderate, surface may be honed down or rubbed with abrasive floor pad. Refinish with floor polish. Extensive damage may require complete tile replacement.	Use suitable products. See sections on maintenance. Select oil-resistant flooring. Pick up spilled oils and greases immediately.
	Use of harmful maintenance chemicals.	Same as for exposure to oils, grease, or solvents.	Same as for exposure to oils, grease, or solvents. Do not use solvent waxes, solvent cleaning solutions, heavily oiled mops, cloths, or oil-base sweeping compounds.

Problem	Cause	Remedy	Prevention
Pock marks.	Women's spike heels.	Floor may have to be replaced or the surface honed.	Use floor material with higher indentation resistance.
	Residual indentation due to highly concentrated static load.	Same as for women's spike heels.	Use proper casters, glides, furniture rests, cups.
Curling at edges.	Usually due to too much water or persistent dampness.	Remove tiles; dry underlayment; re-cement tiles and apply weight.	See sections on maintenance. Do not flood with water.
Holes, scratches, cuts, tears.	Overloading; moving heavy objects.	Patch small holes in linoleum with a mixture of lacquer and granulated linoleum. For vinyls, make a putty with tile scrapings, methyl ethyl ketone, and clear acetate lacquer. Mask area with tape, apply putty. Sand smooth when dry. Some sheet vinyls can be heat-sealed by floor experts. Replace with matching tiles.	Avoid dragging heavy objects with sharp edges over floor. Use hand trucks or rollers where possible. Install appropriate casters.
Fine scratch marks.	Abrasion by soil and traffic.	Clean floor carefully; apply floor sealer and 3 or 4 thin coats of polish.	Use floor mats at entranceways; increase frequency of floor sweeping; use treated floor mops; polish traffic areas more frequently; seed and maintain surrounding lawn areas.
Uneven appearance, i.e., glossy and dull areas.	Uneven subfloor.	Very little can be done short of installing a new subfloor or honing the tile to a smooth surface.	See discussion on subfloors.

Problem	Cause	Remedy	Prevention
Uneven appearance (continued)	Uneven removal of polish during stripping operation.	Strip floor thoroughly.	Check floor machine pads.
	Improper application of adhesive.	Level new floors with heavy roller. Apply low-gloss polish. If severe, replace floor.	Use skilled flooring contractor. Check on correct type of trowel to apply adhesive.
Rust marks.	Metal objects corroded by water or cleaning solutions.	Abrade stained areas with synthetic pads or steel wool; clean and apply polish.	Use plastic floor guards; refinish metal bottoms with lacquer or paint.
Color fading.	Strong cleaning solutions.	Little can be done. Honing or use of harsh floor pads may expose fresh surface.	Use suitable maintenance products.
	Direct sunlight.	Same as for strong cleaning solutions.	Use shades or tinted glass.
Swelling of rubber tile.	Use of oily and superfatted soaps in cleaning solutions.	Clean thoroughly; burnish with No. 00 steel wool; let dry completely.	Use suitable maintenance products.
Shrinking of solid vinyl.	Use of cleaning compounds and polishes containing solvents may extract plasticizer.	Floor may have to be replaced, if damage is serious.	Use suitable maintenance products.
Discoloration of vinyl floors from rubber runners or rubber furniture rests.	Anti-oxidants in rubber reacting with vinyl flooring.	Abrade stained area with synthetic pads or steel wool; clean and apply polish.	Check with supplier of rubber products before use.
Porous and brittle linoleum or cork.	Use of harmful cleaning solutions.	Apply sealer; then finish with floor polish.	Use safe maintenance products.
	Too frequent scrubbing.	Revise cleaning schedule.	See sections on maintenance.

Problem	Cause	Remedy	Prevention
Whitening of asphalt tile.	Inferior tile or use of harmful cleaning solutions.	Rinse floor thoroughly; allow to dry; buff with steel wool or abrasive pad; apply sealer and polish.	Use neutral cleaning compounds in solution with cool water.
Darkening of floor.	Build-up of finish and/or inadequate removal of finish.	Machine-strip with polish remover and steel wool or abrasive pad; then refinish.	Use light-colored polish; strip and refinish at least twice a year or after every four coats; use an effective polish remover; avoid build-up of polish close to baseboards or stationary furniture.
Poor gloss.	Polish film too thin.	Apply polish at rate of about 1,500 sq. ft./gal. Use multiple coats to build up gloss.	See sections on maintenance.
	Surface too porous.	Use water-base sealer; then apply 2 or 3 thin coats of polish.	Use floor sealer with high solids content as soon as practicable after floor is installed.
	Improper cleaning and rinsing leaving residual film.	Machine-scrub surface; rinse thoroughly and mop-dry. Apply floor polish.	See sections on maintenance.
	Unsuitable polish or method of application.	Same as for improper cleaning. Use clean polish applicator; do not re-use polish or allow contamination of polish.	See sections on maintenance.
Streaking of polish.	Too little polish in mop during application.	Strip off polish and re-apply.	See sections on maintenance.
	Use of dirty equipment.	Clean all equipment; strip and refinish.	See sections on maintenance.

Problem	Cause	Remedy	Prevention
Streaking of polish (continued)	Excessive rubbing with applicator.	Strip and refinish carefully.	Have supplier demonstrate proper technique.
	Extremely porous floor.	Strip completely; apply sealer and 3 or 4 thin coats of polish.	Use floor sealer with high solids content and heavy-duty polishes.
	Improper cleaning and rinsing.	Machine-scrub; rinse thoroughly; mop-dry; and re-apply polish.	See sections on maintenance. Have supplier demonstrate proper techniques.
	Improper cleaning solution and/or polish.	Strip and finish with acceptable products.	Use suitable floor maintenance products.
Poor spreading or leveling of polish.	Improper cleaning and rinsing.	Strip completely and rinse thoroughly.	See sections on maintenance. Use suitable cleaning solutions.
	Application of different type of polish without removing old polish film.	Strip completely; rinse thoroughly; apply fresh polish.	Use compatible polishes; strip before changing polishes.
	Use of cationic (germicidal) floor treatments to sanitize and disinfect.	Strip completely; rinse thoroughly, and apply fresh polish.	The floor must be thoroughly rinsed and dried before polishing to discourage reaction of cationic agents with floor polish ingredients.
	Poor application of second coat; unsuitable polish.	Use thinner coats of polish or use a different type of polish.	Use suitable coating product and proper method of application.
Sticky floors.	Too much polish.	Strip and refinish; or dry-buff with No. 00 steel-wool pad to remove excess polish.	Apply thin coats of polish, allowing sufficient drying time between coats.
	Improper cleaning and rinsing before polishing.	Strip completely; rinse and dry thoroughly; then apply polish.	See sections on maintenance.

Problem	Cause	Remedy	Prevention
Sticky floors (continued)	Improper polish.	Strip and refinish with acceptable polish.	Use suitable polishes.
Rapid soiling.	Migration of plasticizer in polish.	Strip and refinish with acceptable polish.	Use suitable products.
	Polish too soft.	Strip and refinish with polymer-type polish.	Use suitable products.
	Polish softened by radiant heating.	Strip and refinish with tougher polishes or those with higher melting points.	Check radiant heating system. Ask supplier for specific recommendations.
Excessive black marking.	Some types of rubber heels, casters, and wheels will mark any surface.	Rub with No. 00 steel wool dipped in general-purpose cleaning solution. On surfaces other than asphalt or rubber, spot-rub with turpentine or naphtha. Rinse well, dry, and apply polish.	Replace offending casters and wheels with casters and wheels made of non-marking plastic or rubber.
	Improper polish.	Strip and refinish with acceptable polish.	Use suitable products.
Powdering.	Polymeric polish incompatible with polish used previously.	Strip completely; rinse thoroughly, dry, and apply finish.	Use compatible polishes; strip before changing polishes.
	Polish too brittle.	Strip completely; rinse thoroughly, dry, and apply finish.	Use suitable products.
	Improper cleaning and rinsing.	Strip completely; rinse thoroughly, dry, and apply finish.	See sections on maintenance.
	Improper buffing equipment.	Strip completely; rinse thoroughly, dry, and apply finish.	Avoid coarse abrasive pads when buffing.

Problem	Cause	Remedy	Prevention
Traffic laning.	Concentration of traffic in certain areas.	Repolish worn areas; buff as necessary to blend in with rest of floor. It is not necessary to repolish the entire floor.	Touch up traffic lanes more frequently than the rest of the floor.
Poor water resistance (water spots, whitening, loss of gloss).	Improper polish.	Strip and refinish with acceptable product.	Use suitable products.
	Improper cleaning and rinsing.	Strip completely, rinse thoroughly, dry, and repolish.	See sections on maintenance.
	Alkaline residues.	Strip completely, rinse thoroughly, dry, and repolish with acceptable product.	See sections on maintenance; test floor for presence of alkaline moisture.

LINOLEUM

Description

Linoleum is the oldest form of resilient floor covering. It was introduced commercially in England in 1864. Linoleum is sold primarily as sheet goods but is also offered in tile form, which has the advantage of easier replacement and affords the purchaser a chance to create individual design patterns. Both forms are supplied in a number of gauges. Sheet linoleum is available in 6-foot-wide sections; this decreases the number of seams to be matched in patterns and the number of crevices where dirt can accumulate. The decorative wear layer consists of oxidized drying oils and natural or synthetic resins to which are added organic fillers (ground cork and wood flour), mineral fillers, curing agents, and pigments. The "mix" is applied by various means to a suitable carrier (burlap, organic fiber felts saturated with synthetic resins or asphaltic compounds, duck, or mineral fiber sheets), consolidated under heat and pressure, and cured at high temperatures.

Because linoleum is a thermoset material, i.e., heat-cured, it is more resistant to temperature changes than thermoplastic coverings, such as asphalt and vinyl asbestos.

A variety of patterns, designs, and colors are possible in linoleum floor coverings. The purchaser has a choice of solid colors as well as mottled, jaspé, and embossed designs.

Since the drying oils used in linoleum are yellow or brown in color, there are limitations to white or pastel shades of color. An interesting

Armstrong Cork Company

Linoleum floor with interesting design effect.

feature of white or very light-colored linoleum is that in service and on exposure to light, the color may become lighter, not darker as one might expect.

Regardless of the thickness of the wear layer or the backing to which the wear layer is attached, the wear surface layer is the same material; that is, there are no grades. *Inlaid linoleum* is the name for all patterns in which the colors are integrally mixed and extended throughout the composition. *Jaspé* is a striped variety made by a modified process. *Molded linoleum* is the name for those patterns not integrally mixed; rather, the pattern is formed by first preparing different colors of linoleum composition, dropping the appropriate color through a grid onto the backing, and then curing the sheet.

There are two commercial thicknesses of linoleum: standard gauge with an over-all thickness of 0.090 inch and a minimum wear layer of 0.050 inch, which is intended for light-duty use, and 0.125 inch gauge backed with burlap, for heavy-duty use. The latter is traditionally called "battleship" linoleum because it was first manufactured in large quantities to meet United States Navy specifications for warship flooring. The once-popular household gauge, 1/16 inch, has completely disappeared from the market. Custom-made gauges can be purchased to meet buyer specifications, provided that orders of sufficient quantity are given.

Linoleum is a good insulating material, and it is more resilient and easier to walk on than asphalt tile, wood, or vinyl asbestos. Properly maintained, linoleum will wear for many years.

An important factor in considering linoleum as a floor covering is the comparatively low cost per unit of thickness. It is possible to install a heavier-gauge linoleum (thus increasing comfort and quietness) for the same cost as other, thinner-gauge flooring materials, except asphalt tile. Asphalt tile, although cheaper, is less resilient, and less resistant to oils and grease.

Along with its durability, linoleum has the advantage of resistance to shrinkage and to oil and grease. A high-density linoleum with high indentation resistance is available for extra-heavy-duty service.

Linoleum is quite sensitive to moisture. It will absorb water when exposed to cleaning solutions or if kept in a moist condition, such as continued exposure to high humidity. When the moisture content of linoleum is high, the material tends to become soft and plastic and shows poor indentation and abrasion resistance. Continuing exposure to high humidity degrades the oxidized oil-resin binder. The nature of the binder also makes linoleum vulnerable to attack by alkaline solutions. It has been found that calcium and magnesium salts have a synergistic action with alkalies that cause leaching of the binder and degradation of the linoleum. Therefore, the use of strong alkaline cleaning solutions in hard-water areas is considered bad practice.

Linoleum's sensitivity to moisture makes it unsuitable as a floor covering in humid areas, or for below-grade and on-grade installations.

All new linoleum has a surface coating or mill finish, consisting of a superficial film of lacquer, topped by a thin coating of bright-drying, emulsion floor polish. This mill finish fills the pores and makes the linoleum more resistant to water, thereby enhancing the luster of the surface. The mill finish will wear off in time, and, unless floor polish is applied to maintain sealed pores, the surface becomes more vulnerable to wear, ingraining of dirt, and absorption of water.

Maintenance

Initial treatment. A linoleum floor should not be scrubbed for 4 or 5 days after the floor has been installed. This waiting period allows sufficient time for the adhesive to set properly.

However, it is good practice to have the floor cleaned lightly and a polish applied as soon as it has been installed. The floor may be mopped lightly with a dilute cleaning solution to remove surface soil following the manufacturer's recommendations on dilution for damp-mopping. Then one or two coats of a good grade of water-base emulsion polish are applied. Care should be taken during these operations not to flood the floor, or to get excess polish "worked into" the seams or joints of the flooring.

The floor should be swept frequently to keep it clean and free of foreign objects, dust, dirt, or other materials which might damage the surface. For this purpose, treated mops or dust cloths are recommended, provided they are treated in such a manner as to leave no deposits of oil or other harmful substances on the floor.

Thorough cleaning. After the four-to-five-day waiting period following installation of new floors, or whenever thorough cleaning of older floors is necessary, they should be scrubbed thoroughly to remove any ground-in dirt or other foreign materials preparatory to the further application of polish.

A neutral soap-base compound or a synthetic detergent diluted with water according to the manufacturer's instructions should be used on linoleum. Compounds containing abrasives or harmful solvents, alkaline compounds with a pH greater than 11.0 at the recommended use concentration, and acidic stripping agents having a pH under 5.0 should not be used.

The cleaning solution is applied to the floor by any suitable means—mop, cloth, spraying, etc. The floor should not be completely flooded.

The cleaning solution should be allowed to remain on the floor for 2 to 4 minutes, but not long enough for it to dry out.

The floor is scrubbed well with a stiff brush under a powered machine, until all dirt and soil are loosened. Fine steel-wool pads or the least abrasive types of synthetic pads may be used under the brush to speed up the cleaning action. The coarse grades of synthetic pads or steel wool are not recommended for this operation. They may strip off the factory finish and scar the surface of the flooring, making it more difficult to maintain.

The spent cleaning solution is taken up using a mop or a wet-vacuum.

The floor is rinsed thoroughly with clean, cool water, but should not be flooded. The purpose is to remove all traces of solution and soil, so that the performance of any subsequent polish is not adversely affected. The rinse water is taken up.

The floor is allowed to dry thoroughly before application of polish. Under ordinary conditions, about 30 minutes are sufficient. A longer period might be required under adverse temperature and humidity conditions.

Applying polish. Liquid water-base emulsion polishes (wax, resinous, and polymer), which are removable with compounds not injurious to the flooring, are recommended as protective and decorative coatings for linoleum floors. Solvent-base polishes are considered less desirable but may be used with reasonable satisfaction.

The polish is applied evenly in a thin, uniform coat with an applicator or mop. If new mops are used, they should be pre-cleaned by soaking in warm water until the size is removed, then rinsed and squeezed damp-dry.

A suggested procedure for application by mop is as follows: The mop is dipped into the polish and the excess squeezed out with a squeeze-type wringer. The polish is applied to the floor by moving the mop in a side-to-side motion across the surface of the floor. The mop should be turned frequently to present fresh surfaces to the floor. Before the mop "works dry," it is re-dipped into the polish, the excess squeezed out and the operation repeated until the entire floor is coated. Excessively heavy coats of polish should be avoided because they will not dry properly. However, the polish should not be spread too thinly or streaking and non-uniform gloss will occur.

The coating is allowed to dry. This usually takes 20 to 30 minutes but varies according to temperature and humidity conditions.

The gloss and appearance of buffable polishes may be improved by buffing with a soft brush or other suitable buffing instrument.

A second coat of the polish is applied in the same manner as the first and allowed to dry. The floor is buffed again if necessary.

On both old and new linoleum floors that have been stripped, a third coat may be needed to cover adequately and protect the flooring.

It is important that the proper film of polish be maintained on linoleum floors. Too little polish will result in excessive soiling and black-marking of the floor and will yield a low gloss. Excessive build-up of polish will tend to show powdering, scratching, and traffic-laning. The correct amount is that which yields a definite film over the floor covering, but which cannot be readily scratched off.

Routine maintenance. Linoleum is relatively easy to maintain, provided proper procedures are employed. Correct cleaning measures will not remove the glossy, protective "factory finish" from the surface of the material. As long as moisture penetration and ingraining of dirt are prevented, maintenance by damp-mopping, sweeping with chemically treated mops, and rebuffing are not too difficult.

The floor should be dry-mopped or swept as needed to remove surface dirt and foreign objects. For this purpose, treated mops or treated dust cloths are recommended, provided they are treated in such a manner that they leave no deposits of oil or other harmful substances on the floor.

When the appearance of the floor warrants, it may be damp-mopped to remove surface dirt and light scuff marks. For this purpose, a clean mop wrung out in clean, cool water or in a very dilute solution of a mild compound is used. The floor should not be flooded. Scouring powders should be avoided; they will cause excessive abrasion of linoleum. The surface should be allowed to dry thoroughly before subjecting it again to traffic.

In the case of buffable polishes, periodic buffing will remove smear and scuff marks and will improve the gloss. Under some types of traffic, where the polish film has worn away without noticeable black marking or soil embedment, re-coating can be done following the damp-mopping as described in page 112. One or two thin coats are applied as needed and the floor is buffed, if desired.

When the floor is noticeably soiled or black-marked, it should be scrubbed lightly with a compound of the type described previously. A fairly dilute solution of the compound will usually suffice, and the manufacturer's recommendations for this dilution should be followed. For this scrubbing operation, just enough mechanical action to remove dirt is used; it is not necessary or desirable to remove all of the previous coats of floor polish. The solution is taken up and the floor rinsed as described previously. This operation is referred to as a "light-duty cleaning," not polish-stripping. If a few stubborn black marks remain after this operation, they can usually be removed on the spot basis with dry No. 00 steel wool.

One or two thin coats of floor polish are applied as needed. The same technique is used as for the first application, except that it is not necessary to coat up against walls, cabinets, or other fixed units where there is no traffic. Staying 6 to 12 inches away from such areas will prevent problems of polish build-up and will reduce frequency of floor stripping.

Spot-cleaning and application of polish can be done at pivot points, drinking fountains, push doors, or other areas subjected to heavy traffic. Separate cleaning and polishing steps may be used, or spray/buff techniques may be employed. In the latter, emulsion polishes are spray-applied to the localized area and burnished with fine steel wool, or fine-grade pads, to loosen the dirt, restore the luster, and provide protection.

Stripping. When obvious build-ups of polish occur on certain areas on the floor, normally once or twice a year, the floor is stripped with a concentrated solution of an efficient, safe, polish remover, using the dilution recommended by the manufacturer.

The stripping solution is applied liberally to the floor by mop or other suitable means. The solution is allowed to remain on the floor for 3 to 5 minutes, but not long enough to dry out.

The floor is scrubbed with a stiff brush under a powered machine until the old polish film is loosened. The less coarse types of synthetic or steel-wool pads may be used to speed up the removal. The stripping solution is taken up with a wet-vacuum or mop. The floor is rinsed well with clear, cool water and the water taken up. If the polish removal is spotty, repeat the stripping operations. The floor is allowed to dry thoroughly. One to three thin coats of polish (as needed) are applied, following the procedure outlined under "Applying polish." Maintenance is carried out as described under "Routine maintenance."

RUBBER

Description

The history of rubber flooring dates from the early 1920's when it was composed of varying amounts of vulcanized natural and reclaimed rubber, inert materials, and color pigments. Since about 1946, rubber flooring has been made from synthetic rubber, specifically styrene butadiene rubber (S.B.R.), which has better aging properties and better oil and grease resistance than natural rubber. In addition to S.B.R., rubber flooring contains reinforcing pigments such as clay, processing oils and waxes, coloring pigments, sulfur, and accelerators. The flooring is vulcanized (cured with sulfur and heat) and, therefore, is a thermoset material rather than a thermoplastic compound.

Rubber floor tiles are available in a variety of thicknesses, including: 0.080 inch, commonly called "80 gauge"; 0.094 inch; 0.125 inch; and 0.188 inch. The most popular commercial and institutional thickness is 0.125 inch. Because rubber tile is uniform in composition, thickness of the tile is a relative measure of its service life. Rubber floor surfacing is also sold for specialty uses in rolls up to 36 inches wide.

Rubber flooring is non-porous, waterproof, and remains flexible and resilient over a wide temperature range. It is alkali-resistant and largely stainproof.

Rubber flooring can be installed over almost any smooth, dry, level, sound surface, which has been properly prepared to restrict transmission of moisture through the floor. It is suitable for use below-grade, on-grade, and above-grade. Outdoor areas are about the only locations where rubber is not suitable as a floor covering.

Because the cost of rubber flooring is higher than most other resilient materials, rubber tile should be used with regard to its outstanding properties of gloss, durability, and resilience. When appearance, ease of maintenance, foot comfort, and reduction of noise level are important considerations, a rubber floor installation should be seriously considered. It is regarded as relatively slip-resistant, and insurance figures indicate that the number of slips on rubber is lower than the number of slips on any other smooth-surface floor covering. However, when the floor is wet, the slip resistance is markedly decreased.

Most rubber flooring is made in a marbleized pattern, but all basic colors are available in rubber flooring, including many pastels.

Rubber flooring is susceptible to attack and deterioration by contact with certain rubber "poisons," including copper and manganese. Soaps of copper and manganese are particularly active, because they will dissolve in the rubber compound; fatty acids are harmful for the same reason. Usually, rubber flooring that is exposed to poisons first becomes tacky and soft. This starts as a surface phenomenon, at the point of contact. The reaction tends to be autocatalytic, i.e., self-enacting. Following the softening stage, oxidation takes place, and the rubber becomes hard and brittle and shows surface cracking and crazing.

Solvents, oils, and grease cause rubber flooring to swell and become soft. If solvents are wiped off fairly quickly, little damage is likely to result; but prolonged contact with solvents and oils will cause irreparable softening and damage. Even superficial softening may result in permanent damage, especially if the floor is walked on while the surface is soft and sticky, and dirt becomes embedded in the surface layer.

Rubber flooring is also susceptible to deterioration by ultra-violet light and ozone in the air. Exposure to ultraviolet light can cause colors to fade. Ozone produces fine cracks in the surface of rubber. Ozone cracking can occur where flooring is exposed to direct sunlight, such as that coming through open doors or windows.

Maintenance

Initial treatment. Rubber floors should not be scrubbed or flooded with excessive water for 4 or 5 days after the floor has been laid. This waiting period allows sufficient time for the adhesive to set properly.

The floor should be swept frequently to keep it clean and free of foreign objects, dust, dirt, or other materials which might damage the surface. For this purpose, brooms, untreated mops, or damp-sweeping tools are recommended.

If necessary, the floor may be damp-mopped during the waiting period, using a mop dipped in a very dilute solution of cleaning compound, and then wrung damp-dry.

Thorough cleaning. Following the waiting period for newly installed floors, or as a treatment on floors already in use, they should be scrubbed thoroughly to remove surface soil and ground-in dirt, preparatory to

Rubber Products, Inc.

Rubber tile floor.

applying a polish. Extra effort may be required initially to remove possible mold-release agents used in the manufacturing process.

A free-rinsing, liquid synthetic detergent cleaning compound or a neutral (non-superfatted) soap, diluted with warm water (100° to 120° F.), should be used according to the manufacturer's instructions. The concentrated cleaning compound should not contain more than 0.001 percent manganese. Free ammonia should not exceed 0.50 percent. Cleaning compounds containing abrasives or solvents should not be used. In addition, alkaline cleaning compounds with a pH greater than 11.0 at the recommended use-concentrations should be avoided. Similarly, acid-stripping agents having a pH under 5.0 should not be used.

The solution is applied to the floor by any suitable means—mop, cloth, spraying, etc.—but the floor should not be flooded. The solution is allowed to remain on the floor undisturbed for approximately 3 to 5 minutes, but not long enough for it to dry out.

The floor is scrubbed with a stiff brush under a powered machine until all dirt and soil are loosened. Fine steel-wool pads, or the mildest types of synthetic pads, may be used under the brush to hasten the cleaning action. The coarse grades of synthetic pads or steel wool are not recommended for this operation. Some of the very smooth, high-gloss rubber floors are scratched by the *finest* cleaning pads. Considerable attention must be employed to minimize scratching.

The spent cleaning solution is taken up using a mop or a wet-vacuum.

The floor is rinsed thoroughly with clean, cool water, but should not be flooded during this operation. The purpose is to remove all traces of solution and soil, so that the appearance of any subsequent polish is not adversely affected. The rinse water is then taken up.

The floor is allowed to dry thoroughly before application of floor polish. Under ordinary conditions, about 30 minutes is sufficient drying time. A longer period might be required under adverse temperature and humidity conditions.

Applying polish. Liquid water-base emulsion polishes (wax, resinous, and polymer), which are removable with compounds not injurious to the flooring, are preferred and are especially recommended for rubber floorings. The pH of the polish should not exceed 10.0 or be less than 5.0. Solvent-base polishes must not be employed, because solvents cause rubber flooring to swell and soften.

It is important that the polish films be light in color and have good color stability to prevent unsightly discoloration after aging.

The polish should be applied evenly in a thin, uniform coat with an applicator or mop. If new mops are used, they should be pre-cleaned by soaking in warm water until the size is removed, then rinsed and squeezed damp-dry. In general, less polish is needed on rubber flooring than on more porous floors. This is so because rubber tile has a smooth face which is relatively non-absorbent.

A suggested procedure for application by mop is as follows: The mop is dipped into the polish and the excess squeezed out with a squeeze-type wringer. The polish is applied by moving the mop in a side-to-side motion across the surface of the floor. The mop should be turned frequently to present fresh surfaces to the floor. Before the mop "works dry," it is re-dipped into the polish, the excess squeezed out, and the operation repeated until the entire floor is coated. Excessively heavy coats of polish should be avoided because they will not dry properly. However, the polish should not be spread too thinly, or streaking and non-uniform gloss will be encountered.

The film is allowed to dry. This usually takes 20 to 30 minutes, but varies according to temperature and humidity conditions. Polishes often dry more slowly on rubber floors than on other more porous floorings. The gloss and appearance of waxy polishes may be improved by buffing with a soft brush or other suitable buffing tool. If necessary, a second coat is applied in the same manner as the first and allowed to dry. However, the second coat should not be applied until the first coat is dry and tack-free. Otherwise, poor re-coating will occur, causing low gloss and possibly streaking. The floor is buffed again if desired.

Routine maintenance. The floor should be dry-mopped or swept as needed to remove surface dirt and foreign objects. For this purpose, treated mops or treated dust cloths are recommended, provided they are treated in such a manner that they leave no deposits of oil or other harmful substances on the floor.

When the appearance of the floor warrants, it may be damp-mopped to remove surface dirt and light scuff marks. For this purpose, a clean mop wrung out in clean, cool water or in a very dilute solution of a mild cleaning compound is used. The floor should not be flooded.

In the case of waxy coatings, periodic buffing will remove smear and scuff marks and will improve the gloss.

Under some types of traffic—where the polish film has worn away without noticeable black-marking or soil embedment—re-coating can be done following the damp-mopping. One thin coat is applied and buffed. When the floor is noticeably soiled or black-marked, it should be scrubbed lightly with a compound of the type previously described. A fairly dilute solution of the compound will suffice, and the manufacturer's recommendations for this dilution should be followed. For this scrubbing operation, just enough mechanical action to remove the dirt is used; it is not necessary or desirable to remove all the previous coats of floor polish. The solution is taken up and the floor rinsed. This operation is referred to as a "light-duty cleaning," not stripping.

If a few stubborn black marks remain after this operation, they can usually be removed on a spot basis with dry No. 00 or No. 000 steel wool.

One or two thin coats of floor polish are applied as the need dictates, using the same technique as for the first application, except that it is not necessary to coat up against walls, cabinets, or other fixed units where there is no traffic. Staying 6 to 12 inches away from these areas will prevent problems of film build-up, and will reduce the frequency with which the floors must be stripped.

Spot-cleaning and re-coating can be done at pivot points, drinking fountains, push doors, or other areas subjected to heavy traffic. Separate cleaning and polishing steps may be used, or spray/buff techniques may be employed.

Stripping. When the floor shows obvious build-up of polish, or when ingrained dirt cannot be removed by routine maintenance, the old polish must be stripped and the floor repolished. The frequency of stripping is a matter of judgment, best left to the chief custodian.

A liberal amount of safe polish remover (diluted in accordance with manufacturer's instructions) is applied to the floor by mop or other suitable means.

The solution is allowed to remain on the floor for 3 to 5 minutes, but not long enough to dry out.

The floor is scrubbed with a stiff brush under a powered machine until the old polish film is loosened. Milder types of synthetic pads or steel wool may be used to hasten the removal action on many rubber floors. If surface scratching is encountered, less-harsh equipment should be used.

The stripping solution is taken up with a wet-vacuum or mop. The floor is rinsed well with clear, cool water and the water taken up. If some film remains, these stripping operations are repeated. The floor is allowed to dry thoroughly. One or two thin coats of polish are applied (as needed) following the procedure previously outlined, and then routine maintenance is continued. For best performance: When a polymer polish is to be used on rubber floors which have a wax polish on them, the old polish should be removed prior to application of the polymer coating.

CORK

Description

Cork floor coverings are made primarily from the outer bark of the cork oak tree, found in southern Europe, particularly Spain and Portugal. The material is manufactured for floors in two forms: sheets (called cork carpet) and tiles. At present, cork flooring in sheet form is manufactured only on special order. Therefore, the discussion here is limited to cork in the form of tiles.

Cork tile, one of the earliest of modern resilient floor coverings, was first produced in the United States around the turn of the century. From that period, until post-World War II, its production consisted of baking cork granules under high heat and pressure without added resin binders, allowing the natural resins of the cork granules themselves to form the necessary binder and create blocks from which the cork tiles were sawed. During that period, practically all cork tile was furnished in heavy gauges, ranging from $\frac{5}{16}$-inch thickness upward. The material was produced without a factory finish. While durable following installation, it had relatively low tensile strength and thus could not be manufactured in today's thinner gauges.

Hedrich-Blessing

Natural cork tile floor.

During the last twenty years, domestic manufacturers modified their process so as to add phenolic or other resin binders to the cork granules prior to their compression and baking. At the same time, the manufacturers reduced both the baking temperature and the length of baking time with the result that the modern version of cork tile has greater tensile strength, more resiliency through the retention rather than extraction of the natural cork resins themselves, greater uniformity of color, and less porosity between the cork granules where the added resin binders act as a fill-in. Also during this period, factory finishing of the surface was introduced.

Cork tile lends itself to many decorative effects. It is used in designs by cutting it into various sizes and by inserting figures cut from tile of contrasting shades. Colors of cork tile, which might be graded as light, medium, and dark, are essentially three shades of brown. The varieties are produced as a result of different degrees of baking. Within these groups are variations of shading which make it possible to achieve blends and patterns of all three. Parquetry and marquetry patterns, medallions, inlaid herringbone, and mosaic effects can be obtained.

Cork flooring is the most porous and resilient of all of the floor coverings considered in this chapter. The former property is not altogether advantageous, but the latter makes cork very quiet and comfortable. Cork is also an insulator giving good protection from heat and cold. The material is practically odorless. The air cells or pores are not interconnected in any regular fashion and therefore there is no tendency to warp or splinter. Cork flooring is not slippery, a quality that makes it an excellent material for floors on inclined walkways or under rugs.

Cork flooring can be divided into four general categories, based on the finish given to the material at the time of manufacture. The four types of surfaces are (1) natural, (2) waxed, (3) resin-reinforced-waxed, and (4) vinyl.

Natural cork tile, as its name implies, is furnished by the supplier without a finish of any kind. Natural cork tile is available in three thicknesses—⅛ inch, 3/16 inch, and 5/16 inch. Only the thickest of these should be considered for commercial or institutional use.

Waxed cork tile is impregnated with a molten wax composition at the factory and does not require a finishing treatment at the time of installation.

Resin-reinforced-waxed cork tile is impregnated with a resin-reinforced wax at the factory. It is less porous and smoother than the first two varieties. Hence, there tends to be less impregnation by dirt.

Vinyl cork tile is the type most recently introduced to the market. It is a denser product with a substantial wear layer of vinyl, polycarbonate, or other polymeric substance intimately bonded to the cork tile surface. It is the most impervious to staining and the accumulation and ingraining of dirt. Sanding, sealing, polishing, and buffing are unnecessary and, in fact, the first two steps should be avoided. Vinyl cork tile is available in only one thickness—⅛ inch.

Formerly, cork floors were not well suited to institutional use, because they did not wear well and were difficult to maintain. Even today, institutional grades of natural cork flooring are limited to special areas of use requiring low impact noise and high foot comfort, and neither natural nor waxed cork tiles are considered sufficiently durable for heavy-duty institutional use. They are not stain-proof, grease-proof, or resistant to soiling. Tracked-in siliceous dirt, cinders, and other abrasive materials will cause roughening and rapid wear of these varieties. The porosity of these types makes for a particularly difficult problem in cleaning; the softening and deteriorating effects of aqueous cleaning solutions add to the difficulties. Natural cork tile and waxed cork tile—especially the former—are quite sensitive to water and alkaline detergents. Floors constructed of these varieties can be ruined by exposure to water.

During the past few years, however, the two newer varieties—resin-reinforced-waxed and vinyl cork—have been perfected to the point where they have quite adequate durability for heavy-duty institutional use and do not impose a severe maintenance problem. In fact, vinyl cork tile will probably have durability equal to that of backed vinyl tile and will withstand relatively heavy traffic. Both resin-reinforced-waxed cork and vinyl cork tile are resistant to deterioration from moderate contact with water. Only these two varieties of cork tile have any resistance to oils, grease, or staining.

Installation

For about 24 hours prior to installation, all cork tile flooring should be preconditioned to the temperature of the area in which it is to be installed. A temperature of about 70° F. is ideal. Cork tile should never be quickly transferred for installation from a low-temperature area to a markedly warmer area or vice versa. Because cork is composed of about 57 percent air in its cellular structure, it is especially sensitive to expansion and contraction caused by changes in temperature.

Preparation of the subfloor before spreading of the adhesive follows much the same pattern as that recommended for other types of resilient floorings with one important exception: Over worn or uneven concrete subfloors, a latex type of patch coat or underlayment should be used. More rigid underlayments, under the impact of traffic transmitted through highly resilient cork tile, will eventually break away from the surface of the concrete, and the tile, with underlayment attached, will leave the subfloor.

All cork tile can be recommended for installation over suspended subfloors having at least an 18-inch air space beneath that is adequately cross-ventilated.

Cork flooring may be installed over concrete slabs in direct contact with the ground, although the slab surface must be at least 12 inches above the grade level and the drainage in the immediate vicinity must be away from the slab. A waterproof adhesive should be used. None of the varieties of cork tile can be recommended for installation below grade level.

Two basic procedures must be followed in the installation of cork flooring which are opposed to those procedures normally used in the installation of other types of resilient floors. These procedures are necessary because cork tile is a highly resilient agglomerate and, while less porous than it was formerly, still has a much higher absorption factor than other resilient floors.

First, it is recommended that the adhesive be spread heavily, and second, the finished floor should be rolled with relatively light equipment. The heavy spread of adhesive is to allow for a certain amount of absorption of the adhesive into the under surface of the tile before the adhesive cement sets. Likewise, allowing for the compressibility of resilient cork tile, a 100-pound (maximum) roller should be used for final seating of the tile to prevent it from sliding with resulting compression, peaking (raised edges), or opening of seams.

In ordinary installations of natural, factory-waxed, or resin-reinforced-waxed cork tile over suspended subfloors, a high-grade lignum paste is used, spread with a trowel. A semi-saturated lining-felt layer should be laid over suspended wood or plywood subfloors. The lignum paste should have a high solids content, because the absorptive characteristics of cork cause the tile to swell when exposed to an undue amount of liquid.

The paste should be spread about 25 to 30 feet ahead of the tile setter, and, after the installation of each area of about 100 square feet, the tile surface should be rolled, preferably diagonally. Rolling again after completion of the entire job is also recommended.

The installation of plastic-topped cork tile or vinyl cork flooring over suspended subfloors follows this procedure, except that manufacturers usually recommend waterproof adhesive in place of lignum paste.

Following installation of cork tile, the subcontractor, according to manufacturers' recommendations, is expected to remove all evidence of excess adhesive and to protect the flooring surface adequately until all construction has been completed.

Maintenance

Initial treatment. Immediately after the installation of natural cork tile and prior to exposure to any traffic, the surface must be sanded to make it level and smooth. The floor is vacuumed but not wet- or damp-mopped. Then it must be coated with a penetrating sealer. Following this, the floor surface must be given successive coatings of liquid or paste wax polish and buffed to enhance the appearance of the finished job.

In the case of waxed, resin-reinforced-waxed, and vinyl cork tile, the sanding and sealing treatments are omitted. With these types, the floor should not be scrubbed for 4 or 5 days after it has been installed. This waiting period allows sufficient time for the adhesives to set properly.

However, it is good practice for these three categories of cork floors to be lightly cleaned and a polish applied immediately following installation. The floor should be mopped lightly with dilute cleaning solution to remove surface soil (following the manufacturer's dilution recommendations for damp-mopping). One or two coats of a good grade of water-base emulsion polish should be applied. Solvent-base polishes (liquid or paste) may be used; in which case, the floor should be buffed to develop a proper luster. Care should be taken during these operations not to flood the floor or to get excess polish worked into the seams or joints of the flooring.

As part of the initial treatment, all cork floors should be swept frequently to keep them clean and free of foreign objects, dust, dirt, or other materials which might damage the surface. For this purpose, treated mops or dust cloths are recommended, provided they are treated in such a manner that they leave no deposits of oil or other harmful substances on the floor.

Thorough cleaning. After the 4- to 5-day waiting period for new cork tile floors, or as a preliminary treatment on previously installed floors, they should be scrubbed thoroughly to remove any ground-in dirt preparatory to the application of a polish.

A neutral soap or a synthetic detergent compound should be used diluted with water according to the manufacturer's instructions. Compounds containing abrasives or harmful solvents should not be used. Alkaline compounds with a pH higher than 10.5 at the recommended use-concentration should not be used. Strong acid stripping agents also should be avoided.

The cleaning solution should be applied to the floor by any suitable means (mop, cloth, spray, etc.), but the floor should not be completely flooded.

The cleaning solution should be allowed to remain on the floor for 3 to 5 minutes but not long enough for it to dry out.

The floor should be scrubbed with a stiff brush under a powered machine until all dirt and soil is loosened from the floor. Fine steel-wool pads or the mildest types of synthetic pads may be used under the brush to speed up the cleaning action. The coarse grades of synthetic pads or steel wool are not recommended for this operation. They may strip off the factory finish and scar the surface of the flooring, making it harder to maintain. The spent cleaning solution should be taken up by use of a mop or a wet-vacuum.

The floor is rinsed thoroughly with clean, cool water, but it should not be flooded. The purpose is to remove all traces of solution and soil, so that the performance of any subsequent polish is not adversely affected.

The rinse water should be taken up. The floor should be allowed to dry before application of floor polish. Under ordinary conditions, 20 to 30 minutes are sufficient, but a longer period might be required under adverse temperature and humidity conditions.

Applying polish. Water-base emulsion polishes are recommended for cork tile that is adequately sealed. Solvent-base polishes may also be used. Freshly sanded floors should be sealed as described under "Refinishing," page 127, before the use of either type of polish. The polishes used may be of the buffable, semi-buffable, or non-buffable types, depending on which is preferred.

The polish is applied evenly in a thin, uniform coat with an applicator or mop. If new mops are used, they should be pre-cleaned by soaking in warm water until the size is removed, then rinsed and squeezed damp-dry. Following is a suggested procedure for application of water-base emulsion floor polishes by mop:

The mop is dipped into the polish and the excess squeezed out with a wringer. The mop is applied to the floor by moving it in a side-to-side movement across the surface of the floor. The mop is turned frequently to present fresh surfaces to the floor. Before the mop "works dry," it is again dipped into the polish, the excess squeezed out, and the operation repeated until the entire floor is coated. Excessively heavy coats of polish should be avoided because they will not dry properly. However, the polish should not be spread too thinly, or streaking and non-uniform gloss will be encountered.

Solvent-base polishes are most easily applied with an applicator or cloth, depending to some extent on whether the polish is a liquid or a paste. Again, uniform, thin coats are best.

The polish is allowed to dry. This usually takes 20 to 30 minutes but varies according to temperature and humidity conditions.

The gloss and appearance of buffable polishes may be improved by being buffed with a soft brush or other suitable buffing device.

A second coat of the polish is applied in the same manner as the first and allowed to dry. Then it can be buffed if desired.

Routine maintenance. The floor should be dry-mopped or swept as needed to remove surface dirt and foreign objects. For this purpose, treated mops or treated dust cloths are recommended, provided they are treated in such a manner as to leave no deposits of oil or other harmful substances on the floor.

The floor is damp-mopped as needed to remove surface dirt and light scuff marks. For this purpose, a clean mop wrung out in clean, cool water or in a very dilute solution of a mild cleaning compound should be used. The floor should not be flooded.

In the case of buffable coatings, periodic buffing will remove smear and scuff marks and will improve the gloss.

Under some types of traffic (where the polish film has worn away without noticeable black marking or soil embedment), re-coating can be done following the damp-mopping. One or two thin coats of polish are applied as needed and the floor is buffed if necessary.

When the floor is noticeably soiled or black-marked, it should be scrubbed lightly with a dilute solution of a good compound of the type described previously. For this operation, just enough mechanical action to remove the dirt is used. It is not necessary or desirable to remove all the previous coats of floor polish. The solution should be taken up and the floor rinsed as described previously. This operation is referred to as a "light-duty cleaning," not stripping.

If a few stubborn black marks remain after this operation, they can usually be removed on a spot basis with dry No. 00 steel wool.

One or two thin coats of polish are applied as needed; the polish should be kept 6 to 12 inches away from fixed objects and baseboards in order to prevent build-up of polish in such areas. The floor is buffed if necessary.

Spot cleaning and polish application can be done at pivot points, drinking fountains, push doors, or other areas which are subjected continuously to heavy traffic. Separate cleaning and polishing steps may be used or spray/buff techniques may be employed in which emulsion polishes are spray-applied to the localized area and burnished with fine steel wool or fine-grade pads to loosen the dirt, restore the luster, and provide protection.

Stripping. The steps described under "Routine maintenance" are repeated as needed until obvious build-ups of polish occur at certain areas on the floor. When this occurs, the floor should be stripped with a concentrated solution of an efficient, safe polish remover, using the dilution recommended by the manufacturer.

The stripping solution is applied liberally to the floor by mop or other suitable means.

The solution should be allowed to remain on the floor for 3 to 5 minutes, but not long enough to dry out.

The floor is then scrubbed with a stiff brush under a powered machine until the old polish film is loosened. The milder types of synthetic pads or steel wool may be used to hasten the removal.

The stripping solution is then taken up with a wet-vacuum or mop. The floor is rinsed well with clear, cool water and the water taken up. If the removal is spotty, these stripping operations should be repeated. The floor is allowed to dry thoroughly. One or two thin coats of polish are applied as needed following the procedure outlined in the section called "Applying polish." Maintenance should be carried out as described under "Routine maintenance."

Refinishing. If the natural, waxed, or resin-reinforced-waxed cork tile has been allowed to become soiled to the point where it cannot be satisfactorily cleaned, or if the floor surface has stains, gouges, and so forth, it can be refinished. While it is probably best to have this job performed by a professional finisher, the following procedure may be suggested.

The tile is sanded smooth and level with No. 00 sandpaper on a sanding machine of the flatbed type. The floor is vacuumed to remove surface dust. Water should not be applied to the newly sanded floor.

Care must be exercised in the sanding operation to control depth of cut and evenness of sanding. For ⅛-inch cork tile, replacing the floor would probably be easier and less expensive than sanding and refinishing because of the thin gauge of the material.

A uniform coating of a good grade of floor sealer (polyurethane, epoxy, oleoresinous, etc.) is applied. This is allowed to dry until hard and then it is burnished with No. 00 steel wool used with a powered machine.

A second uniform coat of the sealer is applied. This is allowed to dry and then it is burnished with No. 00 steel wool. The cork floor may then be polished and maintained as described above.

ASPHALT

Description

The term "asphalt tile" is a carry-over from the days when asphalt and bituminous materials were used as the binders to form the tile. Because of the inherently dark color of these materials, colors of asphalt tile were originally limited to solid, dark shades of black, red, and brown. Since the early 1950's, the trend has been toward lighter colors of tile which, of necessity, contain less asphaltic materials or none at all. Based primarily on color, asphalt tile has been traditionally graded with letter designations from "A" through "D." The old-style "A" solid colors of brown, black, and red have been eliminated because of the demand for light colors and the growing popularity of vinyl asbestos as one of the components of this tile. Currently there are the remaining three color classifications. The "B" colors include the darker shades of black, dark red, and reddish brown. The "C" colors include light brown, light green, charcoal, gray, and sand shades. "D" colors are somewhat brighter and include cream, white, blue, bright red, and yellow as basic colors. The "C" and "D" colors contain little or no asphalt or bituminous materials and are higher priced.

Asphalt tiles are available in three general patterns—marble, color chip, and textured. The marbleized effect is obtained by the introduction of a contrasting color that appears to swirl within the base color. Although white is a common marbleizing color, there is no practical limitation in the use of other colors for this purpose. The color chip patterns, in some cases, produce a terrazzo effect, while, in other cases, a random dot pattern is created. The textured patterns are primarily designed to yield the appearance of cork, stone, tapestry, or carpet.

The dark colors of asphalt tile are made from gilsonite asphalt, fatty-acid pitch, asbestos fibers, inorganic fillers, and coloring matter. Iron oxide and other inexpensive inorganic pigments are often used for coloring. The light colors of tile are made of a variety of light-colored synthetic resins mixed with softeners or plasticizing agents, clay and other inorganic fillers, asbestos fibers, and bright-colored pigments. Coumarone-indene resins have long been preferred because they are inexpensive and light in color.

The thoroughly blended mixture of thermoplastic binder, inert fillers, and color is calendered while hot and sheeted to a uniform thickness, producing a smooth surface, after which the sheet is cut to size. The standard size of the tile is 9 inches square, although the square 12-inch size is becoming increasingly common.

Asphalt tile has been a popular floor covering for many years, but, since the introduction of vinyl asbestos, asphalt has steadily lost ground for institutional use. Good quality asphalt tile is classified as fire resistant (although it will burn) and is resistant to mild alkalies. Although asphalt tile is generally considered to have good alkali resistance, the manufacturers recommend that, in maintenance, strong alkaline solutions should be avoided.

Asphalt flooring is attacked by oils, fatty acids, grease, petroleum spirits, and many organic solvents. Spillage of paint, varnish, or lacquer on asphalt can ruin the floor.

Grease-proof asphalt tile, once produced by most manufacturers, was based on thermoplastic synthetic resins selected for their resistance to oil and grease. The use of special resins and the limited market raised the price for grease-proof tiles over that for the same color class in ordinary asphalt tile. Today, vinyl asbestos tile is used in areas formerly reserved for grease-proof asphalt tile.

While asphalt tile has good resistance to abrasive wear when properly maintained, there are limitations to the type of exposure it will withstand. Continued contact with siliceous dirt, such as the accumulations from a cinder path or driveway, can severely damage the smooth wearing surface and take years off the useful life of the tile, as well as significantly increase maintenance costs. Asphalt tile floors located directly off street entrances may be subject to rapid wear due to tracked-in abrasive dirt. Unless, under such conditions, a rigid maintenance program is carried on, the floor may soon show traffic lanes, worn-off pattern, and dull appearance; difficulty will be encountered in keeping the surface bright and glossy, even after floor polish is applied.

The Perkins & Will Partnership

Floor installation combining asphalt tile and quarry tile.

Asphalt tile has fair durability under normal conditions of traffic and environmental exposure, but it is less durable than all other forms of resilient surfaces, except cork. With normal usage and proper installation, it would be reasonable to expect asphalt tile to give adequate service for 15 years.

A situation where lime or plaster becomes embedded in the surface irregularities of the tile and creates a difficult cleaning job commonly occurs in new construction or during repairs. It is difficult to remove this fine powder by sweeping. When soap solutions are used to clean such tile, the soap reacts with the calcium to form an insoluble and adherent film. Although this film may be quite superficial, it is sufficient to give a white bloom to dark-colored tile and a grayish cast to the light colors of tile. If a floor polish is applied before the precipitated calcium soap is cleaned off, the discoloration becomes sealed in the surface. This trouble can be avoided by protecting the flooring during construction and repair work with a suitable light covering of felt paper.

Asphalt tile has one of the lowest initial costs of the resilient floor coverings available for institutional use. As with all other precut tiles, waste is reduced to a minimum and the standard 9- by 9-inch-size tiles permit relatively easy and inexpensive installation.

The tiles are sold in two thicknesses: a standard gauge, $\frac{1}{8}$ inch or 0.125 inch, and a premium gauge, $\frac{3}{16}$ inch or 0.1875 inch.

Asphalt tile is harder than other resilient floorings; it therefore has a higher noise level and is not as comfortable to walk on as more resilient floor coverings.

The main problems with asphalt tile are associated with its thermo-plastic properties. Exposure to high temperature may soften the tile to the point where it is easily indented by stationary objects, and may be marked permanently by the load. Continued exposure to low temperature may cause brittleness and cracking, especially if the subfloor is not smooth and rigid. Furniture rests that will adequately protect the tile against heavy loads should be used.

Asphalt tile is suitable for installation on any level of floor, i.e., suspended, on-grade, or below-grade, provided the subfloor is dry, smooth, and rigid. The condition of the subfloor is critical to the most advantageous use of asphalt tile. The brittleness of asphalt tile is such that its installation on a non-level floor almost guarantees its failure. A reduced life might result if the subfloor flexed under the impact of normal pedestrian traffic.

Maintenance

Under normal traffic conditions, and with adequate sweeping, damp-mopping, buffing, and application of floor polish, asphalt tile is maintained fairly easily. Under abnormal conditions, some problems of keeping a bright appearance and high gloss may arise. These are best dealt with by increasing the frequency of cleaning and application of floor polish to seal the pores and prevent ingraining of dirt.

Initial treatment. Water should not be used on floors of this type for at least 5 days after the floor has been laid. This will allow sufficient time for the adhesive to harden thoroughly. During this period, the floor should be swept frequently to keep it clean and free of foreign objects or materials which might damage the surface. If the floor becomes extremely dirty, it may be damp-mopped, but only a slightly dampened mop should be used.

Thorough cleaning. After the five-day waiting period, the floor should be thoroughly cleaned to remove dirt and any finish which may have been applied by the manufacturer of the flooring. During this and subsequent operations, the excessive use of water, especially hot water, should be avoided to prevent moisture penetration between the tiles. This can loosen the adhesive and eventually cause warping and cracking of the tile.

A neutral soap or synthetic detergent compound mixed with warm water (100° to 120° F.) should be used according to the manufacturer's instructions. Highly alkaline compounds or those containing abrasives or solvents should not be used. Any alkaline compound with a pH greater than 11 in use-concentration must be avoided. Highly alkaline cleaning compounds can deteriorate the tile, causing embrittlement, and, in some cases, color fading or whitening.

The cleaning solution is applied to the floor with a mop, cloth, sprinkling can, or by spraying. The floor should not be flooded with the solution. The solution should be allowed to remain undisturbed on the floor for 3 to 5 minutes, but not long enough for it to dry out. Then the floor should be scrubbed well.

After the floor is scrubbed, the dirty cleaning solution should be removed from the floor with a mop or wet-vacuum. The floor must be rinsed thoroughly; otherwise performance of the floor polish is likely to be adversely affected. Warm water (90° to 100° F.) should be used and the rinse water kept clean. The floor should not be flooded. The floor should be rinsed twice, using fresh water each time, and allowed to dry thoroughly before application of the polish. Under ordinary conditions, about one hour is sufficient. A longer period will be required under adverse temperature and humidity conditions.

If this cleaning operation fails to remove all stains, soil, and old finish, it should be repeated. If necessary, the floor should be scrubbed lightly with No. 0 or No. 1 steel wool.

Applying polish. Only water-base emulsion waxes and water-base emulsion resin or polymer polishes should be used on these floors. Solvent-base waxes will soften the floor and cause the colors to bleed. Varnishes, lacquers, and polymer or resin polishes containing such detrimental solvents as naphtha, turpentine, or benzine should not be used.

The floor polish should be applied evenly in a thin, uniform coat with an applicator or mop and allowed to dry. This usually takes 20 to 30 minutes, but varies according to temperature and humidity conditions. If the resultant gloss is inadequate, a higher luster may be obtained for the two types of polish, as follows: After additional drying of the first coat (one hour), it may be buffed with a polishing brush; a second coat may then be applied, allowed to dry thoroughly, and buffed. A suitable polishing brush is made of union mixture fibers. This is approximately a half-and-half mixture of tampico and palmyra fibers.

Routine maintenance. The floor should be dry-mopped or swept as needed to remove surface dirt and foreign materials. Never use mops, dusters, cloths, or sweeping compounds that leave deposits of oil on the floor. Oils and solvents, such as gasoline, kerosene, or turpentine, will attack the asphalt or resin binder and cause softening of the tile and color bleeding. Any spilled oily or greasy materials should always be wiped up immediately.

When the appearance of the floor warrants, it may be damp-mopped to remove ground-in dirt and light scuff marks. A clean mop wrung out in clean, cool water or dilute, neutral cleaning compound should be used. The floor should not be flooded. In the case of waxed floors, remaining scuff marks may be removed by buffing.

Worn spots and traffic lanes may be touched up as necessary with water-base emulsion polishes, using the method given above. With waxy polishes, buffing will eliminate the marks caused by overlapping of coats.

Stripping. As required, or at regular intervals, the polish should be removed and a fresh one applied. The methods specified earlier under "Thorough cleaning" should be used.

VINYL

Description

Homogeneous vinyl. This flooring (also called flexible vinyl) resembles rubber tile in appearance. The product is made by mixing vinyl resins, plasticizers, fillers, stabilizers, and coloring matter in a heated mixing machine. The resins, under heat and pressure and the influence of the plasticizer or softening agent, becomes soft and doughlike in consistency. This hot dough is passed between heated, polished steel rollers that squeeze it to the desired thickness in the form of a sheet. After cooling, the sheets are sanded on the backside, polished, and cut into tiles.

Homogeneous vinyl tile can be very attractive, with bright, clean colors and a very smooth, highly lustrous surface. Most flexible vinyl is relatively comfortable to walk on. Although it is not quite as resilient or soft underfoot as rubber tile, it has greater resiliency and "foot-ease" than vinyl asbestos tile. Vinyl tile has good acoustic properties, almost equaling cork in noise absorption. It has the desirable properties of good wear resistance, freedom from damage by contact with oil and grease, and excellent resistance to acids, alkalies, cleaning compounds, and moisture.

Homogeneous vinyl floor covering is expensive. However, this material should be considered when attractiveness and durability are desired. It will vary greatly in price, depending upon color, texture, pattern, and thickness. A solid color will probably cost more than a corresponding thickness of rubber tile.

Armstrong Cork Company

Sheet vinyl flooring.

Vinyl resins are tough synthetic polymers that give the tile excellent wear resistance. At the same time, the tile is flexible yet firm. A vinyl tile floor is able to withstand heavy loads without indentation. The safe load for vinyl tile is generally believed to be 200 pounds per square inch, making it one of the best resilient floor surfaces with respect to indentation resistance.

Vinyl tile floors have been reported to shrink and cup when solvent-base materials were used on them. As a consequence, cleaning compounds and polishes containing naphtha, turpentine, and petroleum distillates are not recommended for use on homogeneous vinyl tile.

When exposed to constant foot traffic, the highly lustrous surface of vinyl tile will become dulled by a myriad of small scratch marks or scuffs. This may show up most in traffic lanes, where the contrast between the worn and unworn areas will be quite obvious by the difference in luster. These surface scratches can pick up material from rubber soles and heels, and the traffic lanes will show discoloration (especially in the case of light or pastel colors). The gloss of the tile surface can be restored by buffing with very fine steel-wool pads. The same technique is effective in removing stains and discoloration.

Keeping the floor well swept and free of abrasive grit will minimize these effects. The application of floor polishes will prolong the life and appearance of vinyl flooring.

Homogeneous vinyl tile can be installed on almost any floor, regardless of grade. On suspended floors, the recommended adhesive is linoleum paste. For on- and below-grade concrete slabs, an alkaline-resistant adhesive is needed; otherwise, a latex-type is used for on-grade, and a chemically set type for below-grade floors. Certain factors are important in the installation of all vinyl flooring. Concrete floors must be well-cured, dry, and clean. The temperature of the tile, adhesive, and floor must be at least 70° F. until 24 hours after installation. The adhesive must be wet when the tile is laid. The floor tiles or sheets must not be tightly abutted and the floor must be thoroughly rolled.

On newly installed homogeneous vinyl floors, difficulties may be encountered in the application of emulsion floor polishes, because of failure to wet and then dry on the surface to a uniform finish. This is usually a result of surface exudation of plasticizer. After two or three cleanings, however, the excess plasticizer will be removed and there will be no further trouble.

Backed (laminated) vinyl. The growth in production of backed vinyl floor coverings has been little short of phenomenal, due largely to the wide variety of decorative offerings at relatively low cost. While backed vinyl is manufactured principally in the form of yard goods 6 feet wide, it is also available in tile form.

The important difference among the backed vinyl and homogeneous vinyl is the wear layer. The latter presents a uniform, continuous wear surface throughout the thickness of tile. The backed varieties have a surface wear layer which may range from a few thousandths of an inch (in the case of roto-printed sheet goods) to 50-thousandths of an inch for the more expensive grades. Backed vinyls are considerably less expensive than the homogeneous product.

There are several varieties of backed vinyl floor covering. One is backed with a vinyl composition, which may be either a fiber-base compound or a plain, solid-color vinyl sheet. It is possible to re-use scrap for making the backing material, and, in these cases, the backing is usually a dark and less brilliant shade of color. In effect, vinyl sheet backed with a vinyl-impregnated base fiber is an all-vinyl composition, although only the top layer contributes the decorative effects and colors.

Another form of backing is similar to the asphalt- or resin-impregnated paper felt that formerly was associated with older forms of low-cost, household types of sheet linoleum. The term "paper felt backing" is still used to describe this form of backing.

Still another variety is a composition backing, constructed principally of asbestos fibers, applied to vinyl sheet goods in the manufacturing process. The combination of a thin film of vinyl resin over asbestos fibers, which is highly resistant to moisture and alkalies, permits the use of these sheet vinyl floors in areas previously excluded from consideration; for example, they may be safely installed directly over most concrete subfloors, below- and on-grade, as well as on suspended floors. Only under extremely saline soil conditions—typical of scattered regions and areas where hydrostatic pressure is excessive—are precautions necessary.

Vinyl-coated jute felt, a popular floor covering in Western Europe, has been introduced recently to the American market. Basically, the roll-goods product is an attempt to combine the advantages of vinyl flooring with those of carpet. It is claimed that the thick felt backing contributes foot comfort and low impact sound, while the vinyl wear surface offers ease of maintenance.

The jute-backed vinyl is manufactured by various methods, two of which are coating the felt with molten polyvinyl chloride and laminating or calendering vinyl film onto the felt backing. The surfaces incorporate slightly textured effects achieved by special embossing.

The backing can be treated with an alkali- and moisture-resistant film to make the floor covering suitable for installation over most subfloors. Lacking this special undercoat, vinyl-coated jute felt should not be used on below-grade floors. The sheet goods can be installed either by cementing in place or loose-laying over clean, smooth subfloors. Thicknesses range up to ¼ inch; widths are 27 inches, 36 inches, and 54 inches.

A new variety of backed vinyl consists of a vinyl wearing surface over a vinyl sponge core, with a backing of either vinyl or asbestos. Available in 6-foot-wide rolls, this variety of vinyl is said to be suitable for use on all grade levels and performs extremely well with respect to foot comfort.

While backed vinyls have the desirable qualities of high surface gloss, bright colors, ease of maintenance, and resistance to oils, grease, chemicals, and alkaline cleaning compounds, their resistance to indentation depends on the character of the backing used. Felt-backed vinyls are much less resistant to indentation than are the homogeneous vinyl coverings.

New trends in styling make use of colored vinyl chips embedded in translucent vinyl to give three-dimensional effects. The chips, in the form of colored, randomly shaped stones or squares, impart a slight texture to floors, which helps to conceal indentation marks made by spike heels. The extent of texturizing is controlled to minimize floor care problems.

The only reason for the existence of laminated or backed vinyl floor covering is that it is cheaper to manufacture than the homogeneous material. A lower initial cost, however, may be misleading, and the product may prove to be more expensive over the long term. It is essential to consider traffic conditions and expected service life when choosing a quality of backed vinyl flooring, especially since the criterion on which price is based is usually the thickness of the wear layer. Backed vinyl for institutional use should be chosen with care.

Most of the advantages and desirable properties of homogeneous vinyl are possessed by the backed vinyl flooring. This is to be expected, because the wear layer is equivalent to that of homogenous vinyl. It follows that the most important considerations are the possible disadvantages.

Special attention must be given to securing a smooth and uniform surface upon which the backed vinyl is to be placed. Care must be taken to apply the adhesive evenly. If the undersurface is rough and irregular, or if nail heads protrude, the impressions show through the surface after a relatively short period.

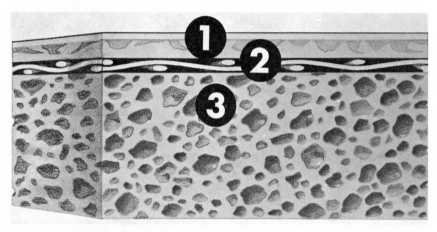

The Flintkote Company

Cross-section of cushioned sheet vinyl flooring showing (1) vinyl-chip layer, (2) woven fiber glass reinforcement, and (3) vinyl-foam backing.

Maintenance

All vinyl floor coverings will look better and give better service when cared for in a regular manner with proper maintenance materials and techniques. Cleaning and polishing improve the appearance, reduce scratching, modify slip characteristics, and make cleaning easier.

Those vinyl floorings which have a very high-gloss surface tend to show scratching and other marks fairly readily and require considerable attention to minimize such marks.

In general, less polish is needed on vinyls than on more porous floors, such as linoleum or asphalt tile. This is because vinyl floors have a smooth "face" which is relatively non-absorbent.

Initial treatment. Vinyl floors should not be scrubbed for four to five days after the floor has been laid. This waiting period allows sufficient time for the adhesive to set properly.

During this 4- to 5-day waiting period, the floor should be swept frequently to keep it clean and free of foreign objects, dust, dirt, or other materials which might damage the surface. For this purpose, treated mops or dust cloths are recommended provided they are treated in such a manner as to leave no deposits of oil or other harmful substances on the floor.

If desired, the floor may be damp-mopped during the waiting period, using a mop which has been dipped in a very dilute solution of cleaning compound and wrung damp-dry.

Thorough cleaning. Following the waiting period for newly installed floors, or as a preliminary treatment on floors already in use, they should be scrubbed thoroughly to remove ground-in dirt and surface soil preparatory to applying a polish.

A neutral soap or a synthetic detergent compound diluted with warm water (100° to 120° F.), according to the manufacturer's instructions, should be used. Compounds containing abrasives or solvents and alkaline compounds with a pH greater than 11.0 at the recommended use-concentrations should not be used.

The cleaning solution may be applied to the floor by any suitable means (mop, cloth, spraying, etc.) but the floor should not be flooded.

The solution is allowed to remain on the floor undisturbed for approximately 3 to 5 minutes but not long enough for it to dry out.

The floor is scrubbed with a stiff brush under a powered machine until all dirt and soil are loosened. Fine steel-wool pads or the mildest types of synthetic pads may be used under the brush to hasten the cleaning action. The coarse grades of synthetic pads or steel wool are not recommended for this operation. Some of the very smooth, high-gloss vinyl floors are scratched by the *finest* cleaning pads.

The spent cleaning solution is taken up, using a mop or a wet-vacuum. The floor is rinsed thoroughly with clean, cool water, but should not be flooded during this operation. The purpose is to remove all traces of solution and soil, so that the performance of any subsequent coatings is not adversely affected. The rinse water is taken up.

The floor is allowed to dry thoroughly before application of floor polish. Ordinarily, about 30 minutes are sufficient. A longer period might be required under adverse temperature and humidity conditions.

Applying polish. Liquid water-base emulsion polishes (wax, resinous, and polymer), which are removable with compounds not injurious to the flooring, are especially recommended for vinyl floorings. Solvent-base coatings are not recommended for homogeneous and backed vinyls.

When a polymer polish is to be used on vinyl floors that have a waxy film on them, the old wax should be removed prior to application of the polymer polish.

It is important that the polish films be light in color and have good color stability on aging. Most vinyl floorings are made in light-colored, brilliant patterns, and colored polish films detract from their beauty.

The polish should be applied evenly in a thin, uniform coat with an applicator or mop. If new mops are used, they should be pre-cleaned by soaking in warm water until the size is removed, then rinsed and squeezed damp-dry.

The suggested procedure for application by mop is as follows: The mop is dipped into the polish and the excess squeezed out with a squeeze-type wringer. The polish is applied by moving the mop in a side-to-side motion across the surface of the floor. The mop should be turned frequently to present fresh surfaces to the floor. Before the mop "works dry," it is re-dipped into the polish, the excess squeezed out, and the operation repeated until the entire floor is coated. Excessively heavy coats of polish should be avoided because they will not dry properly. However, the polish should not be spread too thinly or there will be streaking and loss of uniformity in gloss.

The film is allowed to dry. This usually takes 20 to 30 minutes but varies according to temperature and humidity conditions.

The gloss and appearance of waxy polishes can be improved by buffing with a soft brush or other suitable buffing equipment.

If necessary, a second coat of polish is applied in the same manner as the first and allowed to dry. Buffing may be repeated, if desired.

Because polishes often dry more slowly on vinyl floors than on other, more porous floorings, thin coats should be applied, and a second coat should not be applied until the first coat is dry and tack-free. Otherwise, low gloss and possible streaking will result.

Routine maintenance. The floor should be dry-mopped or swept as needed to remove surface dirt and foreign objects. For this purpose, treated mops or treated dust cloths are recommended provided they are treated in such a manner that they leave no deposits of oil or other harmful substances on the floor.

When the appearance of the floor warrants, it may be damp-mopped to remove surface dirt and light scuff marks. For this purpose, a clean mop wrung out in clean, cool water or in a very dilute solution of a mild cleaning compound should be used. The floor should not be flooded.

In the case of waxy polishes, periodic buffing will remove smear and scuff marks and will improve the gloss.

Under some types of traffic—where the polish film is worn away without noticeable black-marking or soil-embedment—re-coating can be done following the damp-mopping procedure described above. One thin coat is applied and buffed, if desired.

When the floor is noticeably soiled or black-marked, it should be scrubbed lightly with a dilute solution of a cleaning compound of the type described previously. For this operation, just enough mechanical action to remove the dirt should be used; it is not necessary or desirable to remove all the previous coats of floor polish. The solution should be taken up and the floors rinsed as described previously. This operation is referred to as a "light-duty cleaning," not stripping.

If a few stubborn black marks remain after this operation, they can usually be removed on a spot basis with dry No. 00 steel wool.

One or two thin coats of floor polish, as the need dictates, are applied, using the same technique as for the first application, except that it is not necessary to coat areas against walls, cabinets, or other fixed units where there is no traffic. Staying 6 to 12 inches away from these objects will prevent problems of film build-up and will reduce the frequency with which the floors will have to be stripped.

Spot-cleaning and repolishing can be done at pivot points, drinking fountains, push doors, or other areas which are subjected to heavy traffic. Separate cleaning and polishing steps may be used, or the spray/buff technique may be employed.

Stripping. Repeat the routine maintenance steps as needed until obvious build-ups of polish occur at certain areas on the floor. When this occurs—normally once or twice a year—the floor should be stripped with a concentrated solution of an efficient, safe stripping compound, using the dilution-level recommendation of the manufacturer. The solution is applied liberally to the floor by mop or other suitable means, then is allowed to remain on the floor for 3 to 5 minutes, but not long enough to dry out.

The floor should be scrubbed with a stiff brush under a powered machine until the old polish film is loosened. Milder types of synthetic pads or steel wool may be used to hasten the removal action on many vinyl floors. If surface scratching is encountered, use less-harsh equipment.

The stripping solution is taken up with a wet-vacuum or mop. The floor is rinsed well with clear, cool water and the water taken up. If some film remains, these stripping operations are repeated. The floor is allowed to dry thoroughly. One or two thin coats of polish (as needed), following the procedure outlined under "Applying polish," are applied and maintenance is continued as described under "Routine maintenance."

VINYL ASBESTOS

Description

Vinyl asbestos tile is similar to asphalt tile in composition, except that vinyl resins and plasticizers are used in place of asphalt and other thermoplastic resins as the binder. The basic resin, polyvinyl chloride, is a tough, abrasion-resistant, thermoplastic material that is unaffected by most chemicals and solvents. Vinyl asbestos tile presents a uniform, continuous wear surface throughout the thickness of tile.

During the past fifteen years, vinyl asbestos tile has steadily increased in popularity as a floor covering for institutional purposes. It now outsells all other types of resilient floor coverings.

Vinyl asbestos tile is suitable for use in all indoor areas protected from the weather. It can be used over suspended wood floors (which are free from movement or spring), and over suspended, on-grade, and below-grade concrete floors. The use of vinyl asbestos on radiant-heated floors is also considered acceptable, provided that the surface temperature of the floor covering does not become excessive. Most manufacturers suggest 100° F. as the maximum surface temperature, although at least one supplier limits the surface temperature to 80° F. The major concern is that the tile may soften and be susceptible to permanent indentation damage.

Vinyl asbestos tile is a bit more flexible than asphalt. With respect to impact resistance and sound absorption properties, there is little significant difference between the two types of tiles; both types rank substantially lower in these properties than other kinds of resilient flooring.

The maximum static load limit that vinyl asbestos flooring can sustain without forming a permanent indentation is relatively low. Reported values range from 25 to 100 pounds per square inch. Furniture rests to be used on vinyl asbestos should be large enough to distribute the weight of the load adequately and prevent residual indentation.

Vinyl asbestos tile is generally considered to be semi-porous, whereas asphalt tile is porous; solid vinyl and solid rubber are non-porous. The factor of reduced porosity is believed to be largely responsible for the ease with which vinyl and rubber can be maintained.

Vinyl asbestos has good resistance to oil and grease. Another important feature is its resistance to acids and alkalies. The fact that vinyl asbestos is resistant to alkaline moisture is one of the reasons it is suitable for use in below-grade and on-grade concrete slabs. Its alkali resistance has an additional advantage; the tile is able to withstand the use of "strong" cleaning agents and possible misuse of the maintenance chemicals.

Vinyl asbestos tile is available in different thicknesses or gauges: ⅛ inch, ³⁄₃₂ inch, and ¹⁄₁₆ inch. However, for institutional use, only the ⅛-inch gauge is considered acceptable.

Installation techniques require that all tile, adhesive, and areas to be covered must be maintained at 70° F. for at least 48 hours before installation, to permit all materials and surfaces to reach equilibrium. Moreover, the area must be kept at 70° F. during installation and for 48 hours afterwards.

Azrock Floor Products Division, Uvalde Rock Asphalt Company

Vinyl asbestos flooring.

In certain areas, such as California, Florida, and the Gulf Coast region, excessive ground moisture or a high water table may cause excess moisture to penetrate the slab and collect under portions of the tile. In such situations, the most important consideration at the time of installation is proper preparation of the underfloor including measures to prevent excessive moisture penetration in the case of on- and below-grade concrete slabs.

Maintenance

Initial treatment. Vinyl asbestos tile floors should not be scrubbed for four or five days after the floor has been laid. This waiting period allows sufficient time for the adhesive to set properly. However, it is good practice to clean the floor lightly and apply a polish as soon as the floor has been installed. The floor should be mopped lightly with a dilute cleaning solution to remove surface soil (following the manufacturer's dilution recommendations for damp-mopping); then one or two coats of a good grade of water-base emulsion polish are applied. Care should be taken during these operations not to flood the floor or to get excess polish "worked into" the seams or joints in the flooring.

The floor should be swept frequently to keep it free of foreign objects, dust, and dirt. For this purpose, treated mops or dust cloths may be used, provided they are treated in such a manner that no deposits of oil or other harmful substances are left on the floor.

Thorough cleaning. After the waiting period for new floors, or as needed on previously installed floors, the surface should be scrubbed thoroughly to remove ground-in dirt, surface soil, etc.

A neutral soap or a synthetic detergent compound diluted with warm water (100° to 120° F.), according to the manufacturer's instructions, should be used.

Compounds containing abrasives or solvents should not be used. In addition, alkaline compounds with a pH greater than 11.0 at the recommended use-concentrations should not be used on vinyl asbestos tile.

The cleaning solution is applied to the floor by any suitable means (mop, cloth, spraying, etc.), but the floor should not be flooded.

The cleaning solution should be allowed to remain on the floor undisturbed for approximately 3 to 5 minutes but not long enough for it to dry out.

The floor should be scrubbed with a stiff brush under a powered machine until all dirt and soil are loosened from the floor. Fine steel-wool pads can be used under the brush to hasten the cleaning action.

The coarse grades of synthetic pads or steel wool are not recommended for this operation. They may remove the factory finish or may scar the tile surface, making it harder to maintain.

The spent solution is taken up, using a mop or a wet-vacuum.

The floor is rinsed thoroughly with clean, cool water, but the floor should not be flooded during this operation. The purpose is to remove all traces of solution and soil so that the performance of any subsequent polish is not adversely affected. The rinse water is taken up.

The floor should be allowed to dry thoroughly before application of floor polish. Under ordinary conditions, about 30 minutes is sufficient drying time. A longer period might be required under adverse temperature and humidity conditions.

Applying polish. Liquid water-base emulsion polishes (wax, resinous, and polymer), which are removable with compounds not injurious to the flooring, are recommended for vinyl asbestos tile. Solvent-base coatings are not recommended.

The polish is applied evenly in a thin, uniform coat with an applicator or mop. If new mops are used, they should be pre-cleaned by soaking in warm water until the size is removed, then rinsed and squeezed damp-dry.

A suggested procedure for application by mop is as follows: The mop is dipped into the polish and the excess squeezed out with a squeeze-type wringer. The polish is applied to the floor by moving the mop in a side-to-side motion across the surface of the floor. The mop is turned frequently to present fresh surfaces to the floor. Before the mop "works dry," it is re-dipped into the polish, the excess squeezed out, and the operation repeated until the entire floor is coated. Excessively heavy coats of polish should be avoided because they will not dry properly. However, the polish should not be spread too thinly or streaking and a non-uniform gloss will result.

The polish is allowed to dry. This usually takes 20 to 30 minutes, but varies according to temperature and humidity conditions.

The gloss and appearance of waxy polishes may be improved by buffing with a soft brush or other suitable buffing tool. A second coat of the polish is applied in the same manner as the first and allowed to dry. Buffing may be repeated.

On new tile or on older, porous floors which have been stripped, a third coat of polish may be needed to cover and protect the flooring adequately.

The proper film of polish should be maintained on vinyl asbestos tile floors. Too little polish will result in excessive soiling and black-marking of the floor and yield a low gloss. Excessive build-ups will tend to show powdering, scratching, and traffic-laning. The correct amount is that which yields a definite film over the floor covering, but which cannot be readily scratched off.

Routine maintenance. The floor should be dry-mopped or swept as needed to remove surface dirt and foreign objects. For this purpose, treated mops or treated dust cloths are recommended provided they are treated in such a manner as to leave no deposits of oil or other harmful substances on the floor.

When the appearance of the floor warrants, it may be damp-mopped to remove surface dirt and light scuff marks. For this purpose, a clean mop wrung out in clean, cool water or in a very dilute solution of a mild cleaning compound should be used. The floor should not be flooded.

In the case of waxy polishes, periodic buffing will remove smear and scuff marks and will improve the gloss.

Under some types of traffic—where the polish film has worn away without noticeable black-marking or soil-embedment—re-coating can be done, following the procedure described earlier. One or two thin coats are applied as needed and the floor is buffed, if desired.

When the floor is noticeably soiled or black-marked, it should be scrubbed lightly with a dilute solution of a cleaning compound of the type described previously. For this operation, just enough mechanical action to remove the dirt is used. It is not necessary or desirable to remove all previous coats of floor polish. Thus, a fairly dilute solution of the compound will suffice, and the manufacturer's recommendations for the level of dilution should be followed. The solution is taken up and the floor rinsed as described previously. This operation is referred to as a "light-duty cleaning," not stripping.

If a few stubborn black marks remain after this operation, they can usually be removed on a spot basis with dry No. 00 steel wool.

One or two thin coats of floor polish are applied as the need dictates, using the same technique as for the first application, except that it is not necessary to coat the areas up against walls, cabinets, or other fixed units where there is no traffic. Staying 6 to 12 inches away from these objects will prevent problems of polish build-up and will reduce the frequency with which the floors will have to be stripped.

Spot-cleaning and polish-application can be done at pivot points, drinking fountains, push doors, or other areas which are subjected continuously to heavy traffic. Separate cleaning and polishing steps may be used, or spray/buff techniques may be employed in which water-base emulsion polishes are spray-applied to the localized area and burnished with fine steel wool or fine-grade pads to loosen the dirt and restore the luster.

Stripping. The steps outlined under "Routine maintenance" are repeated as needed until obvious build-ups of polish occur at certain areas on the floor. When this occurs—normally once or twice a year—the floor should be stripped with a concentrated solution of an efficient, safe polish stripper, using the dilution level recommended by the manufacturer.

The stripping solution is applied liberally to the floor by mop or other suitable means.

The solution is allowed to remain on the floor for 3 to 5 minutes but not long enough to dry out.

The floor is scrubbed with a stiff brush under a powered machine until the old polish film is loosened. Milder types of synthetic pads or steel wool may be used to hasten the removal action.

The stripping solution is taken up with a wet-vacuum or mop. The floor is rinsed well with clear, cool water and the water taken up. If some film remains, these stripping operations are repeated. The floor is allowed to dry thoroughly. One to three thin coats of polish (as needed) are applied, following the procedure outlined in "Applying polish."

Maintenance is continued as described in "Routine maintenance."

4

CARPET

INTRODUCTION

Soft-pile floor coverings, offering functional, decorative, and psychological values, are manufactured by various methods and are available in many surface styles and fibers.

Rugs are available in standard sizes such as 9 by 12 feet, 12 by 15 feet, etc., and are bound or "finished off" around the entire perimeter. A carpet is cut from a roll of broadloom, of standard width, in whatever length may be needed. Both a carpet and a rug can be "broadloom," since the term has no reference to a type of weave. It simply means that the soft-pile fibers are woven on a loom that is more than 6 feet wide.

Carpet is almost always installed wall-to-wall. Aside from the decorative advantages, this type of installation is practical, because it eliminates the need to maintain the area of hard flooring around the edge of a rug. On the other hand, a rug may be used purposefully: to point up a beautiful wood floor or to accent a special area. In heavily trafficked rooms, rugs can be turned to equalize wear. Also, they are easily rolled up and transported for cleaning or moving.

The use of carpets and rugs began with the Assyrian and Babylonian empires, and a number of basic types persist to this day. Some of the better-remembered ones are: Axminster, braided, Brussels, chenille, embroidered, hooked, ingrain, Oriental, Persian, tapestry, velvet, and Wilton. Here we are concerned only with the modern commercial-grade, machine-made product.

CARPET COMPONENTS

Although we will be discussing carpets made by a variety of methods — that is, weaving, knitting, tufting, looming, and flocking — three basic components are common to all carpets: pile, warp, and weft yarns. Though loosely applied to all carpet, "warp yarns" and "weft yarns" are terms properly associated with woven fabrics.

Pile yarns

These are the upstanding yarns which form the wearing surface of the carpet. They are the only yarns we see and walk upon. The pile yarns may be cut, looped, or a combination of both. As a convenient measure of construction, the amount of pile yarn in a carpet refers to the weight of yarn forming the wear layer plus the weight of the yarn "roots" buried in the body of the carpet. The buried weight of yarn is significant in the case of Wilton weaves and when the yarn is woven through the back.

Warp yarns

In the carpet industry, "warp yarn" is the term used for those backing yarns which run lengthwise through the carpet. There are two types of warp-backing yarns used in weaving carpet: chain and stuffer yarns.

E. T. Barwick Mills, Inc.

Carpeted school library.

The chain warp is often referred to as the "chain binder," because it binds all construction yarns together. The chain binder runs alternately over and under the weft binding or filling yarns, thereby pulling the pile yarn down and the stuffer yarns up for a tightly woven construction.

The stuffer warp is composed of lengthwise yarns, added to give the carpet body or extra weight and strength. They travel on a straight plane. Portions of the pile yarns in Wiltons are also considered to be warp yarns; they form part of the backing and run lengthwise in the carpet.

Weft yarns

The weft yarns (also called "shots") are those backing yarns which run through the carpet in a crosswise direction. Combined with the warp yarns, weft yarns bind the pile yarns together in a woven fabric.

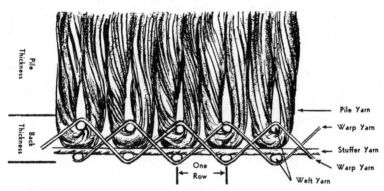

American Carpet Institute, Inc.

General construction of woven carpet.

CARPET QUALITY FACTORS

When we think of carpet quality, we must consider both appearance quality and service quality.

Appearance quality takes into account the styling design, which includes such factors as surface pattern, texture, color, and so forth.

Service quality is concerned with the ability of the carpet to retain its original "look" by resisting soiling, crushing, wear, color change, tuft pull-out, and the like.

Although a discussion of appearance quality is beyond the scope of this manual, it is recommended that no carpet purchase be made solely on the basis of appearance; purchase should also take into consideration the desired service quality.

A number of rules of thumb have been suggested for anticipating the service quality of commercial carpeting. Yet, none of these is completely accurate, because many variables are involved, and it is difficult to reduce these variables to measurable qualities. A common factor by which experienced carpet men judge the quality of any carpet is pile density.

Pile density

The weight of pile yarn per unit of volume is a relative measure of pile density. The denser the pile, or the more tufts per square inch of a specific yarn size, the less weight each tuft must bear. With weight more widely distributed, there will be less flexing within the pile. This is one factor in obtaining greater crush resistance. Likewise, in a dense pile, the support provided is of a collective nature, and more support means less flexing action. Therefore, carpets of denser piles give greater compression resistance and longer wear.

Tourist Court Journal

One measure of carpet quality is tufts per square inch.

Because pile density is difficult to measure accurately, it is commonly calculated from the following construction features: (1) tufts per square inch, (2) pitch, (3) rows (wires) per inch, (4) weight of pile yarn, (5) pile height, and (6) yarn count.

Tufts per square inch. A method of judging closeness of pile construction is to count the number of tufts per square inch. This technique is preferred for tufted and knitted carpets and can also be meaningful when applied to all the weaves. For the woven carpets, the number of tufts per square inch is related to the pitch and rows per inch.

Pitch. This is the number of warp (lengthwise) lines in a 27-inch width of carpet. When we speak of "189 pitch" or "216 pitch," we mean 189 or 216 lines of yarn running through each 27-inch width.

Pitch is indicative of the closeness of a weave crosswise of the fabric. Consequently, the higher the pitch, the finer the weave. Pitch will vary in accordance with the type of weave and the various grades within each weave. A standard pitch for Wilton is 256 and for Axminster, 189.

The term "pitch" does not have real significance for tufted, knitted, or flocked carpets, because their constructions differ radically from woven carpets. In a tufted carpet, the only warp yarn is the stitching which runs the length of the carpet. Therefore, the number of needles per widthwise inch or the space between needles (gauge) parallels the term "pitch." Knitted carpets have no continuous warp lines which can be used as a measure of pitch. Flocked carpets, consisting of individual, upright fibers held in a latex sizing, have no lengthwise or crosswise yarns.

Rows (wires) per inch. Rows are the number of weft shots, or cross-wise units, measured per inch along the length of a carpet. The term refers literally to the number of pile tufts per inch lengthwise of the carpet. As with pitch, the number of rows or wires per inch is indicative of the close-ness of the weave. The number will differ among the different grades of the same weave. For example, it may vary from as low as 4 in an economy fabric, such as a low-density Axminster, to as high as 13 in a densely woven, high-grade Wilton.

Three inches are marked off on the back of the piece of carpet, and the number of weft shots counted. The result is divided by three, to give the number per inch. Thus, 17 rows in three inches of a certain Axminster gives it a designation of 5⅔ rows per inch. The number of wires or rows on the back usually is an indication of the rows of yarn on the face. Axminsters' weft shots are described in "rows"; that of Wilton and velvets, in "wires."

Tufted carpets and knitted carpets have no weft or crosswise yarns; however, it is possible to measure the number of tufts or loops per inch lengthwise for each type of carpet. In tufteds, the number of stitches per lengthwise inch is roughly equivalent to rows in woven carpets. Because of their unique construction, flocked carpets have no tufts to be used as a visual measure of density.

Weight of pile yarn. The total weight of pile yarn per unit surface area (ounces per square yard) is probably the most important factor in wear life. When considered together with pile height, the weight can give a fairly good measure of service quality. The weight of pile yarn per unit of surface area is dependent upon carpet construction, the yarn count, and the pile height.

Pile height. Pile height is the thickness of the wear layer. It is measured from the top of the pile to the top of the back. It does not in-clude the thickness of the backing. If all other factors are equal, particu-larly pile density, a carpet with a higher pile will give longer service wear. The pile heights vary in carpets whose surfaces are textured, high-low looped, or in combinations of cut and loop construction. In these carpet designs, therefore, the average maximum pile height is used to measure pile thickness.

Yarn count. The weight and size (thickness) of a single strand of yarn is also a factor of quality. Carpets require fibers of special weight and size. Examples of systems used to express yarn count are the woolen count, or actual number of yards per ounce, and denier, or number of grams per 9,000 meters.

Tourist Court Journal

Variations in ply of yarn can affect
underfoot comfort and service life.

Additional carpet quality factors

Many other factors influence service quality besides those already described. Here are a few of the more important ones: (1) ply, (2) fiber types and quality, (3) surface construction, (4) body construction, (5) backings, and (6) dyeing methods. These factors will vary considerably according to the weave and the specific piece of goods under consideration.

Ply. This is the number of strands of single yarns twisted to form one pile yarn. The final yarn is designated as 1-ply, 2-ply, 3-ply, 4-ply, and so forth. Ply by itself, however, is not an index of quality. The weight or size of the yarns twisted into the ply must always be considered.

Fiber types and quality. Fibers differ widely in many respects, such as abrasion resistance, twist retention, compression resistance, resilience, soil resistance, stain resistance, wet cleanability, and static generation. The physical properties are also influenced by the fiber denier and thickness. The section on "Fibers" offers greater detail on this subject.

Surface construction. Cut-pile, twist or straight yarn, loop or round-wire, and combinations of each, influence crush resistance, resilience, cleanability, and texture retention.

In general, round-wire or loop construction is more functional than cut-pile but is more difficult to clean. The round-wire gives fuzzier details of design, while cut-pile produces a "luxury" effect and sharp design detail.

Body construction. The form of carpet construction has a bearing on the maximum attainable pile density, tuft retention, and dimensional stability. The choice of designs, textures, and use of colors is limited by the type of loom used to make the carpet. The fibers selected for the body of the carpet are also important, since they affect service life as regards shrinkage, dimensional stability, mildew resistance, and insect resistance.

Backings. Backing yarns are made of various fibers. As a general rule, the stronger the fiber, the longer the life of the carpet. The backing yarns are particularly important in providing the necessary strength to prevent tearing when heavy objects, such as furniture, are moved across the carpet surface. By adding more fibers to the back of the carpeting, the life of the carpet is prolonged. Additional heavy yarn running the length of the carpet is the common method of increasing the amount of backing fibers. These are called "stuffers." Some of the fibers used as backing yarns are:

Jute—comes from the sisal plant that grows in India and the Philippines. It is spun into a strong and durable yarn that adds strength, weight and stiffness to carpet backing. A woven jute burlap is generally used as the backing fabric for tufted carpets.

Kraftcord—tightly twisted yarn made from wood pulp. It has the advantages of uniform diameter and availability, because it is produced from American wood pulp.

Cotton—used in a chain stitch, cotton fiber has surprising strength. It is also used as a stuffer to lend bulk and durability to carpet backings.

Rayon—heavy strands of rayon are woven into a tough, durable backing.

Wool—the most expensive backing material. In high-quality carpetings like chenilles, wool is used to add performance and value.

For woven carpets, backing yarns and pile yarns are woven together to form the carpet. But for tufted and flocked carpets a separate sheet of backing is needed. Called the "prime backing," this most frequently consists of a 10-ounce jute sheet.

Certain synthetic materials may also serve as backings. Woven polypropylene strips (recently put on the market) are now being used in tufted carpet construction. New forms of non-woven polypropylene backings are in the final testing stages and should soon be available for commercial use. A new kind of backing, based on urethane foam reinforced with nylon scrim, should soon be on the market.

When polypropylene serves as a backing, some sort of adhesive may be needed to bind the yarns of the tufted carpet in place. Synthetic materials are of special value in carpet backings because they aren't susceptible to shrinkage or mildew. Furthermore, they are proof against wicking, which occurs when stains absorbed on the back of the carpet seep through to the surface of the carpet.

Of side interest to the commercial carpeting field is the use of powdered polyethylene as a backing material for tufted carpets. Although powdered polyethylene has been used in Europe for more than ten years, it was only introduced in the United States in 1960. The biggest user of powdered polyethylene in this country is the automobile industry. Powdered polyethylene is now used instead of rubber and styrene latices for automobile carpet backing because it offers these advantages: (1) The carpet coating operation is faster; (2) Coating costs are lower; (3) The finished carpet can be molded to fit the contour of the floor, eliminating cutting and sewing operations.

The use of a double jute back for tufted carpets has increased considerably in the last few years. Tufted carpet is made by stitching yarn into a sheet of jute, 10 ounces per square yard, and then back-coating with latex to bind the yarns in place. While the cement is still wet, a second jute sheet of equal weight is bonded to the latex.

Reinforced backings can be a woven-mesh fabric, tightly woven burlap, or similar fabric. Scrim backing is a woven-mesh fabric that is laminated to the regular carpet backing and usually impregnated with a latex compound coating. It is primarily used on tufted carpets but is also found on woven and knitted carpets. Scrim backing cloth may have a weight range from 4 to 12 ounces per square yard, plus the additional weight of the adhesive used to bind it to the fabric.

Some purposes served by scrim backing are:

(1) It increases the carpet's "dimensional stability"—the ability to resist stretching and shrinking.

(2) It counteracts excessive humidity effect on carpet—swelling and buckling.

(3) It gives the carpet greater "hand" or "feel," i.e., more body.

(4) It strengthens the carpet by further securing the tufts in place.

(5) It prevents the corners of rugs from curling.

Dyeing methods. There are a number of methods used to dye carpet fibers. However, no matter which method is used, the quality of the dyes and the mode of application should result in satisfactory color-fastness to light and to wet-cleaning procedures.

Raw-stock-dyeing: The wool is dyed in bulk before it is spun. This ensures uniform color throughout a large batch.

Skein-dyeing: Yarn (in skeins) is dyed after spinning, but before weaving.

Solution-dyeing: In the manufacture of man-made fibers, the dye is added to the raw material while it is in liquid form; the material is then formed into solid threads, and the dye is part of the yarn.

American Carpet Institute, Inc.

Wilton carpet loom.

Package-dyeing: Spun and wound yarn is placed on perforated forms. Dye is forced through the perforations to "soak" the yarn with color.

Piece-dyeing: After the carpet is woven, the whole piece of goods is dyed.

Print-dyeing: After the carpet is woven, the pattern is screen-printed with pre-metalized dyes in as many as six colors. Deep penetration of the pile is achieved by an electromagnetic technique.

As the technology of dyeing synthetic fibers has advanced, the number of special effects that can be achieved with the different methods of dyeing has increased. Of special interest are the color choices made possible by skein-dyeing and piece-dyeing yarns for tufted carpets. Take the case of acrylic carpet fibers. When two different acrylic yarn components are plied together, skein-dyeing offers three choices for color and effect in the same bath operation: (1) color-on-white, in which only one of the yarn components is dyed; (2) tone-on-tone, in which the dye is distributed in different intensities on each yarn component; and (3) two-color or cross-dye effects, in which each yarn component is dyed a different color in the same bath.

Similar techniques can be applied in piece-dyeing nylon and acrylics to create decorative two-color effects. In fact, when nylon is used, three-color or three-way cross-dye effects can be imparted to the material in one dye bath.

Two important recent methods of dyeing are space-dyeing and resist-printing. For space-dyeing yarns, a special machine applies two or more colors to the yarn at predetermined intervals prior to tufting. To make resist-printed carpet, a dye-resist agent is printed on tufted carpet prior to piece-dyeing.

An important breakthrough in dyeing tufted carpets has been achieved by a printing technique that employs pre-metalized dyes. This new method provides a deeper penetration of the dye and a better definition of pattern on tufted carpets than was possible with the older method of drumprinting. In the new technique, plain tufted carpets are silk-screened with a pre-metalized dye in a shallow trough. An electromagnetic charge, applied under the carpet, rapidly drives the dye deep into the pile. It is possible by this process to print-dye piles up to 1¼ inches in height. The carpet is continuously processed through a series of printing troughs in each of which a different color is applied by the silkscreen method to build up a final pattern containing up to six colors. The carpet is then cured to set the dyes, after which it is washed and dried.

Print-dyed tufted carpet may become a serious competitor of Wilton and Axminster carpets. With deep dye-penetration and good definition of pattern, print-dyed tufted carpets are equal in appearance to Wilton and Axminster carpets. Also, the new dyeing process has a relatively low cost, and tufted carpets are inherently more economical to produce than woven fabrics.

WOVEN CARPETS

Velvet carpets

Velvet carpets have a relatively simple form of construction as compared to Axminster and Wilton weaves. At one time, carpets having cut pile made on the velvet loom were termed "velvet," and those made with looped pile were known as "tapestry" or "loop velvet." The more popular term for looped-pile carpets made on a velvet loom is "round-wire velvet."

Because they are made with only one pile yarn, velvet carpets are primarily of solid colors. "Salt and pepper" and "tweed" effects are possible, however, if the carpet is made of "moresque" yarn (two or more strands of different colors twisted together to form a single yarn). "Striped" effects are obtained by a different technique. At least two manufacturers offer velvets in geometric patterns made by a modified loom.

Modern velvet looms produce woven carpets in a wide selection of solid and tweed colors and in a variety of surface textures. Among the textured effects available are: tight loop—loop pile, single or multi-level; plush effect—straight yarn in cut pile; tree bark effect—high and low looped pile; frieze effect—tightly twisted yarn in cut pile; and variform surface—use of cut and uncut pile.

A *high-quality velvet* has 8 to 10 wires per inch and a pitch of 216 to 270 per 27-inch width, or 64 to 100 tufts per square inch.

Less expensive or medium-grade velvets run 7 to 9 wires per inch with a pitch of 189 to 243 per 27-inch width, or 49 to 81 tufts per square inch.

The *lowest-priced velvets* have only 6 to 7 wires per inch and a pitch of 162 to 189 per 27-inch width, or 43 to 49 tufts per square inch.

The various grades of velvet carpets differ as to the number of shot yarns used per row of tufts to bind and hold the tufts in place; 1-shot, 2-shot and 3-shot constructions are used. The most common is the 2-shot velvet, in which each row of tufts is gripped by two crosswise yarns.

The pile yarns in velvet carpet can be woven through the back or interwoven with the backing yarns. The tufts can be anchored and made secure by use of special compounds applied to the back of the carpet.

Wilton carpets

The Wilton loom differs from a velvet loom in that it has a Jacquard mechanism. This permits it to handle up to six different-colored pile yarns to weave a design in a carpet. Following the design pattern, the loom selects and uses only one color of yarn to form a pile loop at any point in the carpet, burying the other pile yarns in the body of the carpet.

Some time ago, carpets having a loop-pile surface construction were referred to as "Brussels," while the term "Wilton" was reserved for cut-pile carpets made on the same loom. Today, a Wilton carpet refers to any carpet woven in a Wilton-Jacquard loom, and the Brussels carpets are known as "round-wire Wilton" or "round-wire Jacquards."

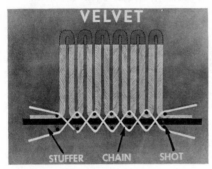

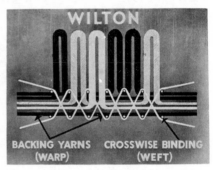

American Carpet Institute, Inc.   *American Carpet Institute, Inc.*

The ingenious Jacquard mechanism permits the weaving of patterned carpets of multiple colors—usually limited to five, or one color for each "frame" of yarn on the loom. The loom also makes possible the weaving of carpets with sharply delineated sculptured- and embossed-texture patterns. These "carved" patterns are created by varying the pile height, using high and low loops, or using combinations of cut loop tufts and "straight" or tightly twisted yarns in various combinations.

The Jacquard process uses punched cards, analogous to a player piano roll or an IBM card, to control the loom's selection of pile yarn. The pattern of holes in each card corresponds to the color design of the carpet. Laced together in order and suspended in the loom, the cards match the entire surface design of the carpet. The cards move past a mechanism in the loom, which selects and lifts the pile yarns into position to be looped over the wires. The patterns of the holes in the cards determine which color of yarn the mechanism will lift to the surface, and which it will leave to be buried in the body of the carpet. Therefore, for each tuft of yarn showing on the surface of the carpet, there may be anywhere from one to four strands of yarn beneath the face, depending upon how many colors or frames are used. The pile yarns in Wiltons can be woven through the back or interwoven with the backing yarns. While the modern

Wiltons are usually limited to five frames, the loom can be set up to add many additional colors by "planting" other color yarns.

Generally, the addition of each frame or color in a Wilton carpet will add more total yarn to the carpet pile. Thus, a three-frame Wilton carpet will give a greater pile weight than a two-frame Wilton of the same yarn size and density. The one-frame Wilton is identical to velvet carpet for all practical purposes. Therefore, it should be regarded as a velvet carpet.

The service quality of a Wilton carpet depends primarily on the weight of pile yarn in the wear layer, the yarn count, and the pile height. Secondary factors, affecting over-all quality, are back construction, yarn twist, twist retention, and yarn quality.

The *pile density* of a Wilton carpet is controlled by the *pitch* (number of lengthwise lines of yarn in a 27-inch width), the wires per inch (weft shots or crosswise units per inch along the length of carpet), and the yarn count (weight and thickness of a single strand of yarn). Pitch can range from 162 up to a maximum of 256, while wires per inch generally range from 6 to 10.

Years ago, one of the finest-grade Wiltons had 13 wires per inch, a pitch of approximately 9.5 per inch (256 per 27-inch width) or approximately 123 tufts per square inch, 3 shots per wire and 5 to 6 frames of pile yarn. Today, however, a top-quality Wilton can be made with 180 pitch and 8 to 9 wires per inch (53 to 61 tufts per square inch) by using heavy 3-ply or 4-ply yarns to provide the necessary pile density.

The *pile depth* is controlled by the height of the wire used in forming the pile loops during weaving. A dense, low-pile Wilton of a given pile yarn weight will usually give better service life than a deep-pile, low density Wilton of the same back construction and pile weight.

A minimum order of approximately 200 to 500 square yards, depending on style desired, is normally required for custom designs. A premium will probably be added to the carpet cost for orders of lower quantities.

Wilton carpets have been employed in the commercial field for over one hundred years. This weave offers a strong, densely constructed carpet with a wide variety of pattern and texture. The carpet design can always be duplicated since the punched cards which determine the pattern can be stored and reused just like a player piano roll.

Axminster carpets

Axminster carpets are made on highly organized looms which draw pile yarns from small spools wound with the various colored yarns to be used in the carpet. The spools are locked together, end-to-end, in a frame which equals the width of the carpet.

The sequence of colored yarns on the spools determines the eventual surface pattern, since each frame provides one row of tufts across the carpet, and each strand of yarn on the spools provides a single pile tuft. The spool frames are positioned in an overhead endless conveyor which brings the spools down to the loom. As each frame arrives in place, the loom inserts and cuts a row of pile tufts from the strands of yarn on the spool.

When the spool frame is lowered in position, the ends of the yarn strands on the spools are inserted between the warp threads in the loom. As the needle inserts the weft yarn across the shed, a comb curls the ends of the spool yarn under the weft and back up between the warp strands. As another pass of the needle binds the looped strands in place, a knife cuts the strands from the spools, leaving the two ends of each strand protruding upward to form a pile tuft. The spool frame is lifted back into the conveyor which carries it around to be re-used in sequence, and the next spool descends to provide another row of pile tufts.

The Axminster loom simulates hand weaving, because each tuft of yarn is individually inserted into the pile; thus, every tuft can be of a different color. This design flexibility offers unlimited scope in pattern and color. Extremely complicated patterns are ideally suited to Axminster carpet. Symbols, crests, multi-color flowers, complex geometric figures, and abstract patterns are a few of the design possibilities offered by this weave. It is possible to duplicate almost any design in an Axminster carpet.

Because of the nature of the loom, the texture of a conventional Axminster carpet is usually limited to a cut-pile of even height. A variation in pile height can be achieved by using especially treated (reverse-twist) yarns which "shrink" after steaming. Tufts can also be omitted in certain areas, creating a textured design.

Axminster carpeting can ordinarily be identified by a number of special features:

(1) The back of the carpet has a double-weft (widthwise-yarn) shot, which gives the backing a ribbed appearance. Because the backing is usually coated with a latex solution or heavy sizing, the double shots may be hard to recognize. (Sizing is a paste-like substance that coats the backing, adding strength and rigidity to the backing fibers.)

(2) The stiffness of the backing—due to the double shot and heavy sizing—usually will permit Axminsters to be rolled one way only. They can be rolled lengthwise, not crosswise. (This is not always true, because some manufacturers make what is called a "soft-back" Axminster.)

(3) Although texture variations are possible, Axminsters are notable for even-height pile.

(4) Axminsters are made with cut pile because of the nature of the loom. Exceptions are possible only by modifying this loom. One major producer has an entire line of "modified" Axminsters.

(5) Multi-color effects are easily woven on Axminster looms; floral designs are quite common. All-over color patterns of any kind are likely to be Axminsters.

Although most grades of Axminster have a standard pitch of 189, a maximum of 216 is also used. The pile yarn is held firmly in an upright position because of the arrangement of the crosswise yarn, making available more pile yarn in the wear layer and contributing to good tuft retention.

Grades can be identified by the number of tufts per inch, as indicated below:

Top-quality Axminster may have as many as 8 to 11 rows per inch and a pitch of 189. This combination of rows and pitch results in approximately 56 to 77 tufts per square inch.

Medium-quality grades have from 6 to 7 rows per inch and a pitch of 189. This construction yields about 42 to 49 tufts per square inch. Quality can be improved in this grade construction by increased yarn weights.

Lower-quality grades have from 4 to 5 rows per inch and a pitch of 189. The number of tufts per square inch is approximately 28 to 35. While good-quality Axminsters can be made in this construction, most carpet in this grade is intended to fill a demand for low-cost, multi-colored, designed carpet.

For multi-colored carpet, Axminster carries the lowest cost, and additional savings can be realized through large-volume purchases.

KNITTED CARPETS

Knitting carpets is the most recent manufacturing method employed by the carpet industry. It is somewhat similar to weaving, in that the pile and backing yarns are fabricated in one operation. Knitting differs from weaving, however, because the carpets are made by looping the pile and backing yarns together with different sets of needles on a large machine.

The commercial use of knitted carpets has grown substantially since this method of manufacturing was introduced in the early 1950's. Inasmuch as the production rate for knitted carpets falls between the high-speed tufting process and the conventional weaving methods, knitting makes possible carpet manufacture offering excellent performance at moderate cost.

Although the design possibilities attainable in knitting are limited, new techniques are broadening the styling variations. Recent developments indicate that a free-form pattern will become available in the near future. Currently, most knitted carpets are of looped pile texture, available either in solid colors or tweeds. Textural designs, however, can be created by varying the pile height of the loops. Cut pile and combinations of cut and loop pile can be achieved by a shearing operation.

The knitted carpet can be identified by "grinning," i.e., bending the carpet to expose the backing, and looking for the continuous looping of the pile yarns from row to row. A coating of latex is used on knitted carpets to provide additional body to the fabric. The bulk of the pile yarn appears on the surface.

Tourist Court Journal

Identifying a knitted carpet by "grinning."

Any of the pile fibers used in woven or tufted carpets can be used in knitted carpets. An important feature of knitted carpets is that they can be furnished in any width. Thus, there could be some cost savings by ordering widths to fit different-sized areas.

TUFTED CARPETS

Tufting is one of the new important methods for making carpets. In operation, the tufting machine behaves like a giant sewing machine with hundreds of needles. A yarn threaded through each needle eye is moved through a backing fabric. As the needle is pulled out, a loop or tuft is formed and held by the backing fabric. A heavy coating of latex is applied to the back of the fabric to anchor the tufts permanently in place.

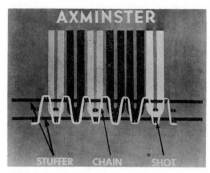
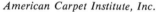

American Carpet Institute, Inc.

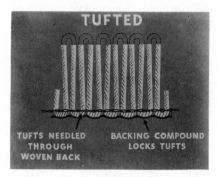

American Carpet Institute, Inc.

Whereas looms and knitting machines fabricate the entire carpet, including backing and pile, tufted construction is concerned only with the pile. The pre-formed backing fabric is generally made of jute, although cotton canvas is also used. New backing-fabric materials have been developed, which are laminated to the tufted carpet to provide increased dimensional stability. One of the distinguishing features of tufted carpets is the lengthwise direction of the rows of loops. By contrast, in any woven carpet, the rows run across the width of the carpeting.

The popularity of tufted carpet has increased rapidly since its commercial introduction about 1949. Low costs are made possible with high-speed production techniques. Electronic control of both the yarn feed and the needle action permits variations in needle insertion and the height of pile tufts, thereby creating texture patterns in the carpet surface. Additional effects are possible by the formation of cut pile and loop pile, as well as combinations of both.

Various pattern attachments have been used successfully on tufting machines to produce a variety of high-low effects. The usual restrictions in pattern because of the straight-line stitch formation have been overcome by equipment that shifts the jute back and forth to yield a zigzag tufting line. When the shifting needle plate is used with a pattern attachment, the high and low loops give the appearance of an almost random pattern.

An alternative to the standard straight-line tufting machine is the use of stitch-displacement needle bars, sometimes called "stepover" or "sliding needle bar" machines. With this equipment, the needles shift back and forth, and the jute is fed without lateral motion in the normal fashion.

Conventionally made of solid-color or "moresque" yarns, tufted carpets are now being made in multi-color patterns. The same range of colors and color patterns associated with velvet carpets is possible in the tufting process. The use of electric hand-tufting machines, in combination with the normal multi-needle equipment, has also made it possible to insert individual tufts of different color into a carpet of a solid ground color.

In the past, continuous filament nylon has not been used in cut-pile tufted carpets. Today, it has been shown that it is possible to use the continuous filament nylon economically in cut-pile tufting operations on standard machines. Shedding, a serious problem in cut-pile carpets with staple nylon, is eliminated when continuous filament is used. The variety of dye techniques that can be used with continuous filament nylon makes it possible to produce cut-pile carpets in unusual styles and textures.

The quality of tufted carpets depends upon a number of factors including yarn quality, amount of pile yarn per unit of area, quality of backing material, and thickness and quality of the latex coating applied to the carpet. All good tufted carpets have a backing reinforcement weighing not less than 4 ounces per square yard. The weight of the latex coating varies from 12 to 28 ounces per square yard.

A *high-quality tufted carpet* has 7 to 10 stitches per inch of length, up to 8 needles per inch (56 to 80 tufts per square inch), and backing fabric weighing 12 to 13 ounces per square yard.

Average-quality tufted carpets have 5 to 7 stitches per inch, 4 to 6 needles per inch (20 to 42 tufts per square inch), and backing fabric weighing 8 to 10 ounces per square yard.

Custom-tufted carpet is available, at a premium price, from most manufacturers. The carpet is made to fit the area according to a room layout submitted in advance. Specially designed area rugs are especially suitable to the custom tufting process.

LOOMED CARPETS

The term "loomed carpet" is used here to describe a bi-component carpet of tightly woven, low-loop fabric, made on a converted, upholstery-type loom, to which a sponge-rubber cushion is bonded. Because of the tightness of weave and the popular use of round, cross-section nylon, these carpets are often referred to in the trade as "sponge-bonded, high-density pile, nylon carpets." The same construction is also offered with wool and acrylic piles, although the volume produced with these fibers is considerably lower than with nylon.

When loomed carpets were first introduced in the mid-1950's, the surface style resembled upholstery fabric and the backing consisted of latex foam. The carpets wore well in service and exhibited good cleaning characteristics. However, difficulty was encountered in proper installation and in seaming the foam back. The development of loomed carpets was relatively dormant from 1955 to 1959, after which several important modifications were made. Sponge rubber was used in place of latex foam to correct the seaming problems and provide longer cushion life. The construction was further modified to make use of tightly woven pile yarns in loop form; and the technique of custom-texturizing feeder yarn was improved.

Loomed carpets are intended for use in heavy-traffic areas subject to much abuse. Because of the limitations in styles and the very low pile, they are not suited for areas requiring high-style designs. These carpets are not as soft underfoot as conventional carpets, since resilience depends solely on the rubber cushioning. Airborne noise is not reduced quite as well as with high-pile carpets; however, sound absorption is considered more than adequate for most situations where loomed carpet will be used.

The pile layer is made separately with a tabby weave which gives a staggered diagonal pattern across the weft yarns. The pile is, therefore, formed on a combination of warp and filling yarns. Included in the construction is a single-filling yarn of high-tenacity rayon and one ground warp of cotton. A high-strength filler yarn is necessary to achieve adequate tuft bind (15 pounds). Since the pile yarns are not woven over wires, the carpet has a characteristic single-level, low loop. A good-quality pile has 16 ounces per square yard of a round, cross-section, fully delustered nylon; a pile height of 0.15 inches; a pitch of 223; and 8 rows per inch. Yarn is dyed in a knitted form, then de-knitted before weaving.

The pile back is treated with an adhesive which forms a waterproof barrier and serves as a tie-coat for the sponge rubber. Sponge rubber is applied to the pile fabric in its relaxed state by flowing on the sponge in batter form and heating the backed carpet to cure the rubber. The final gauge of the sponge rubber is held to 3/16 inch by the laminating process.

FLOCKED CARPETS

Flocked carpets are a relatively recent addition to the family of commercial carpets. Although the flock industry is rather new in this country, the process itself is old. In fact, as early as the fifteenth century, flocked wallpaper was being produced in Europe. Only in recent years, however, has flocking for carpeting really come into its own.

There are three basic methods of applying flock: by beater bar, by spraying, and electrostatically. Each process starts with the coating of the adhesive on the material to be flocked. In the beater bar process, the material being treated passes over a series of square bars which vibrate it. When the flock is sifted onto the material, the vibration causes the fibers to stand on end and produce a pile effect. In the spray system, the flock is sprayed from a gun using a special nozzle. This process is generally used in coating irregularly shaped objects and has very little utility for flocking carpets.

E. T. Barwick Mills, Inc.

Flocked carpet.

In electrostatic flocking, specially treated flocked fibers are introduced into an electrostatic field. The fibers align themselves with the electrostatic lines of force and become charged. When the charged fibers encounter the object to be coated, they are moving vertically at a high speed, and they become firmly embedded in the adhesive. A permanent bond is established after the adhesive has dried and cured. The balance of the discussion will be restricted to the electrostatic process, which appears to have greatest potential use in the commercial carpeting field.

Fiber is supplied to the carpet manufacturer as a continuous, loose rope of filaments on large spools. These are dyed and an electrostatic finish applied. The dyed tow is then cut to predetermined lengths by a flock cutter. The only fibers presently used in this system are round, cross-section, uncrimped, straight fibers of nylon, Type 6,6. Although a 27-denier, fully drawn fiber, and a 45-denier, undrawn fiber have been used, the *undrawn* fiber is preferred by industry for most applications. Adhesive, at the rate of about one pound per square yard is applied to a woven jute backing which weighs 10 ounces per square yard. The fibers are given an electrostatic charge which transports them at high velocities to the coated jute. The process permits the fibers to be uniformly embedded in an upright position across the face of the adhesive. Approximately 17,500 individual fiber ends to each square inch, standing 4.5 millimeters (about 0.2 inches) deep, are fastened to the backing. The adhesive is then cured in ovens and the carpet given a double-jute back in the usual manner. A good-quality pile will contain between 18 to 20 ounces of nylon fiber per square yard.

Flocked carpets may be dyed before construction, as indicated above, or after construction by a print-dyeing technique.

The use of relatively heavy fibers, 27-denier as compared to the usual 15-denier, uniformly packed in an upright position is claimed to increase wear life significantly. Resilience and compression resistance are also said to be improved as a result of the uniform distribution of the upright fibers. The smooth, uncrimped fibers of nylon make the carpet easy to clean, since there is less surface area on each fiber to which dirt can cling.

Flocked carpets have a single-level, cut-pile surface, which offers a velvet or velour appearance.

The use of flocked carpets should be further increased when they become available with synthetic backings of polypropylene. A new and expanding potential application for flocked carpets is in outdoor applications and in areas of extremely high humidity. For withstanding outdoor conditions, these carpets will probably consist of polypropylene pile fibers embedded in a coated backing of non-woven polypropylene.

FIBERS

As a result of the tremendous strides being made in the development of synthetic fibers, the number of fibers available for carpet use has increased. Moreover, the present synthetic fibers have been vastly improved since their introduction. There is also every indication that continuing research in the field of synthetics will result in new fibers, as well as improvements in the types presently available.

Considered as a group, man-made fibers accounted for approximately 70 percent of broadloom surface fiber consumption in 1964. Wool, which at one time was the single most important fiber in poundage used, was surpassed in 1964 by nylon. Acrylic and modacrylic fibers are rapidly increasing in use and may in the next few years equal and perhaps exceed wool for carpet use. The consumption of polypropylene, though still very small compared to the other fibers, could become a very important factor in the carpet industry within the next ten years.

Although there are no figures available to indicate the exact proportion of various fibers used in the commercial field, there is growing evidence that the use of synthetics is following the same pattern seen for the entire industry. Large institutional users are turning more and more to synthetic fibers, which offer greater uniformity, longer wear life, and brighter colors.

The face yarns presently used in significant quantity for commercial carpet are made of wool, nylon, and acrylic. Other available materials include polypropylene, cotton, rayon, and acetate.

Wool

This product is still considered to be the traditional carpet fiber despite its steady decline in consumption. Used in woven carpets for centuries, it is now used extensively in tufted carpets, knitted carpets, and rugs. In commercial-grade carpets, wool accounts for 35 to 45 percent of the pile yarn used. For residential carpets, wool represents about 30 percent of total usage.

Carpet wool is obtained from the native, unimproved sheep of a number of countries, such as Syria (Aleppo wool); Iraq (Awassi-Karadi wool); Argentina (Cordova wool); Pakistan (East Indian wool); and New Zealand. Chinese wool, the major type of thirty years ago, is no longer available to U. S. carpet manufacturers, as a result of the severing of trade relations with China.

Wool from each country has unique qualities; even within a country, different breeds of sheep yield different wools. Some wools are long; some short. Others are fine, or tough, or lustrous, or springy. The various wools are blended together for the purpose of achieving the over-all quality desired for carpet use.

The outstanding characteristic of wool is resilience, i.e., the ability of the fibers to recover quickly after a load has been removed. This feature, in combination with good resistance to abrasion and moderate fiber strength, produces a level of appearance durability that has become the standard for the industry.

In the past, wool had the disadvantage of being attacked by moth and carpet beetle larvae. When purchasing carpets, therefore, it is customary to specify that the wool pile component be treated with a moth repellent, such as a silicofluoride compound.

Space Planning Services, A Division of Carson Pirie Scott & Co.

Wool carpet in area of law library.

Woolen yarn is made up of interlocked long and short fibers; worsted yarn uses only the long wool fibers, laid parallel. Woolen yarns are softer, bulkier, and rougher than worsted yarns. Today, the pile of most wool carpets is composed of woolen yarns.

An identifying characteristic of wool is that it burns slowly and extinguishes quickly, without smoldering. Burned wool leaves a crusty ash and emits an odor similar to that of scorched feathers.

Material specifications should call for thoroughly scoured carpet-type fiber. Virgin fibers should be used although fibers recovered from the carpet yarn manufacturing process may be used with a minimum of 85 percent of virgin fiber.

Nylon

Nylon, today, is the largest single fiber produced for all markets. Although it represents well over 45 percent of the total yardage used in residential carpeting, its application in commercial installations is believed to be about 30 to 40 percent of the total used. The increased use of nylon is attributed to nylon's exceptional resistance to abrasion and the wide range of available colors and designs. In the commercial field, its biggest use is in areas of average traffic, such as offices, lounges, and some reception areas. The use of nylon in heavily trafficked areas has grown at a much slower rate.

Nylon, the first truly synthetic fiber, was introduced in apparel textiles by du Pont shortly before World War II and has since become synonymous with strength and abrasion resistance. Staple nylon, engineered for carpet use, was introduced for soft floor coverings in 1947.

Since its first use in carpets, the nylon fiber has been modified both chemically and physically to adapt it to specific industry needs. Each development in carpet nylon resulted in a correspondingly wider market for the finished product. Heat-set nylon, developed in 1953, enabled carpet stylists to create a number of texture variations by using it alone or in combination with non-heat-set nylon. In 1955, carpet manufacturers were offered an alternative in lusters, and stylists pioneered designs which used bright and delustered nylon, separately and in combinations. The greatest step forward, however, came in 1958 with the introduction of bulked continuous-filament nylon, or "BCF." This opened the way for nylon in loop-pile constructions. After 1962, fibers with different dye performance were developed, so that combinations in the same carpet could be used to produce a wider variety of multicolor effects by piece-dye methods.

Nylon is produced today in two forms: (1) *staple nylon,* which is composed of specially engineered fibers cut into short staple for spinning

E. T. Barwick Mills, Inc.

Nylon carpet in office area.

yarns; and (2) *continuous filament nylon,* which is composed of long continuous strands of the fiber.

Chemically, there are two types of nylon—termed "Type 6" and "Type 6,6." The former represents a long-chain polymer of caprolactum, a chemical containing six carbon atoms. The latter represents a long-chain polymer, resulting from the polymerization of adipic acid and hexamethylenediamine, two chemicals each containing six carbon atoms.

Since the two types of nylon are different in basic chemical structure, the method of carpet manufacture must differ depending on which type is used. As a result, processibility, dyeability, and physical properties differ slightly. Yet, in the end product (carpets), the two types of nylon perform in a a similar manner.

Nylon 6 melts at 414° to 428° F., while Nylon 6,6 sticks at 445° F. Both form hard beads when they melt. The flame of a match is well over 1,000° F., and hot tobacco ashes are well over 500° F.

Nylon fibers are produced with different cross-sections, depending on the design of the spinnerettes used in the manufacturing process. The highly bulked fibers have a trilobular or triskelion cross-section, which gives the fiber greater covering power, especially when coupled with the texturizing crimp applied to the fiber. It is believed that the soiling problems associated with nylon are related to the shape of the fiber and the extent of crimping. The round, cross-section fibers are inherently less bulky than the trilobular form, are more translucent, and have a smoother surface. Yarns made with these fibers do not have the covering power possible with multi-lobe fibers. However, they are well-suited for construction of carpets with high-density surface yarns.

Durability, coupled with medium resilience and lustrous color-effect possibilities, has led to a steady increase in the use of nylon in carpeting. High static generation, the tendency of staple nylon to form pills that stay attached to looped-pile textures because of nylon's high strength, and the former high fiber cost retarded the sale of nylon carpets. The factor of price is now becoming less critical since fiber costs have come down and it is possible to use less nylon than wool in the pile yarn for comparable wear. Although the use of continuous-filament nylon has eliminated pilling, the problem of static has not been completely resolved.

Staple nylon is used for cut-pile fabrics and for blending with wool. The blended yarns generally consist of either 70 percent wool and 30 percent nylon, or 80 percent wool and 20 percent nylon. Although these blends are still available, their use appears to be waning in favor of 100 percent nylon yarns.

A new nylon was introduced January, 1965, under the trade name Antron, by E. I. du Pont de Nemours. Although this nylon is still generically classed as a Type 6,6 fiber, it is said to contain an added ingredient to improve soil resistance and reduce static build-up. Antron is classed by the manufacturer as a premium nylon for heavy use conditions. It has the same general physical properties as Type 6,6 nylon. Its round, cross-section form and slightly lower luster lend themselves to construction of high-density piles. Although offered at the present time as a bulked, continuous filament, it should be soon available in staple form. Thus far, it has only been used in Wilton and velvet constructions with pile weights on the order of 32 ounces per square yard. Carpets made with this fiber are colored by the yarn-dyeing process, using acid dyes. It is anticipated that piece-dyeing techniques will shortly become available.

Nylon fibers in the 27- to 45-denier weights are finding use in carpets prepared by the flocking technique. Although not a significant factor in today's market, it is anticipated that these flocked carpets will increase in popularity.

Material specifications for staple nylon should require the use of carpet-type fiber, with average fiber diameter of 15 denier or higher. Virgin-type carpet fibers, as so graded by the prime fiber producer, should be used. Fibers of virgin grades recovered from the carpet yarn manufacturing process may be used with a minimum requirement of 85 percent virgin fibers.

Filament nylon should be a continuous-filament, high bulk or textured, carpet-type yarn. Individual filament size should be at least 15 denier.

Because of nylon's exceptional resistance to abrasion, carpets made of all nylon pile do not require the same ounce-weight as wool carpeting. In conventional carpet constructions, a minimum of 20 ounces per square yard of nylon is required to give adequate coverage. This weight of nylon appears to be adequate for lightly trafficked areas, typical of residential floors. For commercial service, a minimum of 22 ounces is recommended for all tufted carpets. Important exceptions to these minimum requirements are the sponge-bonded, high-density, nylon pile carpets, which are constructed with 16 ounces per square yard of a special nylon. In flocked-carpet construction, from 18 to 20 ounces per square yard of nylon fiber appears to be adequate. (For additional specification requirements, see Table 15, page 185.)

Acrylic

First used in carpets in 1957, acrylic and modacrylic fibers have rapidly increased in volume production. It is estimated that, in 1964, acrylics accounted for 21 percent of the total surface fiber consumed for broadloom carpets. As soon as additional manufacturing facilities become available, it is expected that consumption of acrylics will rise even faster than before.

Acrylic fibers are composed primarily (85 percent or more) of the chemical "acrilonitrile," while modacrylics contain lesser amounts of acrilonitrile in chemical combination with modifying materials. The acrylic family of fibers, available only in staple form, is characterized by high wear life, comparing favorably in this characteristic to wool. Its tenacity, elongation at the breaking point, and breaking toughness exceed that of wool, while its moisture retention is considerably lower than that of wool fiber. Acrylics have excellent resistance to weak acids and to most strong acids. Whereas carpet wool is attacked by weak alkalies and destroyed by strong, cold alkalies, acrylics show good resistance to weak alkalies and moderate resistance to strong, cold alkalies. Their good resistance to dry-cleaning solvents and other common solvents permits acrylics to be treated with a wide variety of stain-removing chemicals. Additionally, like other man-made fibers, acrylics are not damaged by moths or carpet beetles, nor are they subject to the deteriorating effects of mildew. To their disadvan-

Space Planning Services, A Division of Carson Pirie Scott & Co.

Acrylic carpet in conference room.

tage, they have a greater tendency than wool toward pilling and bearding, which decrease texture retention. Since the acrylic fiber strengths are less than those of nylon, pilling is not a serious factor. When pills form, they usually wear off after moderate traffic.

At the time acrylics first appeared on the market, there was some concern about their potential flammability hazard. These fears appear to have been related to the highly plush fibers used in sweater manufacture. To guard against this possible hazard, carpet manufacturers often blend acrylics with modacrylics in commercial-grade carpets. The latest acrylic fibers have been substantially improved, to the point where they are considered to be no more flammable than wool.

Chemstrand's acrylic carpet fiber, trade-named Acrilan, has outstanding performance characteristics for carpet use. Its bean-shaped cross-section distinguishes it from other acrylics, such as du Pont's Orlon, which has a figure-eight, cross-sectional configuration.

Acrilan is readily dyeable by all methods using basic and acid dyes. When blended with a slightly modified Acrilan, which has no affinity for dyes of the acid, chrome, neutral pre-metalized, or other wool types, it is possible to achieve two-tone pattern effects in the same dye bath.

A bi-component acrylic fiber was introduced in 1963 by du Pont, under the trade name Orlon 33. Two filaments of different denier, 12 and 18, are welded parallel to each other, giving a figure-eight cross-section with a nominal 15-denier gauge. Because of the different shrinking ratios of the two filaments, the bi-component fiber assumes a coiled shape in its dry equilibrium state. The coiled form is said to improve texture retention, which has been a problem with conventional acrylic fibers. Available in staple form, the bi-component acrylic fiber theoretically can be used in all forms of carpet. So far, it has been used only in woven constructions.

A new acrylic fiber, characterized by a round cross-section and blended with about 30 percent modacrylic fiber, is available in 13 colors. It is supplied only as a solution-dyed staple fiber from the manufacturer. Velvet carpets, woven with this fiber, may soon become available.

Acrylic and modacrylic specifications should call for carpet-type fiber, with average fiber diameter of 15 denier or higher. At least 85 percent virgin fibers should be required.

The industry generally recommends that for specification purposes, the ounce weights for acrylics and modacrylics be the same as those used for wool. (For further details, see Table 14, page 184.)

Polypropylene

The latest man-made fibers to be offered for carpet use are made of polypropylene, which is grouped as an olefin. Although there are two classes of olefins, polyethylene and polypropylene, only the polypropylene has been introduced in a fiber form suitable for use in carpet construction. Polypropylene was first offered to the commercial and domestic carpet market in January, 1962, as a bulked continuous filament. The first offerings were solution-dyed fibers available in nine colors.

Since then, a number of improvements and variations have been made. The first woven carpet, for commercial installation, a solution-dyed velvet with a level-loop tweed effect, was shown in January, 1965. A staple fiber that could be piece-dyed was introduced in June, 1965. A modified polypropylene in continuous filament form that could be piece-dyed was also introduced early in 1965. A special class of dispersed dyes was developed for use with the staple form of polypropylene fiber, and the original nine colors offered to the trade have now grown to 30 colors, with more to come.

Polypropylene is characterized by high strength, but its resiliency is less than that of nylon. In respect to durability, strength, and wear resistance, however, polypropylene is considered comparable to nylon.

The main selling points of polypropylene carpet fiber are absence of static build-up, relatively low specific gravity, and excellent stain resistance.

Compared to other fibers, polypropylene is virtually static free. Moreover, it is possible to attain greater surface coverage with an equivalent weight of fiber. Polypropylene is resistant to acids, alkalies and bleaches, while its low moisture absorption contributes to its excellent soil and stain resistance and to its high wet-cleanability. Its appearance recovery after cleaning is reported to be excellent. As a synthetic, it is also resistant to mildew, fungus, and bacteria.

Along with its advantages and interesting potentialities, polypropylene as used at present has a few drawbacks. Limited experience with polypropylene indicates that its texture retention is not as good as that of nylon and is far inferior to that of wool. This may be due to its low compression resistance and slightly poorer resilience when compared to nylon. The fact that the colors of polypropylene are not as bright as those of nylon has led to some unfavorable comment regarding over-all carpet appearance, even when the carpet is new.

When polypropylene was introduced to the trade, a minimum weight of 22 ounces of surface yarn per square yard was specified for commercial production. Although this fiber has not been extensively field-tested, there is an indication that slightly lower pile weight may be acceptable in certain light traffic areas. Tentatively, the same ounce weights recommended for nylon are suggested for polypropylene.

Polypropylene has one of the lowest softening ranges (285° to 330° F.) of all synthetic fibers. Its melting point, depending on source, ranges from 325° to 350° F. Although not considered flammable, polypropylene fibers will melt and form a hard crust or bead when exposed to heat from ashes and cigarettes. Commercial grades of continuous filament olefins have shown no tendencies to pill or fuzz. While it is too soon to say whether the staple fiber will react in the same way, it is believed that there will be no problem of pilling or fuzzing. The staple fiber is presently being used in tufted carpets with a 34- to 36-ounce pile weight and a double-jute back.

Because of its thermal properties, the yarn can be heat-set in a twisted state to extend the styles beyond those presently available.

Polypropylene is not available in blends with other fibers, nor does it seem likely that any will be offered. At the present time it is available only in tufted and velvet constructions.

Cotton

Although it has high wear resistance, cotton fiber is not ordinarily used in commercial carpet as a face yarn. Its chief disadvantages are low compression resistance and low resilience; hence cotton pile crushes readily. Also, cotton has poor soil and stain resistance. The chief advantages of cotton yarn are low cost and availability in many bright, clear, and light shades.

Cotton burns rapidly, leaving a soft gray ash. The smoke has an odor resembling burning paper. When the flame is extinguished, the carpet will continue to smolder.

Rayon

Carpet rayon is chemically termed a "regenerated cellulosic" fiber, since it is made by a series of chemical reactions from the cellulose found in cotton linters and wood pulp. Rayon, in a chemical sense, is essentially the same as cotton and hence has similar performance characteristics. Physically, however, rayon is much different from cotton, so that inherent performance characteristics due to the chemical composition are modified by the possible variations in physical form. The effect of heat on rayon is the same as for cotton.

The translucent and lustrous appearance of rayon contributes to its apparent rapid soiling rate; soil particles are more visible and the change in appearance is more noticeable. Rayon also has the low resilience associated with cotton and relatively poor abrasion resistance. Some of these defects are partly overcome by delustering the fiber and producing more uniform fibers.

Continuous filament rayon yarn is used to create special texture effects, because the yarn shortens in length with wet heat.

Acetate

Acetate, like rayon, is produced by chemically treating cotton or wool and then reacting the cellulose with acetic acid. Its performance is similar to that of rayon in a number of respects.

PADDING

The term "padding" includes all of the following: underlay, lining, cushion, and pads. Although the use of an underlay or pad beneath the pile floor covering is not a substitute for carpet quality, it serves a number of useful functions. It (1) provides extra insulation against extremes of cold or heat, (2) adds extra sound-absorbing qualities, (3) lengthens the life of the carpet, (4) improves underfoot comfort, (5) cushions the shock of walking, and (6) absorbs crushing forces on pile.

The conventional hair-type underlays are made of felted cattle hair. They may have a waffle design to provide a slip-resistant surface and improve resiliency, and sometimes they are reinforced with backings of jute fiber (India fiber) or with burlap center interliners. Where burlap reinforcing is used, the hair is punched through burlap fabric and then compressed to a uniform thickness. Starch sizing or adhesive of sufficient quantity is sometimes used to provide a strong bond between the fibers and the burlap core.

Before construction of the underlay, the hairs and fibers to be used are cleaned, washed, and sterilized. Many manufacturers also permanently moth-proof the underlay to protect it against the larvae of moths and carpet beetles.

The conventional hair-type underlays are sold in all standard widths, i.e., 27 inches, 36 inches, 54 inches, 6 feet, 9 feet, and 12 feet. Special widths can be made to specification. These underlays are available in weights of 32, 40, 48, 54, 64, and 86 ounces per square yard.

Some underlays made of hair or of hair and jute are coated with rubber on one or both sides to hold the fibers together securely and to provide additional cushioning. In some instances, the underlay has an animal-hair, waffle top and a jute back reinforced with a designed rubberized material. The rubberized cushions are available in all standard widths and range in weight from 32 to 56 ounces per square yard.

Cushions made of hair and sponge rubber are also available. In making these combination cushions, animal hairs and jute fibers are punched through burlap backing and bound to the burlap by a synthetic latex; then the fiber side of the felt is bonded to a foam rubber coating. A typical construction of 44-ounces-per-square-yard combination cushion consists of 25 ounces of fibers, 4.5 ounces of burlap backing, 4.5 ounces of latex sizing, and 10 ounces of foam rubber.

Foam and sponge rubber cushions are made as flat sheets, with or without perforations. The cushion backs have different designs, e.g. waffle, ripple, grid, and V-shaped ribs. A carpet-laying problem associated with slip-resistant rubber pads is the difficulty encountered in stretching the carpet across the pad during the installation operation. Therefore, a scrim or burlap fabric is usually bonded to the rubber padding. When laid with the fabric side up, these underlays permit a taut and even stretch of the carpet. Sponge and foam rubber cushions are available in widths of 36 inches, 54 inches, 6 feet, and 9 feet, and in thickness from ¼ inch to 7/16 inch. The weights of high-density rubber cushions range from 38 to 75 ounces per square yard.

Rubber cushioning bonded to carpet is available in two forms. One kind of rubber cushioning, prepared and manufactured prior to application to the rug or carpet, is bonded to the carpet in strip form by means of an adhesive. This type of cushioning can either be sponge rubber or latex foam. In this case, the lamination process is generally done by a company other than the carpet manufacturer. This type of custom work makes it possible to obtain any form of carpet construction with a bonded rubber cushioning back. The other general class of rubber cushioning is manufactured and cured in place on the back of the carpet or rug in seamless widths.

Rubber cushioning is a general term describing such elastomeric materials. We should go further than this definition and distinguish between sponge rubber and latex foam, often referred to as simply sponge and foam.

Both latex foam and sponge rubber are filled with air cells. Sponge, having a thicker cell wall, is usually heavier than foam. In addition, sponge is more often made from a solid, whereas foam is usually made from a liquid mix. Sponge rubber is made only by a few rubber companies, and carpet must be sent to these plants where the sponge is laminated to the finished carpet. Sponge can be made in widths up to 6 feet.

Two kinds of foam are made. The first is a separate sheet which is laminated to the carpet in much the same manner as sponge. The other form of latex foam is applied in a continuous process to the back of the carpet as a liquid. The coated carpet is then heated, causing the liquid to foam in place and become cured. The heavier the mix density, the longer it takes for finished carpet to pass through the oven to foam and cure.

Latex foam can be colored without affecting its performance. In its natural state, latex foam is cream-colored. Unlike sponge rubber, latex foam can be made by the mill, usually in a 3/16th-inch thickness, in widths up to 15 feet, on a continuous seamless basis.

The quality of rubber cushioning can ordinarily be estimated from its density, expressed as ounces or pounds per square yard. The danger in full acceptance of *density* as the sole measure of *quality* is that density can be adjusted by the use of "fillers" in latex. Some filler is normally used in the mix, whether foam is made separately for lamination, or foamed in place on the carpet. The filler is usually fuller's earth or clay. Unfortunately, it is virtually impossible to tell how much filler has been added by looking at the foam. To obtain a true estimate of the filler content, it is necessary to burn the foam sample and analyze the ash for inert ingredients. Inexpensive foam can be made easily by adding more filler to the mix. However, excessive amounts of filler tend to speed foam decomposition and have other deleterious effects on durability.

In a recent federal specification (DDD-C-95 dated April 16, 1965), approved by the United States General Services Administration, rubber cushioning must meet the following density requirements:

(1) Cushioning shall average not less than 3/16 inch in thickness.

(2) The weight per square yard shall be not less than 3.5 pounds (56 ounces) or more than 4.25 pounds (68 ounces).

(3) The compressibility (i.e., weight required to compress one square inch to 75 percent of its original thickness) shall be not less than 5 pounds or more than 9 pounds.

(4) The compression set shall be not more than 15 percent after being compressed 50 percent of its original thickness for 22 hours at a temperature of 158° F.

(5) Cushioning foamed in place and cured on the carpet should tear before pulling free from the carpet after being stored at 90° F. for 96 hours. Laminated cushioning attached to the carpet by an adhesive should have a minimum strip strength of 2 pounds per inch of width.

(6) The cushion should not deteriorate, i.e., become sticky, or crack when bent back on itself, after being subjected to accelerated aging conditions.

The government's minimum requirement of 56 ounces per square yard is believed, by some, to be much higher than necessary. Among reputable producers, 38 to 40 ounces are now being used for commercial qualities. According to a representative of a latex company, when a producer goes as low as 32 ounces, wearing problems can be expected.[1] A minimum of 38 ounces has been suggested as being sufficient to be labeled high-density foam.

A new type of foam, namely, vinyl foam, is expected to be available soon. This product, made from a combination of solids and liquids, will be 3/16 inch thick. However, it is expected to be lighter than the so-called

---

[1]C. Wells Moore, Southern Latex Co., quoted in an article by Ed McCabe in *Home Furnishings Daily,* June 11, 1965.

high-density foam. It is claimed that vinyl foam does not decompose, and that it has other inherent advantages which make it a satisfactory replacement for rubber.

Another new type of backing is the molded-rubber back, which can be added by the carpet mill. In this process, liquid rubber is coated on the carpet back, and then rolled out with an embossed roller to provide a slip-resistant designed surface.

Underlays of different material will vary in their effectiveness. Felted pads of jute or hair have two defects—they may mat down in time, and they may develop mildew, especially if their fibers (primarily animal and vegetable) get too wet during shampooing. Nevertheless, hair-type pads are desired for their impact resistance and lack of color transfer to carpet. When properly cleaned, sterilized, and treated, hair-type pads are suitable for use on all grade levels and on radiant-heated floors.

Although more expensive, sponge and foam rubber retain their resilience much longer than hair pads and permit a variety of improved construction designs. They have high resistance to humidity and vermin and are non-allergenic. Rubber cushionings are suitable for use on all grade levels, but some of the denser grades are not recommended on radiant-heated floors.

When purchasing any type of carpet underlay, it is wise to make sure that the padding is suitable for the particular installation. It might be well to obtain assurance from the manufacturer on this matter, as well as a guarantee that the padding is free from holes, tears, lumps, wrinkles, tackiness, or other defects which might impair its serviceability.

Before installing the underlay, make sure the area is dry and clean. Installations should be made with as few seams as possible, and where joints are necessary, edges should be butted together.

CARPET SELECTION GUIDELINES

There is no sure and simple method for predicting the service quality of a carpet. A number of helpful guides do exist, however, which can be used to advantage by purchasers.

The General Services Administration of the United States Government, working in cooperation with the American Carpet Institute, Inc., recently prepared a master classification of commercial carpets. This work has been incorporated in Federal Specification DDD-C-95, dated April 16, 1965, entitled "Carpets and Rugs, Wool, Nylon, Acrylic, Modacrylic." For any serious purchaser of commercial carpets, reading of this specification is recommended. (The specification may be purchased for 15 cents from the United States Government Printing Office, Washington, D. C.

20402.) Given in the specification are requirements for the common carpet fibers, chain, filling and stuffer yarns, backing material, backing reinforcement, attached rubber cushioning, and back coating. The specification also describes requirements for color fastness and various physical requirements and tolerances. A wide variety of construction types are described, including Axminster, velvet, Wilton, tufted, knitted, and modified carpet constructions. Some of this information is shown in Table 13.

As a guide in the selection of the quality of carpeting to be used in various areas, the following suggestions are offered. It should be kept in mind that each installation must be judged carefully as to the peculiar traffic conditions expected. In some areas, it might be advisable to use a heavier, better grade because of the peculiar wear factors in these situations. As a basis for estimating probable carpet performance in use in the library, the levels of traffic might be illustrated as follows: Light—conference rooms, informal reading areas, audio-visual rooms, and rare book rooms; Medium—open-stack areas, reading rooms, technical processing room areas, and micro-film reading areas; Heavy—entrances, stairways, meeting rooms, and such focal points of traffic as the circulation desk, card catalog, and reference desk.

Carpet having wool, acrylic, or modacrylic pile yarn in the range of approximately 20 ounces per square yard or more should be satisfactory for light traffic. Fabrics of 25 ounces per square yard or more of pile yarn should be satisfactory for medium traffic areas. Those having 36 ounces per square yard or more of pile yarn should be satisfactory for heavy traffic. Carpet having 100 percent nylon pile yarn in weights of 20 ounces per square yard or more should be satisfactory for medium traffic. Those having 28 ounces per square yard or more should be satisfactory for heavy traffic.

Pile density

A number of years ago, the American Hotel Association recognized the importance of pile density and pile height in estimating the relative wearing qualities of pile floor coverings. It was proposed that wearing qualities of different carpets would be judged by comparing the pile density squared times pile height (D^2H).

The density factor took into account pitch, rows (wires) per inch, and pile yarn weight. The relationship was expressed by the formula:

$$D = 2RPB$$

where D is the density of the pile,
           R is the number of rows per inch lengthwise,
           P is the pitch, and
           B is the weight of the pile yarn in grains per inch.

TABLE 13
TYPICAL COMMERCIAL CARPETS

	Velvet Heavy	Wilton Heavy	Axminster Medium	Knitted Heavy	Tufted Heavy
Type of Carpet / Traffic Level					
Description	single-level loop pile, woven through back	single-level loop pile, woven through back	single-level cut pile pattern	single-level loop pile	single-level loop pile
Tufts/sq. in.	60	53	47	36	60
Pitch	216	180	189	—	—
Rows (wires)	8	8	7⅓	—	—
Shots	2	2	3	—	—
Frame	—	3	—	—	—
Pile weight (oz./sq. yd.)	42	54	26	37	42
Total weight (oz./sq. yd.)	60	75	56	58	80
Pile height, inches:					
Minimum	0.200	0.250	0.200	0.230	0.250
Maximum	0.250	0.300	0.310	0.290	0.300
Material of construction:					
Pile	wool	wool	wool	wool	wool
Chain	cotton or rayon	cotton or rayon	cotton or rayon	cotton, rayon or nylon	—
Filling	cotton or jute	cotton or jute	jute or kraftcord	jute or kraftcord	—
Stuffer	cotton, jute, kraftcord	cotton, jute, kraftcord	cotton or rayon	—	—
Backing	—	—	—	—	jute or cotton (min. 10 oz./sq. yd.)
Back coating, oz./sq. yd.	8	none required	6	14	12 to 28
Backing reinforcement, oz./sq. yd.	—	—	—	—	4 or more
Tuft bind, oz. (force required to pull a tuft or loop loose)	80	50	16	32	100

All things being equal, a fabric with twice the pile height of another should be twice as durable. Furthermore, if the pile heights were the same and the density of one fabric twice that of another, then the denser fabric should have approximately four times the durability.

Suggested carpet specification based on pile density

It has been previously indicated that durability and service quality depend to a large degree on the pile density of a carpet. This in turn is largely determined by two factors: weight of yarn in the pile, and height of pile.

Since both of these factors can be evaluated by analysis (total weight of pile yarn as ounces per square yard of carpet, and pile height as thousandths of an inch), it is possible to set up specification requirements which, if met, will result in adequate levels of pile density.

A study done for the American Hotel and Motel Association has produced such a specification, which has been adopted by the Institutional Research Council as a standard for acceptance of carpet service quality by that organization. In the development of the requirements for this specification, round-wire, all-wool velvet carpet was used as the reference level of performance under commercial conditions of average heavy traffic. The density factors were set on the basis of ounce weight and pile height for this type of carpeting.

Requirements are presented for two levels of traffic conditions, illustrating the necessary variation in pile yarn weight and pile height for average heavy traffic and average medium traffic. For an explanation of these terms, see the section "Building areas and traffic conditions," below.

The specification takes into account the differences in service quality attributable to carpet construction. Grade limits are set according to the method of carpet manufacture. It is believed that the minimum requirements for other construction types give durability qualities comparable to the round-wire velvet used as the reference level of performance.

The specification requirements will ensure satisfactory service life, provided the carpet construction conforms to accepted commercial practice and the materials of construction are of good quality.

The recommended weights and pile heights for wool, acrylic, nylon, and polypropylene carpets are summarized in Tables 14 and 15.

Building areas and traffic conditions

Foot-traffic conditions within a building vary widely. The type, size, and location of a building area determines the level of traffic to which a particular space will be subjected.

For example, lobbies, public rooms, corridors, and stairways will normally receive heavy traffic. Office areas usually encounter medium traffic. A classification of different building areas, according to the extent of traffic that may be expected, is given in Table 16.

TABLE 14

MINIMUM SPECIFICATION REQUIREMENTS BASED ON PILE DENSITY
FOR WOOL OR ACRYLIC CARPETS

	Average Heavy Traffic		Average Medium Traffic	
	Minimum Weight per Square Yard (Ounces)	Average Pile Height (Inches)	Minimum Weight per Square Yard (Ounces)	Average Pile Height (Inches)
Axminster carpet	36	0.200-0.310	28	0.200-0.310
Knitted carpet	42	0.250-0.300	36	0.200-0.250
Tufted carpet	42	0.250-0.300	36	0.200-0.250
Velvet carpet:				
Woven through the back	42	0.200-0.250	32	0.175-0.230
Not woven through the back	36	0.200-0.250	28	0.175-0.230
"Twist"	—	—	42	—
Wilton carpet 42		0.200-0.250	34	0.200-0.250

There are other carpetable building areas not included in Table 16. Consultation with commercial-carpet specialists will make it possible to classify such areas according to level of foot traffic.

Carpeting wears out much faster upon stairs than on level areas. Especially hard wear occurs at the leading edge of the steps. For this reason, it is especially important to use a very good pad under the carpet on the stairs, regardless of the quality of the padding you use elsewhere. Carpet of cut-pile construction is sometimes preferred for stair installations, since it shows less "grin" at the rounded edges of the stair.

Heavy wear can be distributed over more of the carpet if, at the time of installation, an extra foot or so of carpeting is folded under one or two of the risers at the top of the flight. Occasionally thereafter, the whole carpet can be shifted downward an inch or two—preferably before wear becomes noticeable. There will be some expense at each shifting, but the practice will help make a stair carpet last as long as the same carpet used on the floor area. Such shifting is a job best left to a professional craftsman.

TABLE 15
Minimum Specification Requirements Based on Pile Density for Nylon or Polypropylene Carpets

	Average Heavy Traffic		Average Medium Traffic	
	Minimum Weight per Square Yard (Ounces)	Average Pile Height (Inches)	Minimum Weight per Square Yard (Ounces)	Average Pile Height (Inches)
Tufted carpet	28	0.190-0.290	22	0.190-0.290
Velvet carpet	28	0.210-0.290	22	0.210-0.290
Woven through the back	28	0.210-0.290	22	0.210-0.290
Loomed carpet* 16		max. 0.150	—	—

*Sponge-bonded, high-density nylon pile.

TABLE 16
Building Areas Classified by Expected Foot Traffic

Applications	Average Heavy Traffic	Average Medium Traffic
Office buildings	Reception areas, aisles, open work areas, stairways, and elevators	Executive offices, staff areas
Banks, stores	Entranceways, lobbies, stairways, elevators, aisles, and selling areas	Executive offices, semi-private office areas, aisles, and selling areas
Churches, funeral homes	—	Entranceways, stairways, aisles, areas under seats or benches, chapel and altar areas
Restaurants, clubs	Dining areas, bars and grills	—
Schools	Corridors, classrooms, libraries, and stairways	Administrative offices and faculty lounges
Planes, trains, railroads, ships	Aisles, dining areas, and lounges	Staterooms and compartments
Libraries, hotels, motels, hospitals	Lobbies, stairways, elevators, corridors, public rooms, meeting and banquet rooms, wards	Executive offices, staff lounges, private rooms, waiting rooms, and guest rooms
Professional offices	—	Reception areas and consultation rooms for doctors, dentists, lawyers, etc.
Theatres, bowling alleys	Lobbies, stairways, lounges, and aisles	—

Extra-heavy traffic conditions

It should be noted that the commercial-carpet recommendations given here are *minimum* specifications for *average* heavy and medium foot-traffic conditions. Yet, traffic conditions in some building areas are often substantially higher than the average. As a result, these areas demand carpets with yarn-weight requirements higher than the minimums specified for normal heavy traffic use.

For example, large motion picture theatres and department stores in major metropolitan centers use carpets containing as much as 70 to 90 ounces of pile yarn per square yard because of the extra-heavy traffic they encounter.

It is not unusual for theaters, stores, offices, and other building areas subjected to *heavier-than-average* traffic to use carpets with 50 to 60 ounces of pile yarn per square yard.

Consultations with commercial-carpet specialists can help determine whether a particular area would require carpeting with specifications above the yarn weights recommended for average heavy traffic conditions.

KEY POINTS FOR PURCHASERS

As with any other basic building material, early and careful planning in the selection of carpet for a public area offers many advantages. It will provide sufficient time to choose the correct grade of carpet and the most desirable styling. It will expedite delivery and installation of the carpet to conform with the over-all building schedule. Possibly the most important advantage is that good planning will enable the architect and builder to design a building and interior with carpet in mind. This will not only help prevent installation problems, but can reduce costs.

Following are a number of key points to consider in specifying carpet:

(1) Consult with commercial-carpet specialists as early as possible. In the case of new building construction, call in the carpet specialists when plans are still in the drawing-board stage.

(2) Take full advantage of the extensive knowledge and background offered by the commercial-carpet specialists in selecting and specifying the grade and style of carpet that will provide the best possible service within the proposed budget. Consider anticipated service life and the length of time you may have to live with the present installation before replacement is economically possible. A good rule of thumb in purchasing carpet is to estimate "a dollar per yard per year of service life."

(3) The planning of building areas should be done with acoustical factors in mind. If carpet is chosen, other sound-conditioning treatment may be unnecessary.

(4) Anticipate the carpet installation when laying out the several interior areas. Carpets are manufactured in various widths: 27-inch, 36-inch, 54-inch, 9-foot, 12-foot, 15-foot, and 18-foot. Planning room dimensions and modules with these widths in mind will hold carpet waste to a minimum.

(5) Carpet pile heights vary. Plan door sizes so that they will swing freely over the carpet and padding specified.

(6) If the building specifications call for carpet, consider the use of economical subflooring materials such as plywood. Important savings can be realized in this way.

(7) Different areas within the same building are subjected to varying conditions of traffic and soiling. Stairways, for example, usually receive considerably more traffic and wear than ordinary floor areas. For areas likely to be subjected to especially heavy traffic, consider the purchase of carpets of heavier grades than those to be used in areas with much less traffic. Carpets of different grades, but with identical styling and appearance, are available from most manufacturers. An alternative suggestion is to purchase an extra supply of the same carpet for future replacement of worn carpet in areas of extra-heavy traffic.

(8) Consider the local soiling conditions when selecting color and design. Just as in clothing, light colors will tend to show soil more readily than darker tones. Medium shades, tweed stylings, and multi-color patterns tend to camouflage soil most effectively.

(9) The anticipated direction of traffic flow across a public space should be considered when planning placement of seams in a wall-to-wall carpet installation. The commercial-carpet specialist and the experienced carpet installer are the best sources of advice on seam placement.

(10) Take advantage of the styling services offered by carpet manufacturers' design studios. The artists and technical experts employed by the mills can furnish assistance in the selection of designs, colors, and textures that will be coordinated with the other furnishings and over-all decor of an interior.

(11) Take a good look at all of the stock commercial-carpet lines offered by several manufacturers. Besides providing a wide assortment of grades and stylings, they offer the advantage of being available for quick delivery for any size of installation.

(12) If you allow enough lead time in selection, and the size of the public area is 200 square yards or more, consider the custom-design services offered by most manufacturers of commercial-grade carpet.

(13) Make sure that the carpet selected is permanently mothproofed. All carpets made today by major American manufacturers are mothproofed for the life of the carpet even after repeated shampooings.

(14) Consult the commercial-carpet specialist and the carpet installer for recommendations on the correct padding and proper installation method needed. Always specify the best installation job possible.

INSTALLATION

Carpet for institutional service is generally installed in two ways: stretched over or bonded to the subfloor. In a stretched installation, the tackless method is used. This employs stripping, which consists of strips of wood about one inch wide through which are placed rows of sharp pins. The strips are securely fastened to the subfloor, against the wall or baseboard, with the pins projecting at an angle pointing toward the wall. When laid, the carpet is stretched fairly tight and hooked over the pins; thus the carpet is held firmly in place without visible tack heads.

In the second type of installation, bonding to the subfloor is used with carpets which are delivered with a foam rubber backing as an integral part of the carpet. Sponge-bonded carpet is laid like sheet goods and cemented to the floor. The carpet must be measured carefully before cutting to conform to the room dimensions, because there is no margin for correction by stretching. A waterproof cement is preferred for fixing the carpet to the floor. However, for temporary situations, a release adhesive with good horizontal strength and low vertical adhesion can be used. It is imperative that a special seam adhesive be used to cement the butted edges together; otherwise, the carpet seams will lift and become unsightly.

The removal of carpet that has been cemented to the subfloor is a more difficult task than taking up a stretched carpet. Although there is no easy way to accomplish this, the use of a terrazzo grinding machine has been suggested as a method for removing residual rubber and adhesive from the subfloor surface.

A recent development in bonded installations is the use of a laminated sheet of felt paper between the carpet and the floor. The carpet is bonded to the top surface of the felt sheet, and the bottom surface of the sheet is bonded to the floor. When replacement of all or part of the carpet becomes necessary, the carpet is peeled away from the subfloor carrying one layer of the felt paper with it. The remaining layer of felt paper with its adhesive is removed by a floor grinding machine.

The question of whether to install carpet by the stretch method or by bonding it to the subfloor usually arises when potential buckling may be a problem, e.g., when book trucks are to be used in carpeted areas of libraries. This question is not easily answered; no general claim can be made that one technique is superior to the other. Considerations peculiar to the particular installation must be taken into account.

Certain carpets can only be installed by the stretch method. If such is chosen, the purchaser may risk the chance of buckling but gains certain advantages, one of which is cost. Stretched carpet is generally less expensive than the same quality of carpet bonded to the subfloor. Also when stretched carpeting must be replaced, very often the underlay can be saved and used with the new carpet.

Proper installation of carpet is extremely important. A faulty installation job can be listed as the first cause of a buckling problem arising later. Another important factor related to the buckling of stretched carpet is the size of the area to be covered. A very large area, if unbroken by stabilizing factors such as pillars, bookstacks, furniture, and so forth, can be a problem to cover by the stretch method, and buckling is more likely to occur. Where the area to be carpeted is large and the anchorage is inadequate, bonding of the carpet to the subfloor will probably be required.

Certain other factors may have some influence on the choice between stretched carpet or bonded. For example, changes in humidity and temperature may have an effect on the dimensional stability of carpeting; thus, it may be important to consider whether and how effectively the building is air-conditioned before making the choice.

To sum up: The person who must decide how carpet is to be installed should consider (1) the ability of the supplier to do the best possible job of installation, (2) the proper underlay material for the carpet chosen, (3) the amount of funds available, (4) the size of the area, (5) stabilizing factors, which might eliminate the problem of buckling, and (6) the presence of good air-conditioning equipment.

A MAINTENANCE PROGRAM

Floor surface coverings are required to retain their original appearance for a prolonged time period, despite a large number of factors: abrasion by traffic; weight of fixed and moving objects; settling of air-borne dust; grinding-in of dirt; formation of dulling oil films; oxidizing effects of the atmosphere; exposure to color-fading light rays; attack of industrial gases; accidental contact with assorted stain-producers; extreme variations of temperature and humidity; attack by insects, fungi, and animals; periodic contact with cleaning agents; and daily brushing.

The effect of many of these detractors from appearance can be minimized by a well-planned and properly executed maintenance program. It is the purpose of the remainder of this chapter to serve as a reference guide for personnel concerned with all aspects of carpet maintenance.

Regardless of how carefully an institution is cleaned, decorative fabrics will become soiled. Because of their function as floor coverings, rugs and carpet receive the greatest amount of soiling. Further, since carpet is a pile fabric, having a depth of ⅛ inch or more, dirt not only collects on the surface, but works itself into the carpet. Under the pressure of foot traffic, the dirt becomes embedded in and around the pile tufts.

Soiling naturally shows more rapidly on pastel- and light-colored carpets. Even with the daily and weekly care recommended, these colors will probably become soiled in most locations. This soiling becomes especially serious when light colors are used where traffic is heavy, or where the air contains large quantities of greasy soot and dust. The oil and grease content of the dirt particles, often as high as 10 percent, causes them to cling tenaciously to the pile fibers, and even daily use of a vacuum cleaner may not remove all of them. This grease-laden dust eventually causes some discoloration of light-colored carpet.

The problem of light-colored soil on dark carpet can be as annoying as when the reverse color situation exists.

A carpet needs and deserves regular cleaning. This will ensure maximum durability for the fabric and preservation of the original color scheme and decorative effect worked out when the floor covering was purchased.

At least four elements enter into a planned maintenance program for carpet and rugs. These are (1) daily care, (2) weekly cleaning, (3) seasonal cleaning, and (4) irregular care.

DAILY CARE

Surface dirt is always easier to remove from a carpet than embedded dirt. Therefore, it is recommended that light cleaning with a vacuum cleaner be done every day on each carpet or rug so that dirt and dust deposited on them will be removed before it has a chance to work its way into the pile. Daily cleaning is especially desirable on heavy-traffic areas or near an entrance from the street. In the latter case, it is suggested that carpets be readily removable for commercial cleaning.

Non-slip carpet walk-off mats are recommended at entrances to aid in keeping at a minimum dirt, dust, snow, rain, etc. that might be tracked on the installed carpet. An institution can buy such mats and maintain them itself; or it may rent them from a franchised dealer who delivers clean mats weekly or bi-weekly. One manufacturer produces mats with rubber nosing on the ends to prevent curling. Mats with a slip-resistant back can be used on hard floor surfaces at entrances, while mats with a special plastic gripper back to prevent creeping are used on top of the carpet.

Surface litter may be removed by a soft-bristled broom or with a carpet sweeper. The latter is preferable because it raises less dust. After the rug has been swept, the pile should be brushed gently in the direction of the lay of the pile so that it all inclines in the same direction.

The use of light-weight vacuum cleaners as maintenance tools is becoming increasingly popular. These units are easily transported in cleaning carts and afford effective removal of loose dirt.

A heavy-duty vacuum cleaner is essential for proper care. The machine that does the best job combines a strong suction with a revolving brush and beater bar. Upright vacuums are usually of this type, and some canister and tank types have attachments which contain a brush and beater bar.

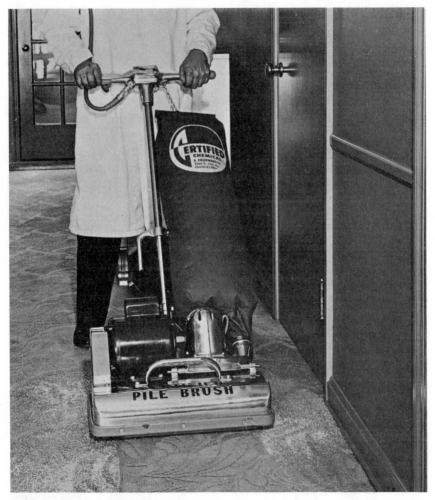

Certified Chemical & Equipment Co.

Pile-brush vacuum cleaner.

The motor-driven brush and beater-bar type not only removes surface litter but, because it opens the pile surface, is also an excellent aid in removing deeply-embedded soil. It further aids in keeping the pile upright. This type of machine is ideally suited for maintenance of heavy-traffic areas where its deep soil removal and pile-raising ability will materially aid in the maintenance of carpet.

The more common commercial vacuum is the suction-only, tank-type machine. The more powerful the suction and the better the pile opening devices—such as stationary brushes—that these machines have, the better they function as vacuum cleaners. This type of machine will do an excellent job in light-traffic areas and in removing surface litter and can operate readily in the "difficult to reach places," such as under furniture.

Where the maintenance operation is large enough, both types of vacuum cleaners can be utilized to good advantage.

Caution: Tank-type vacuums are often equipped with metallic or plastic combs, sometimes referred to as a "gleaner." While these combs are helpful in raising the pile of a cut-pile carpet, they can be detrimental to loop or round-wire carpet. They can pull or snag the loop pile, breaking pile yarns and causing loose ends.

On loop-pile carpet the comb should be raised so that it does not contact the pile. This can be done either by using the lever provided for raising the combs or by a set-screw adjustment.

Where sprouting (see page 207) has occurred or where such a condition is caused by the vacuum cleaner, the sprout is simply clipped. Sprouts should not be pulled out.

Be sure to keep any vacuum mechanically fit for best results. Brushes should be kept clean and replaced when worn-out, and the dirt bag should not be allowed to fill more than half way.

WEEKLY CARE

At least once a week, all carpet areas should be given a thorough cleaning with a vacuum cleaner. This should be done twice a week for heavy-traffic areas. Rooms which are seldom used should also be cleaned at least once a week to remove dust deposited from the air and to help prevent moth infestation.

Areas of extra-heavy traffic need special attention and require dry cleaning frequently to maintain a satisfactory surface appearance. Dry cleaning has the advantage of allowing an area to be cleaned and open to traffic within a relatively short time. However, it should be used only if there is adequate ventilation to remove solvent vapors. Two general types of products are available for use: a solvent solution, and a solvent-saturated, inert-particle (powdered) cleaning compound.

The solvent-cleaning should be left to professional cleaning personnel, since it requires special equipment and more than usual care in handling volatile solvents. Inherent also in the use of grease-dissolving solvents is the danger that excess solvent will penetrate through the pile and soften any latex coating in the backing.

Instructions for use of a powdered cleaning compound are:

(1) Be sure there is adequate ventilation before starting work.

(2) Clear the area of all movable objects.

(3) Open up the pile and remove loose dirt from the entire area with a mechanical pile brush or with a heavy-duty vacuum cleaner.

(4) Pre-spot stained areas.

(5) Sprinkle absorbent material liberally over a small area. Follow manufacturer's suggested dosage.

(6) Work the powder into the pile with a long-handled brush or with a mechanical, absorbent-powder brush. The amount of mechanical action required will depend on the degree of soiling. An electrically powered divided-weight machine equipped with a long-bristled, fairly stiff brush, is well-suited for this work. In order to be effective, the powder must contact the fiber. Therefore, the brush should be worked in two directions at right angles to each other in order to "hit" all sides of the pile yarn.

(7) Repeat steps 5 and 6 for the entire area.

(8) Allow the material to dry completely as indicated by a drying out of the powder and the disappearance of a strong solvent odor.

(9) Vacuum the entire area.

(10) Repeat step 3.

(11) Replace objects that were removed from the area.

Two manufacturers of this type of cleaning compound provide a special powered brush which, in one case, can be rented and, in the other, purchased. Some professional maintenance services are qualified to provide carpet care based on the use of this cleaning method.

Liquid cleaning compounds are available containing synthetic detergents and solvents that do not produce the problems listed for straight solvents. Personnel can apply these mop-on cleaning compounds by means of short-string cotton mops or sponge mops. This type of cleaning removes surface soil only and does not replace periodic machine-shampooing that loosens and removes soil embedded in the pile. Mop-on cleaning compounds leave no dry powder residues in the carpet and do not require pickup application. They are sudsless and dry within one hour.

It may become necessary in some areas of extra-heavy traffic to use a water-base cleaning compound to maintain an acceptable level of cleanliness. This may be achieved by use of the mop-applied cleaning compound or by special equipment that minimizes over-wetting of the carpet and reduces the time the area will be closed to traffic.

There is a carpet scrubbing machine that combines the scrubbing and vacuuming function in one unit. Two sponge-rubber or rubber pads are given a slight circular movement as they reciprocate on the carpet, simulating the scrubbing action of a brush in the hand. The vacuum nozzle follows the pads, picking up the suds.

Another type of carpet cleaning machine presuds the shampoo before the latter is spread on the carpet. This prepared lather is then rubbed over the carpet with the usual rotating brush, after which the foam is wet-vacuumed from the surface.

SEASONAL CLEANING

Although there is no established rule governing how often a carpet must be wet-shampooed, it is fairly certain that at least one such shampooing will be required each year.

Plant-cleaning

Generally, if the carpet or rug can be easily picked up, it should be "plant-cleaned" rather than cleaned on location. However, plant-cleaned rugs usually shrink. Loose rugs which are cut to fit close to walls will be undersize when returned from plant-cleaning.

Plant-cleaning includes the following general steps: (1) removal of embedded solid soil by mechanical agitation; (2) washing or shampooing; (3) rapid drying; (4) mildew-, vermin-, and mothproofing; (5) resizing; (6) drying.

There are several good reasons for preferring plant-cleaning. (1) It removes more soil than is possible on location. (2) The first step in plant-cleaning (i.e., dirt removal by mechanical means) takes out embedded soil which cannot be removed by normal on-location methods. (3) It cleans the back of the fiber covering, which is impossible in on-location cleaning. (4) Rinsing operations remove emulsified soil and cleaning solution that cannot be removed in on-location cleaning. (5) Due to the thorough rinsing operation, plant-cleaned carpets resoil more slowly than location-cleaned carpets. This is because many cleaning agents, when added to the carpet pile, enhance its dirt-catching properties. Some synthetic detergent residues, if not rinsed properly in plant-cleaning, or if left in the pile during location-cleaning, are especially good dirt catchers. The characteristics of the synthetic detergent used will determine the extent to which it performs as a resoiling agent. (6) The rapid drying process in plant-cleaning lessens the danger of damage due to fungicidal action, which has been, until very recently, always present in on-location cleaning.

All dust and soils contain spores, fungi, and molds, as well as bacteria and nutriment for micro-biological growth. In the presence of highly humid conditions, at normal summer temperatures, conditions for active growth of these fungi and molds are sometimes reached within forty-eight hours on damp rugs or carpeting. Odors from this source can persist indefinitely. Recent developments involving the addition of "mildew proofing" agents to on-location shampoos may mitigate this problem.

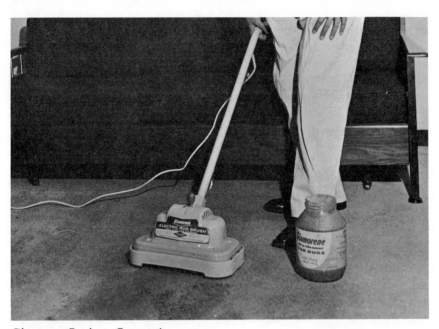

Glamorene Products Corporation

Portable brush machine designed for use with
"powdered" dry cleaner.

On-location cleaning

It is not practical to send out the bulk of institutional carpeting for cleaning. In most cases, cleaning must be done on location. On-location cleaning methods cannot entirely remove soil which is deeply embedded in the pile or base of the rug. Frequent vacuuming will reduce the amount of soil which penetrates to the base of the pile and will thus make it possible for on-location cleaning to produce better results.

Carpet may partially be overwetted during an on-location cleaning process, and, if the floor covering shrinks as it dries, a tension will be produced tending to pull the covering away from the walls. It is therefore important that floor coverings be installed securely. It is recommended that low-quality or inexpensive tufted carpet be purchased with polypropylene back (polybac) instead of prewoven jute so as to avoid dimensional change from overwetting. Polybac eliminates shrinkage; it is used in carpet walk-off mats (mentioned on page 190).

Equipment. A portable tank-type machine or a central vacuum system with a wet separator should be used. Only heavy-duty vacuums should be considered for this application since drying time will be dependent on the quantity of moisture left in the carpet.

Wet-shampooing machines, most of which are of the rotary type, are the most suitable equipment developed to date. A three-gallon tank is desirable and a controlled feeding system essential. Commercial machines for on-location cleaning usually weigh slightly over 100 pounds and have brushes 12 to 16 inches in diameter which rotate at 160 to 200 rpm. The usual speed is between 190 and 200 rpm. Brushes which operate between 190 and 200 rpm give better cleaning and reduce pile damage, but are considered more difficult to control than the machines which operate at lower brush speeds.

Commercial machines may operate in either a clockwise or counterclockwise direction, but any machine can be set to operate in either direction by merely changing the motor leads. It is important that all machine brushes used by a group of operators rotate in the same direction, since it is difficult for operators alternately to use machines on which brushes rotate in different directions.

One manufacturer of floor machines now has available a foamer attachment that fits on the housing of any rotary machine. This self-contained solution tank and foam builder eliminates the need of the usual solution tank. Rotary foam shampooing has two advantages over rotary liquid shampooing: (1) The carpet is dry in 30 to 60 minutes instead of 4 to 6 hours—important for public areas. (2) It is impossible for personnel to overwet the carpet, which may cause shrinkage. In rotary foam shampooing, one man does the shampooing and another removes the dirty suds with a wet-vacuum pickup before any re-absorption takes place. New synthetic detergent shampoos containing foaming solvents are quite effective in cleaning all types of carpet fibers.

One manufacturer of floor machines recently introduced a new type of carpet shampooing machine that releases foam and brushes in a reel action, as a pilelifter does. This kind of cleaning involves two operations and two machines. First the carpet is shampooed, and then the foam is removed—either a wet-vacuum is used to pick up the damp foam or the foam is allowed to dry, following which an upright vacuum is used.

The advantages of reel foam cleaning are quick drying and elimination of overwetting and shrinkage. The disadvantages are the high cost of equipment and the inability to clean heavily soiled carpet. With this method, carpet must be shampooed more often to keep it presentable.

Another manufacturer of floor machines has introduced equipment which combines the reel foam shampooing and wet suction pickup in one machine. This one-man, one-step, one-machine operation saves time and labor and, by instantly picking up the foam, eliminates entirely the possibility of re-absorption of the dirty foam by the carpet.

Pile setting is necessary after rotary shampooing (either liquid- or foam-type) and after reel foam shampooing. Especially important on high-pile and cut-pile carpet, pile setting gives the carpet the best possible appearance by eliminating heel marks, foot prints, etc.

Before the development of nylon, circular brushes were made of natural fibers. These varied from soft tampico to medium palmetto and the stiffer palmetto and bassine fibers. One manufacturer sells a brush made with a central ring of tampico, an intermediate ring of palmetto, and an outside ring of bassine.

New brushes should be soaked in a synthetic detergent solution of the concentration used for cleaning for two or three hours prior to use. All-bassine brushes are not recommended for cleaning carpet, since they are very stiff and can cause damage to the pile tufts. Brushes which have been previously used do not require soaking before being re-used. The all-palmetto fibered brush is considered safest for general use and provides adequate agitation for proper cleaning. Tampico fibers by themselves are too soft to be of any value.

The trend is toward all-nylon brushes. Nylon brushes are available in various degrees of flexibility, have superior wear-resistance, do not readily "flatten," and do not become excessively sharpened. The over-all brush firmness grades differ—soft, medium, and hard, and each brush is a blend of fibers of different thicknesses.

Before new nylon brushes are used on carpet, they should be run on cement. This softens the bristle ends and eliminates pile yarn damage such as twist reduction or fuzzing.

Polypropylene brushes offer an advantage over existing natural fiber types. Due to lack of moisture acceptance, the polypropylene brush does not soften, mush, or flatten after continuous use, thereby giving a constant brushing result and more even cleaning.

Care of equipment. Brushes must be regularly cleaned to remove soil and the loose pile which builds up on and between the bristles. The suction hose should be wiped dry at frequent intervals, since the water picked up by the hose will be dirty. During cleaning, it will be impossible to keep the hose from occasionally striking furniture or walls and a dirty hose will leave marks which will be difficult to remove. Dirty water dripping from the hose can also cause unsightly stains on walls and furniture. The wet pick-up tank should be emptied frequently (at least once per 500 feet) and washed and rinsed every day after use.

Shampoo materials. Until about ten years ago, most on-location wet shampoos were made with a soap base. Today, as a result of a study sponsored by the American Hotel Association, soaps are not considered acceptable for on-location cleaning. The study concluded that soaps create undesirable odors and increase the re-soiling rate.

Generally, a well-balanced carpet shampoo will be composed of a blend of surface-active agents rather than of a single synthetic detergent base. While all the ingredients might serve a useful cleaning function, it is more likely that at least one of the components will be specifically included for its "high foam" properties and another will serve as a foam booster and stabilizer.

A carpet shampoo must satisfy a number of general performance requirements in order to be considered acceptable by modern standards.

It must (1) readily produce foam with water of varying degrees of hardness; (2) produce a foam that is stable in the presence of soil; (3) effectively clean by emulsifying oily-type soils, dissolving water-soluble substances, cleaning inert particles from the fibers, and dispersing and suspending soil in the foam; (4) have sufficient lubricity to minimize frictional wear from the brushes; (5) have no deleterious effect on the various carpet components; (6) be relatively mild, as measured by pH; (7) leave no soil-attracting residues; (8) have no effect on standard carpet dyes; (9) not cause excessive wetting of the backing.

Extra values that are sometimes incorporated into carpet shampoos include mildew-, moth-, and germproofing agents, optical brighteners, anti-soil additives, and corrosion inhibitors.

A novel product approach to carpet cleaning utilizes absorbent particles in the shampoo. The presence of these particles is said to permit more complete removal of dirt and to act as a soil retardant. The cleaning program with this product is basically the same as for regular on-location wet-shampooing. However, it is suggested that the wet-vacuum pickup operation can be omitted if the feed rate of detergent is reduced to permit only a very thin (1/16 inch) uniform layer of suds to form on the carpet. The dried carpet must be vacuumed to remove dried shampoo, absorbent particles, and soil particles.

Miscellaneous equipment and supplies. These include: a stiff brush for "laying" the pile, cardboard strips for protecting the wet rugs from metal on furniture which can cause rust marks, a drip pan in which to rest brushes when not in use, and spotting solutions.

Personnel. The use of a two-man crew is essential to proper timing and efficient work. The crew should consist of an operator and a helper. The operator should be experienced in all phases of carpet cleaning, with a knowledge of the construction of carpets so as to be able to vary his procedures to obtain best results under varying conditions of pile heights, weaves, and twist. The helper assists in moving furniture and equipment, and hand-brushes the corners of the room. He operates the wet-vacuum pickup while the shampooing is in progress.

Street shoes should be changed before the cleaning process, as wet rugs readily pick up soil. Special slippers or sneakers should be provided for the cleaning crew.

Electrical circuits. Machines and vacuums are equipped with ¼- to 1-horsepower motors and both machines will be in use at the same time. Therefore, ample current should be provided for both the cleaning and vacuum operations. Electrical connections should be inspected daily and all equipment grounded. Short circuits would be disastrous in wet operations.

Scheduling. Carpets will dry at a rate which is dependent upon the amount of fluid used, the amount of air circulating over the carpet, and the weather. Low relative humidity and high temperature promote rapid drying.

Cleaning operations should be scheduled to take advantage of weather conditions. Rainy seasons, which are prevalent in some sections of the country, can be ruinous to location-cleaned rugs. Humidity is fairly constant over large areas, and a good rule might be to consult weather reports in the local press. Relative humidity below 70 percent will allow fair drying. If rugs must be cleaned during periods of high humidity and if air circulation is poor, the minimum amount of cleaning solution which will produce satisfactory cleaning should be used.

Drying rates can be improved by increasing air circulation over the surface of the rug with fans. Combination fans and electric heaters are also available. The hot air delivered by such units will decrease the drying time and will be very helpful under adverse conditions of drying. Where conventional shampooing machines are used, drying will normally require from 5 to 36 hours. Where rotary machines with a foamer attachment or reel-type foamer machines are used, drying will require from 30 to 60 minutes. During drying, shampooed areas should be roped off from traffic; this will facilitate subsequent maintenance and increase the time between cleaning operations.

Furniture moving. If possible, move all the furniture from the room before starting the cleaning operation. If this is impractical, move the furniture to one side of the room and clean the vacated area. The furniture should then be moved back to positions where it will be placed permanently and the shampooing process repeated on the remainder of the floor.

Be sure to put strips of cardboard under the legs of the furniture moved onto cleaned areas; otherwise furniture stains, which are very difficult to remove, will be absorbed by the damp carpet. The cardboard protectors must be left in position until the fabric is completely dry. This will normally require at least 36 hours, since drying under the cardboard will be slower than on exposed portions of the carpet.

Cleaning should start at a far corner with work proceeding toward exits. Doors and windows should be left open to accelerate drying.

Preparation of solutions. Measuring devices, pails, and shampoo concentrates should be kept in a specified area for mixing. Plastic pails are preferred in order to avoid rust stains from metal. A waterproof tarpaulin spread on the floor will prevent soiling. Good measuring equipment is essential, because careless use of concentrates will leave excess amounts of synthetic detergent residues in the carpet and in some cases actually detract from the cleaning process.

Small graduated vessels, designed to measure liquid ounces or cubic centimeters, are available in photographic, drug, and hardware stores. Use these to measure the correct amount of shampoo concentrate for the solution being prepared. Do not resort to guesswork. Capacity of pails, mixing vessels, and machine storage tanks should be measured and marked. Tepid water may sometimes be used; hot water, *never*.

Vacuum cleaning. Efficient removal of all loose soils before the wet-shampooing will materially increase the effectiveness of the job and the duration of the brightness effected by the shampooing. Therefore, immediately before shampooing, the carpet should receive a thorough cleaning with a heavy-duty vacuum cleaning system such as a portable tank-type vacuum.

Spot removal. All stains should be removed before wet-shampooing. (See section on "Spots and stains," page 210.)

Wet-shampooing. Excessive moisture and residues are to be avoided at all times. It is therefore important to use shampoo materials properly and to use only the amount and concentration necessary to accomplish good cleaning. Under conditions of normal soiling, carpets of average pile thickness, such as medium velvet and good Axminsters, can usually be cleaned satisfactorily with from 6 to 9 quarts of ready-to-use shampoo per 108 square feet. It is seldom advisable, even under adverse cleaning conditions, to use more than 12 quarts of solution for 108 square feet. The exact amount will depend upon the operator and his judgment of what the particular job requires.

Little benefit is realized by increasing the concentration beyond that recommended for cleaning heavily soiled areas; it is more practical merely to increase the brushing time. Badly soiled areas of a carpet or rug should be cleaned again by returning to these areas later, rather than keeping the machine brushing in one place for a long period. The solution should be fed to the brushes slowly and continuously, rather than in spurts, to prevent wetting of the carpet backing.

Whenever very heavily soiled carpets or rugs are encountered, one cleaning will usually be insufficient to restore original brilliance. In cases where re-cleaning is indicated, best results can be achieved by a second cleaning 24 hours after the first. This allows much of the first quantity of solution to dry out before the second is added. In addition, the 24-hour period markedly increases soil removal by the shampoo, making the repeat cleaning more efficient than two immediately successive cleanings.

Satisfactory cleaning usually requires the use of enough shampoo to produce a minimum amount of foam on the rug during the cleaning operation. Excess foam indicates that more synthetic detergent or solution than is required has been used. It may also indicate undue wetting. It is important that only the proper amount of solution be used. Low-sudsing biodegradable synthetic detergents eliminate the necessity of wet-vacuum pickup. Steps taken are: (1) shampoo with low suds, (2) set pile with hand brush, (3) dry-vacuum carpet when dry.

Proper rotary brush operation contributes greatly to the results obtained with on-location cleaning. Operators should be instructed to operate with the brush flat, which will give better mechanical action and cleaning, and will also do much to prevent streaks. Many operators believe that they must heel or toe a brush if it is to move across the rug properly, but this is not true. Properly trained operators can satisfactorily manipulate the brush when it is running almost flat. The operator should also use care to obtain proper overlapping of each run across the carpet, since improper overlapping will result in streaks.

Wet-vacuum pickup. The wet-vacuuming operation should follow cleaning with as little time lag as possible, generally not more than 2 or 3 minutes. Under such conditions, about 10 percent of the solution applied to the rug will be removed from the pile surface, carrying with it soil and contributing to the brightness of the shampooed carpet.

Studies indicate that if the vacuuming can be carried out within 5 to 10 seconds behind the rotary brush, it will be possible to remove a much larger percentage of the solution applied to the rug. However, such an interval of removal can be obtained only where the brush and vacuum are parts of the same machine. This is the advantage of having a shampooer and vacuum pickup in one machine.

Multi-Clean Products, Inc.

Shampooing and wet-vacuum pickup.

Treatment after shampooing. Immediately after vacuuming, the carpet should be brushed uniformly to regularize the lay of the pile and to eliminate superficial marks of the rotary brush. Where the rug has been badly marked by the rotary brush, it will, in general, be impossible to eliminate such marks by hard brushing. The remedy for this condition, as has already been noted, lies in proper use of the rotary brush during scrubbing.

Shading is decreased and appearance possibly brightened and regularized by brushing in the direction of the pile lay, although the rug will be more resilient if brushed against the pile lay. The main point is to brush uniformly in the same direction with regular strokes.

The use of a mechanical pile brush is recommended to restore the pile to its original height. When using a pile-lifting machine or pile brush to set damp pile, make sure the brushes are clean. The carpet should be force-dried if possible, by circulating warm, dry air over the carpet. The use of fans, hot-air blowers, and dehumidifiers will measurably reduce carpet drying time.

IRREGULAR CARE

Irregular care consists of correction of mechanical damage to the installation and restoration of burned, permanently stained, and crushed areas. Some of the mechanical defects encountered in institutional and commercial installations are loose ends, snags, sprouts, holes, rough seams, open seams, and loose and buckled carpet. These conditions are unsightly and may become hazardous. They usually get worse if not given prompt attention. Repairs of most of these defects call for the services of a skilled carpet mechanic.

Loose ends, snags, and sprouts

Loose ends, snags, and sprouts should be clipped with scissors, never pulled. If a bare area remains, the pile yarn can be replaced by burling.

Burling and tuft-replacing procedures

Obtain matching yarns. Remove damaged tufts either with scissors or tweezers. Insert a curved needle under the shot and sew in loops. If the carpet is cut pile, make the loops higher than the surrounding tufts; then, using nap scissors, trim the loops flush with the surface of the pile. When repairing loop pile fabric, the same technique is used, except that the loops are made the same height as the carpet pile.

Another method of burling is tuft setting. Matching yarn is obtained. Damaged pile is removed. A clear drying latex-based cement is put into the bare spot. The yarn is placed in the "U" of the tuft-setting needle. A light tap of the hammer will drive the yarn into the backing of the carpet.

Patching

Damaged areas and holes that are too large for burling can be patched. With a "knee-kicker," the carpet is kicked toward the damaged area and stay-tacked from all sides. After the damaged area is blocked in and the tension relieved, a rectangle or square is outlined. The nap of the carpet following the outline is opened up by use of a screwdriver or similar tool. Then a sharp knife is worked carefully between the opened rows of yarn and the damaged area cut out. The cut should always be made between the shots and rows of face yarn, never across the shot or face yarn. The pattern match and direction of the pile are checked, and the number of shots and rows is counted when cutting out the patch.

Face-up tape is placed under all four sides of the cut-out. The edge of the cut-out should be on the middle of the tape. The carpet is lifted at the edge of the cut-out and seam cement applied on the entire tape by squeezing the cement from a plastic dispenser. A piece of carpet scrap can be used to spread the cement and also coat the carpet edges.

The patch is inserted by forcing an awl through the center and then bending the edges downward with the other hand. When the edges of the patch are in contact with the tape, the awl is removed and the center of the patch is pushed down. This will push the edges of the patch outward to contact the edges of the cut-out. No pile should be trapped between the edges. A weight is placed over the patch and the cement allowed to cure. Where sponge-bonded, high-density pile carpet is used, stained and damaged areas may be cut out and replaced with plugs. The plugs are cemented in place, with no visible loose threads and no need for sewing. When evenly soiled, the plugs are impossible to detect.

Rough seams

This condition occurs most frequently at cross seams. Loops that originally were caught and hidden in the seam and have worked up to the surface with use are cut. The protruding ends should be cut with nap scissors to a height slightly less than the height of the surrounding pile.

Repairing seams

An open seam must be given immediate attention. It not only presents a tripping hazard, but will spread, extending the opening and causing the carpet edges to fray. Prior to damage to the edge of the carpet, the seam can be easily repaired. Sewn seams can be re-sewn. The taped seams require an application of cement and stay-tacking.

If the edge of the carpet is damaged, the following procedure is recommended:

(1) Stretch the carpet towards the seam and stay-tack. Place nails 3 inches apart, about 4 inches away from the center of the seam. Repeat this step on the other side of the seam. The carpet will now bulge between the two rows of tacks.

(2) Cut the tape at the seam and remove it. Place edges of carpet one on top of the other and determine the amount to be cut off each edge. The cut should be made parallel to the seam and down its entire length.

(3) Lay sufficient face-up tape on the floor for the entire length of the seam and fasten it at both ends. Place the carpet with cut edges on the center of the tape and check the fit. Lift the edges of the carpet, exposing the tape.

(4) Apply a seam cement to a 4-foot section of the tape, using a piece of waste carpet for an applicator. Also apply some of the cement to the cut carpet edges to lock in the tufts.

(5) Set the carpet edges on the tape and butt gently together, using either a knee-kicker or a "crab." The seam may then be rolled with a porcupine roller. The tapered points of the roller perforate the carpet back and tape to improve the bond. This section is held in place by tacking on each side of the seam about half an inch from the edge and spacing the tacks

about every 2 inches along the length of the seam. On a concrete floor, use bags of sand to hold down the edges of the carpet.

(6) This procedure is repeated, by 4-foot sections, for the length of the entire seam. Remove tacks or weights when the cement has cured.

Loose and buckling carpet

If the carpet has worked loose around the doorways or the walls it should be re-fastened. Otherwise, buckling may develop. Humid weather can cause a large installation, which has not been properly stretched, to buckle. Buckling can be a hazardous condition and can also contribute to accelerated soiling and wear. If buckling persists, the installation should be restretched.

Burns

If lighted cigarettes, matches, or glowing ashes fall on a carpet, a charred or glazed spot may result. This effect is more pronounced with the man-made fibers—particularly nylon and acrylic—than with wool.

The charred, and sometimes fused, spot of a synthetic fiber is more resistant to wear and scuffing than a comparable burned area of wool. Therefore, the discoloration with synthetics will persist under traffic abrasion for a longer period than with wool.

A charred area in wool carpet can usually be removed with a fine grade of sandpaper or other abrasive; a depression in the carpet may result from this treatment. A burn on a synthetic carpet will cause the man-made fibers to melt to a hard black bead, which can only be removed by clipping it from the surface. If clipping is followed by brushing, carpet appearance will be noticeably improved. In severe cases, replacement of the burned tuft or patching of the burned spot with another piece of matching carpet may be necessary.

It is recommended that the area around ash trays or other receptacles for lighted cigarettes and matches be protected against accidental dropping of these items.

Permanent stains

Some stains will contain dyestuffs, such as shoe polish, ink, etc., which will not be removed by spot cleaning, but will permanently change the color of the surface yarn. Clipping or replacement of the stained tufts may be possible in some cases, while patching may be required with a small but seriously stained area. For larger areas of premanent stain, consideration might be given to the possibility of having the carpet re-dyed. Some carpet manufacturers, as well as professional cleaning agencies, offer this service.

Crushed carpet

All carpet will become depressed if subjected to heavy loads for long periods of time. In many cases, the crushed area can be "teased" up by application of steam and brushing in the following manner:

(1) Moisten the area with water and cover it with several layers of clean, dry cloth.

(2) Place a hot electric iron ("wool" setting on the temperature dial) on the cloth and press down with moderately heavy pressure. During the pressing operation, a small cloud of steam will escape around the base of the iron. Continue to press until the escape of steam has nearly but not completely ceased, usually about 10 seconds.

(3) Brush the hot, damp tufts erect with the fingertips or a dull knife.

SPECIAL PROBLEMS

Carpets are as nearly perfect as manufacturing methods will permit. Because no machine is perfect, however, a carpet woven by a loom is also not perfect. After a carpet leaves the loom, it is sent to the finishing room. Here, all the obvious imperfections and irregularities are repaired by a hand-tailoring operation. The carpet is then given a final, careful inspection. If passed, the carpet is shipped to the dealer as commercially perfect; rejects are labelled "imperfects" or "seconds" and disposed of on that basis.

Certain factors in the construction of soft-pile floor coverings can account for undesirable effects that may develop shortly after installation. A knowledge of the special problems associated with a soft-pile floor covering will help the reader realize that his difficulties are not peculiar to his carpet but to all carpets. Most of the difficulties are minor and are not likely to diminish the serviceability of the carpet.

Shading

Carpets and rugs, after they have been laid, seem to change color in certain spots. Viewed from one direction, the spots will appear lighter; from another direction, darker. These spots may appear in heavy-traffic areas as well as in areas of little traffic. This phenomenon is called "shading."

The pile in a new rug stands nearly vertical. But as the rug is used, the pile fibers in different areas become inclined or bent in different directions under the pressure of foot traffic or the movement of heavy furniture. This causes a variation in light reflection.

Shading may occur in both plain and figured carpets and rugs. It is more noticeable on plain color carpets because of the wide expanse of color, unbroken by any pattern. On figured rugs, shading is most noticeable when there is little contrast between the colors or shades in the pattern. Hard-twist or frieze carpets, looped-pile carpets and other texture weaves show shading to a lesser degree than do the cut-pile or smooth-surface types.

One way to minimize shading, if it appears on a plain-colored rug, is to make sure that the lay of the pile is pointed away from the light. A good rug cushion also helps prevent excessive flattening of the pile. A vacuum cleaner, particularly one with a motor-driven beater bar, will do much to lift and straighten crushed pile tufts. Shading is difficult, if not impossible, to remove permanently, but wet-shampooing is sometimes effective.

Shading is not a manufacturing defect. It is an inherent feature of pile fabrics, and in luster-type carpets and rugs, shading actually enhances the richness of the coloring.

Shedding

When the pile is cut, short ends of fiber are left in the surface of the carpet. With wear and vacuuming or sweeping, these short ends gradually work loose. This condition is referred to as fluffing or shedding.

This condition does not constitute a defect, and there is no danger of excessive fiber loss. The amount of fiber removed by shedding in the lifetime of the carpet is only a small fraction of the total weight of the carpet fiber.

The only remedy is time. Shedding does not reduce the life and quality of the carpet and stops as soon as the loose fibers have been removed.

Sprouting

During manufacture, extra-long ends of yarn may become curled into the pile and thus escape inspection. After a short period of service, these yarn ends may work up and protrude above the surface, a condition called "sprouting." Sprouting does not mean that the carpet is coming apart. It is only necessary to clip or shear the protruding end to make it even with the pile surface. The tuft should never be pulled out as the fabric may be injured.

Discoloration

Carpets are normally quite fast to light and do not fade unless excessively exposed to the direct rays of the sun. Judicious use of window shades or other window-covering materials usually solves the problem of too much sun exposure. Where carpets will by necessity be exposed to much sunlight, it is advisable to have the manufacturer specify colors with ratings of high light-fastness.

Carpets in service, despite normal maintenance, will gradually change in color and this change is frequently classified as fading. The color change is due to the accumulation of grease-laden dirt in the pile, and the degree and rapidity of this change is dependent upon the amount and nature of the accumulation. The higher the grease content of the soil, the greater its tendency to cling tenaciously to the pile fibers. This kind of soiling shows most rapidly on light-colored pastel carpets. The original color and tone of a carpet may be restored by dry cleaning or shampooing. Thorough cleaning is the only remedy for such a condition.

Carpets of light pastel tones are best used only in locations where there is little traffic or where the dust content of the air is relatively low. Carpets of stronger colors such as red, dark green, or blue, which do not show discoloration too readily, can be selected for more heavily trafficked or dusty areas. Since the dust in the air is normally not controlled, discoloration is not considered a justifiable complaint to be addressed to carpet manufacturers.

Pilling

Pilling is more serious than the difficulties thus far described. It is the formation of fuzzy balls made by friction and held on the surface by long fibers that are too strong to permit the pills to break away. This defect is especially associated with staple nylon used in loop-pile construction and to a much lesser extent with acrylic fibers. Its occurrence is rare with wool fibers. The only method for dealing with pills after they have formed is to shear or clip them from the surface.

Manufacturers can minimize this pilling tendency by complete impregnation of the base of the tufts with backsize and stiff brushing and shearing in the finishing. Continuous filament nylon in loop construction is more resistant to pilling than staple nylon.

Bearding

Bearding refers to fiber that has come out of its anchorage and works its way to the top of the pile. This condition is associated with "slippery" man-made fibers rather than with wool. Should bearding continue for a long period, it can result in substantial loss of fiber.

Static electricity

Considerable research has been done in attempts to reduce the buildup of static electricity created by the friction of walking on carpets and rugs. A recent development shows promise of eliminating this problem, which produces a slight shock when a person touches a metal object. Carpets woven of a blend of wool and stainless steel fibers have been tested at Cornell University's School of Hotel Administration, with results that indicate that the carpet is almost static-free, even in low-humidity climates.

There is also evidence that the carpet does not attract soil as readily as conventional carpet and is easier to clean.

The stainless steel fiber was developed by the Brunswick Corporation. Originally, the fibers were extruded to a hair-like fineness of 12 microns in diameter, later to 9 microns, and can be made as small as 7.5 microns. They are reasonably good conductors of electricity, which means that the buildup of static electricity is greatly reduced. The fibers, when tested by Brunswick, proved to combine high tensile strength with "softness" and pliability, making them suitable for use in carpets and cloth.[2]

Mildew

Molds causing mildew develop most often on cotton, rayon, wool, wood, and paper. Synthetic fibers—such as nylon, acetate, acrylic, and modacrylic—are mildew-resistant. Yet, since carpeting is usually made from a blend of fibers, the danger of mildew damage exists for most carpets.

Molds, as they grow, cause considerable damage and often leave a musty odor. They discolor yarns, sometimes eating into them so severely that the yarns rot.

Some of the precautions that should be taken to prevent mildew are:

(1) *Keep carpets clean.* Soil can supply sufficient food for mildew to grow under certain conditions of moisture and temperature.

(2) *Get rid of dampness.* Reduce the sources of high moisture. Make certain outside drainage is adequate. Waterproof concrete, brick, and other masonry walls above ground.

(3) *Dry the air.* Heat can be used to dry out dampness. Turn up the heat; then open doors and windows to let out the warm moisture-laden air. To dry air in closets and other small areas, burn a small electric light in them continuously. Dehumidify the air mechanically.

When mildew or musty odors develop, the following steps may alleviate the condition:

(1) Remove any visible mold by vacuum or brush.

(2) Do everything convenient to dry the area in question.

(3) Shampoo by "on-location" technique; then spray or treat with a fungicide recommended by a carpet specialist. Fungicides such as zinc naphthenate, quaternary ammonium naphthenate, dichlorophenol, and salicylanilide are effective if properly applied.

---

[2]See Richard A. Compton, "Carpets Woven of Wool and Stainless Steel," *The Cornell Hotel & Restaurant Administration Quarterly* (February, 1967), and Gerald F. Barry, "Textile Applications of Metal Fibers," *Modern Textiles Magazine* (June, 1967).

Vermin

Protection against the ravages of moth and carpet beetle larvae is needed for wool. The synthetic fibers are not prone to attack by these insects.

When looking for evidence of moth damage, the spots to check are those portions of the carpet which extend under radiators and under pieces of heavy furniture, which are not regularly moved for cleaning. The turned-under portion of wall-to-wall carpeting is also subject to attack by the webbing moth and carpet beetle.

Thorough and frequent cleaning with a vacuum cleaner and daily exposure to light and air are the best ways to prevent moth damage to carpets in use. Occasional cleaning of the back, when possible, is also advisable. Heavy furniture should be moved now and then, and the carpet under it thoroughly cleaned. As a further protection, carpet on stair risers and under radiators should be treated with a mothproofing or moth-repelling solvent spray.

When greater protection against moth damage is desired, the fabric may be treated with a mothproofing solution by a professional rug cleaner as a part of the commercial cleaning process. If rugs are to be stored, or if certain rooms are to be closed for a period of time, the carpet should be completely and thoroughly cleaned, face and back, with a vacuum cleaner. It may then be sprayed with a solvent-type mothproofing or moth-repellent solution. The carpet is then rolled immediately, wrapped in heavy brown paper, and the edges sealed with a heavy gummed tape. It is also desirable to clean the sources of moth infestation, such as the floor cracks and under the quarter round and base board. These places provide a fertile breeding place for moth larvae, especially when filled with lint and soil accumulations.

When purchasing new carpets, specify that the wool be "permanently mothproofed."

Spots and stains

Nothing detracts from the appearance quality of a carpet as much as spots or stains; almost every carpet is the victim of accidental spillage from time to time.

Knowledge of spot-removal techniques is of sufficient importance to warrant calling in experts to educate all personnel concerned with maintenance operations. Informative free literature on the subject is available from each major carpet manufacturer.

The suggestions given in this section are intended to illustrate problems encountered in actual use and the general types of materials for dealing with them. The reader is strongly urged to invest in commercial spot-removal kits rather than attempt to prepare his own solutions.

The two most effective ways to prevent permanent stains are to start spot-removal treatment as soon as possible and to use the correct spotting fluid. Experience, in most cases, has shown that prompt action—even though it is only blotting up spills or scraping off solids—can measurably reduce the intensity of the dry stain and simplify subsequent stain-removal efforts.

ServiceMaster Industries Inc.

Removing spots from carpet.

Commercial carpet can be subjected to a wide variety of stains, depending on the location in which the carpet is used. Carpet exposed to public traffic is most frequently marred by chewing gum, candy, grease spots, burns, and food or beverage stains. Unfortunately, such stains are not usually noticed until some time after they have occurred, making their removal difficult.

There are a number of general rules for spot removal: (1) Blot up spilled materials with absorbent paper, cloth, towelling, or a clean sponge. (2) Try to identify the stain. If this is not possible, treat as an "unknown" stain. (3) In treating the stain, begin at the outer edge and work towards the center of the stained area. Do not brush or rub the spot any more than is necessary. Excessive rubbing may result in a distortion worse than the stain. (4) Use only stain removers that have previously been checked for possible deleterious action on a sample of the carpet involved. (5) Do not rush the job. Some stains require considerable time and effort to remove. (6) Do not allow a wetted area to dry too slowly. Blot as much as possible and then leave a weighted pad of clean cloth or paper towels on the wet area to remove as much liquid as possible.

A variety of stain-remover chemicals are available. A simple two-solution kit is recommended by the American Carpet Institute as being safe for general use. One of these solutions can be prepared by adding one teaspoonful of a neutral synthetic detergent, such as those used on fine fabrics, to a quart of water. Then add one teaspoonful of white vinegar, a weak acid that will serve to neutralize any alkaline materials. The second solution should be a dry-cleaning fluid (solvent), similar to those used to remove spots from clothing.

The following procedures are suggested for dealing with known and unknown stains:

Oily materials

Oil, grease, hand cream, ballpoint pen ink

Remove excess materials; apply a dry-cleaning fluid; dry the carpet; repeat application of solvent if necessary; dry the carpet and brush pile gently.

Oily foodstuffs, animal matter

Coffee, blood, tea, butter, salad dressing, milk, ice cream, gravy, sauces, chocolate, egg

Remove excess materials, absorbing liquids and scraping semi-solids; apply detergent-vinegar-water solution; dry the carpet; apply dry-cleaning solvent, dry the carpet and brush pile gently.

Foodstuffs, starches, sugars, and special stains

Candy, soft drinks, alcoholic beverages, fruit, washable ink, urine, excrement

Blot up liquids or scrape off semi-solids; apply detergent-vinegar-water solution, dry the carpet. Re-apply solution if necessary; dry carpet and brush pile gently.

Heavy grease, sticky substances

Paint, lipstick, tar, crayon, chewing gum

Remove excess materials, apply a dry-cleaning fluid; apply detergent-vinegar-water solution; re-apply dry-cleaning fluid; dry carpet and brush pile gently.

For the removal of a wide variety of stains, four types of removers are recommended: absorbent materials, synthetic detergents, solvents, and chemical stain removers such as bleaches. A suggested list of such cleaning agents might include the following:

Synthetic detergent solution	Alcohol
7 percent ammonia solution	10 percent hydrofluoric acid
7 percent acetic acid solution	Rust remover
Paint-oil-grease remover	Amyl acetate
Paste-type paint remover	1 percent hydrogen peroxide bleach
Benzene	½ percent chlorine bleach

5 MASONRY FLOORS

Masonry floors are constructed of such materials as natural stone, brick, and ceramic tile. They also include poured masonry floors such as concrete and terrazzo. As a general rule, such floors are hard and durable. They offer a wide range of colors, patterns, textures, and designs. When properly installed, they are especially suitable for use in areas intended for heavy traffic. Many of these floors are especially resistant to staining and to deterioration by solvents, acids, and alkalies.

MARBLE

Description

Geologically, marble is a metamorphic, recrystallized *limestone* composed predominantly of crystalline grains of calcite or dolomite or both, having interlocking or mosaic structure. Commercially, all calcareous rocks capable of taking a high polish are called marble.

TABLE 17

GENERAL CLASSES OF MARBLE

Class of Marble	Comments
Calcite	Almost pure lime carbonate rocks.
Dolomite	Contains a high percentage of magnesium carbonate.
Serpentine	Silicate crystallized with carbonates.
Onyx	Formed from processes of solution and precipitation.
Travertine	A precipitate from hot springs characterized by irregular cavities and bonding.

Marble is found throughout the world and in nearly every state in the United States. However, in the United States large, active quarrying operations are limited to relatively few states, among them, Alabama, Arkansas, Georgia, Missouri, Tennessee, and Vermont. Marble as a building material varies in color, texture, soundness, finish and panel size.

Color. The colors, veining, clouds, mottlings, and shadings in marble are caused by extraneous substances introduced in minute quantities during

215

formation of the stone. Iron oxides make the pinks, yellows, browns, and reds. Greys, blue-greys, and blacks result from bituminous deposits. The greens are caused by mica, chlorite, and silicate.

It is necessary to see a complete showroom collection to appreciate the full color range of marble; a great variety of colors, tints, and hues are available. Some of the general color classes are black, blue-grey, buff-brown-yellowish, greyish-pink, green, pink, reddish-brown, white, white-bluish, white-brownish, and white-creamy. Within these classes are an elaborate assortment of sub-hues with exotic names such as Carthage Ozark Rouge, White Georgia Golden Vein, Southwest Pedrara Mexican Onyx, Appalachian Havlin Grey Pink, Granox Veined Champion Pink, and so on.

Texture. The term "texture," as applied to marble, means size of grain, degree of uniformity, and arrangement of constituent minerals. Grains of calcite, the chief constituent of most marbles, are crystalline and have definite cleavage which show bright reflecting faces on a broken

Carthage Marble Corporation

Floor made with large tiles of
Fior di Pesco Carnico marble from Italy.

Carthage Marble Corporation

Parquet floor tile of walnut travertine marble.

surface. In most marbles, the cleavages appear about equally prominent in every direction. In some marbles, however, the grains are elongated. The size of the grain is usually labeled as fine, medium, or large.

Soundness. Marbles are classed by the producers into four groups: A, B, C, or D. The groups are defined by the Marble Institute of America in its *Marble Engineering Handbook* as follows:

Group A—"Sound marbles and stones with uniform and favorable working qualities."

Group B—"Marbles and stones similar in character to those in Group A, but with somewhat less favorable working qualities. They may have occasional natural faults. A limited amount of waxing and sticking may be necessary." (Waxing, sticking, and filling are methods used in the marble trade to repair and improve the appearance of marbles containing natural flaws, voids, veins, etc. Materials such as wax, shellac, coloring, and marble dust are used for this purpose.)

Group C—"Marbles and stones of uncertain variation in working qualities. Geological flaws, voids, veins, and lines of separation are common. Standard shop practice is to repair these natural variations by sticking, waxing, and filling. These techniques have recently been greatly improved by the use of new adhesives. Rodding, liners, and other forms of reinforcement may be freely employed when necessary." (Rodding is a method of reinforcing a slab of marble by cementing stainless steel or aluminum rods to the back of the slab. A liner is a thin slab of marble that is cemented to the back of the original slab in order to reinforce it.)

Group D—"Marbles and stones similar to Group C, subject to the same methods of finishing and manufacture, but with a larger proportion of natural faults. These have also a maximum variation in working qualities. This group comprises many of the highly colored marbles prized for their decorative qualities."

Marbles used for monumental, structural, or veneer purposes and which are to be exposed to the weather are generally selected from Group A. Marbles in Groups B, C, and D are usually selected for their color and decorative effects. Occasionally, carefully selected marbles from these groups are used on surfaces exposed to the weather.

Finish. Although marble may be obtained in a variety of surface finishes, the three most frequently used are the polished finish, the honed finish, and the sand and/or abrasive finish. Marble with either a honed finish (a velvety smooth surface with little or no gloss), or a sand and/or abrasive finish (a flat non-reflective surface) is recommended for floor installations. The mirror-like glossy surface of polished marble is used almost exclusively for interior wall surfaces and is not generally recommended for floors. In the selection of a floor marble, special attention should be paid to the ability of the marble to withstand severe wear, i.e., its hardness and abrasion resistance.

Panel size. Panels of extreme size (over 7½ feet by 5 feet for the A group and 5 feet by 4 feet for the B, C, and D Groups) usually command a premium price and do not always show marble at its best. Smaller panels facilitate matching and color blending and offer a wider selection at more attractive prices. The choice, for lower price and greater availability of material, should be made from standard thicknesses. When plans and specifications call for exterior marble in thicknesses greater than two inches, this usually means that stone masons and not marble setters will claim the work. Marble setters are responsible for all interior marble and for exterior marble and veneer 2 inches thick and less.

Installation

Marble should be handled only by marble contractors or under the direct supervision of the marble sub-contractor. Chipped and spalled corners and edges and scratches and stains on exposed surfaces are much easier to prevent than to repair. Marble should be stored on a resilient, non-staining material, such as fiberboard, and with a waterproof covering, if outdoors. Slabs should always be stacked on edge rather than laid flat, and supported by "A" frames or braced, rather than leaned against a wall.

Once installed, marble should be protected from the work being performed by other finishing trades. Lime in plaster, for instance, can leave tell-tale traces on marble surfaces. Paint spatters can be difficult to remove, especially the oil-base types. Marble floors, though tough and durable, deserve the protection of corrugated cardboard or other covering until

Carthage Marble Corporation

Installation of marble flooring.

after construction debris has been removed from the building. Good marble sub-contractors always observe these precautions and should be permitted to protect their work according to their prior experience and judgment.

Water repellents are generally considered unnecessary on the exposed surface of marble. Most marbles have a vapor transmission of less than 1.25 grains per square foot and qualify as vapor barriers. Rates of absorption are less than two-tenths of 1 percent by weight after a 48-hour soak for the majority of marble types. Where marble is in constant contact with moisture, non-staining, waterproofing, or damp-proofing materials are recommended on the back of slabs.

Sealants of the synthetic rubber variety are quite satisfactory, when formulated for natural stone and used with suitable primers. Pink staining, a problem in the early use of polysulfide sealants placed in direct contact with masonry mortar, can now be prevented. Portland cement, waterproof white portland cement, and gypsum molding plaster all meet requirements for mortars and jointing materials for marble work.

Maintenance

Few, if any, flooring materials can surpass marble for beauty and permanence. Because of its durability, marble is too often considered a material which needs no care at all. However, as with all flooring materials, maintenance is needed, although comparatively little effort is required. While neglect will detract from the beauty of marble, it will not seriously impair its serviceability. Proper maintenance of marble is largely a problem of avoiding harmful cleaning agents and procedures. If maintained properly and systematically, marble floors, including stair treads and landings, should not require any drastic cleaning action or strong cleaning solutions.

Acids should never be used to clean marble; they react chemically with the marble and will etch the surface. This condition makes the surface even more susceptible to damage in the future. Alkaline salts, such as sodium carbonate, sodium bicarbonate, and trisodium phosphate, may injure marble, if used frequently. After being absorbed into the pores of the marble, these materials crystallize into large particles and eventually their accumulation disintegrates the surface of the marble. Soaps should not be used for cleaning marble. Soaps will cause gummy precipitates which will be difficult to remove, and their residues may cause the floor to be slippery. Use of ammonia water is not recommended, as it may cause surface yellowing.

For routine maintenance of marble, a mildly alkaline cleaning compound is recommended. It should contain no abrasives, acids, or alkaline salts capable of harming marble or its jointing materials. It should not discolor, etch, or react with any marble. The compound should be free-rinsing, even in hard water, and not leave any residue capable of contributing to soil retention. Generally, neutral synthetic detergents are considered safest for washing marble.

For removing soils that are not affected by washing, a mildly abrasive, inert scouring compound is recommended. Its use is not intended for routine daily maintenance or for normal use on polished marble. The compound should be free-rinsing, even in hard water, and not leave any residue harmful to the marble surface. Coarse abrasives should not be used at any time.

Marble floors must be cleaned regularly in a manner that will not leave a slippery film. A marble floor should always be wet first with clear, clean, warm water before washing with the cleaning solution. Pre-wetting helps prevent absorption into the marble of salts in the cleaning solution and makes rinsing easier. Scrubbing or mopping can be done either by hand or by machine. After cleaning, the solution should be wet-vacuumed or mopped up. The floor should then be rinsed thoroughly with clean water and wiped with a well-wrung mop or squeegeed free of water. Care should be taken to keep metal parts of the mop or machine from injuring marble surfaces.

Between washings, routine maintenance should consist of vacuuming or sweeping. Sweeping compounds containing oil, sand, or abrasives and oily dust mops should not be used. Dampened white pine sawdust is satisfactory as a sweeping compound.

Polishes are not recommended, and special trade preparations should not be necessary, but a colorless sealer will bring out color and offer extra protection. The sealer should be applied with a soft applicator using just enough to seal all the pores of the surface. Care in obtaining a non-yellowing sealer is essential.

Stain removal

Specific stains of almost all types, which are unaffected by the above washing operations, can usually be removed from marble if the proper treatment is used. If surface discolorations remain after treatment, the floor marble may be rehoned, resanded, or regritted.

The poultice method of cleaning marble is especially applicable to long-neglected or stained marble surfaces. Powdered cleaning compound is mixed with hot water, or a liquid compound is mixed with whiting, to form a paste. The marble is pre-wetted and the paste applied to a depth of about one-half inch. The paste is kept moist for 48 hours and then removed. One application will usually result in a clean marble surface. However, deeply embedded stains or dirt may require repeated applications.

Before using any of the specific stain removal treatments described below, wet thoroughly around the stain area with clear water to keep the stain from spreading during the removal treatment and to prevent a stain ring.

Organic stains: Organic matter, e.g., wood, leaves, flowers, paper, may cause pinkish brown stains on light-colored marble when moisture is present. If out of doors, the normal action of the sun and rain will clear up the trouble and no remedial treatment is necessary in the majority of cases. Indoors, or if the action must be hastened, hydrogen peroxide applied either as a wash, in a poultice made with whiting, or with white blotting paper, will be found effective. If hydrogen peroxide is used as a poultice, add household ammonia to start the action.

Tobacco stains can usually be removed by using the techniques mentioned under "Organic stains."

Urinal stains can be guarded against by scattering an abrasive compound around the urinal or toilet and leaving it overnight. If there is a stain due to neglect, the poultice method should be used, adding a bleaching agent such as hydrogen peroxide.

Iodine stains will disappear in time without treatment. However, they may be removed quickly by applying a poultice of alcohol and whiting.

Metallic stains: Stains from iron and steel have the appearance of rust. A fresh stain may be so superficial on a smooth finish that it can be removed by vigorous rubbing. Light scrubbing or rubbing with an abrasive should smooth over any roughening of the floor surface. If this treatment fails, it will be necessary to convert the insoluble rust to a soluble colorless compound. Application of sodium hydrosulfite should be made to the stain, then dampened and left in place not more than a half hour. Immediately following, a solution of sodium citrate should be applied. This treatment may be repeated if necessary. Some etching of polished surfaces may result but this can be corrected by re-polishing.

Copper and bronze stains are usually greenish or muddy brown in color. To remove them, a dry mixture of one part of ammonium chloride (sal ammoniac) and four parts of whiting or powdered talc is added to ammonia water and stirred until a thick paste is obtained. This poultice is placed over an area larger than the actual stain, to prevent spread of the stain, and left until dry. It is removed with a wooden paddle and rinsed thoroughly. The process may be repeated if necessary.

Lead stains are bright yellow or orange. When the source of the stain is removed, the stain will disappear through atmospheric action.

Ink stains may be removed by first removing all surface ink and then covering the ink spot with a blotter soaked with alcohol, followed by another blotter soaked in ammonia. As a final step, the remaining color can be removed with bleaching powders. Some inks are metallic in nature and may be removed by reducing agents, as suggested under "Metallic stains."

Oil, grease, fats, etc.: Oil and grease stains are usually light brown or yellow in color. They can usually be removed by the proper use of a solvent, such as acetone and amyl acetate in equal parts. A saturated clean cloth, white blotting paper, or poultice with whiting and solvent should be applied over a larger area than the stain and left until dry. The area should be rinsed thoroughly and the treatment repeated if necessary.

Paint should be removed from marble as soon as possible, using a razor blade or knife edge.

There are two methods of removing paint stains:

(1) Apply benzol in a ½-inch-thick whiting poultice to an area larger than the stain; remove poultice when dry, and bleach remaining color. Rinse and repeat as required.

(2) Apply varnish paint remover, either liquid or paste, over stained area; scrub with a fiber brush and bleach remaining color. An oil solvent can be used to remove any remaining oil stain.

Perspiration stains should disappear with the use of oil solvent followed, if necessary, with a bleach.

Linseed oil stains that have become oxidized will be difficult to remove. Oil solvent followed by a bleach, if necessary, may be used.

Refinishing

Occasionally it may be necessary to restore the finish to small areas of a marble floor. The basic method is to use abrasive bricks or coated abrasive papers in successively finer and finer grades until the finish (hone) is restored to its original smoothness.

Where a marble floor surface is rough, begin refinishing with a No. 80 abrasive followed in succession by Nos. 120, 220, 320, and 600. In place of the last, pumice stone can be used. Abrasive bricks or coated abrasive papers are available from most marble finishing plants and many hardware stores.

When a smooth surface has been achieved, sprinkle a polishing powder, such as tin oxide, on the area and rub briskly for several minutes with a damp cloth, continuing until polish appears.

When large areas of marble require refinishing, it is best to seek the advice of an experienced marble contractor.

TERRAZZO

Description

Terrazzo had its origin before the sixteenth century with the Venetians who developed the art of laying terrazzo from the Romans' use of marble mosaic floors. The use of terrazzo has continued through the years and it is found in thousands of buildings where traffic is extremely heavy.

Good terrazzo has a smooth surface that is a mixture of 70 percent or more coarse aggregate and 30 percent or less portland cement matrix. The aggregate is waste marble or granite chips. The chips are usually run through a crusher and then over screens which sort the chips by size. The chips are graded by number from 0 to 8 depending upon their size. For example, #0 chips range from 1/16 to ⅛ inch; #8 range from 1 to 1⅛ inches. Care is taken that only a certain color of chip is run through at one time, so that a desired color or color combination may be selected later. Many colors and designs can be incorporated into a completed terrazzo floor. Often, colored pigments are added to the matrix to produce special patterns and effects.

Terrazzo combines the durability of marble with the strength and economy of concrete. Properly laid, it is a durable installation and only simple care is needed to preserve its attractive appearance and natural sheen. Ease of maintenance is one of the principal reasons why terrazzo is found in so many buildings where traffic is heavy.

Terrazzo is recommended for almost all floor areas, both exterior and interior, except for those subjected to acids or strongly alkaline concentrations. Reinforced, precast terrazzo units with abrasive inserts are widely used as treads and steps.

Precast terrazzo tiles are available for installation on all grade levels and over any sound subfloor construction. Typical sizes are 8, 12, and 16 inches square.

Portland Cement Association

Terrazzo floor and stairway.

Installation

The mixture of chips and cement matrix is applied to a base of concrete. Metal strips are almost always used in terrazzo installations to divide the surface into sections. This is done to control cracking and to achieve designs specified by the architect. Then the surface is ground down and polished to a very smooth finish.

Sand cushion (floating) terrazzo is used where structural movement is anticipated from settling, expansion, contraction, or vibration, which may cause injury to the terrazzo topping. This method requires that the over-all thickness of the underbed and topping be at least 3 inches. The concrete slab is covered with a thin bed of dry sand, over which is laid a waterproof membrane and reinforcing wire mesh. The terrazzo underbed is installed to ⅝ inch below the finished floor line; divider strips are put in place and then the terrazzo topping is poured.

Bonded-to-concrete terrazzo is used in all general areas—corridors, lobbies, rooms, sidewalks, etc. The minimum over-all thickness most common is 1¾ inches. However, when additional reinforcing is desired, 2 or 2½ inches should be designated. The terrazzo contractor thoroughly cleans and soaks the base slab with water; then slushes it with dry portland cement to ensure a good bond. The underbed is then installed, followed by the placing of the divider strips and terrazzo topping.

Monolithic terrazzo is installed ⅝ inch thick and is bonded to or made integral with the prepared slab. Monolithic terrazzo is an economical type of terrazzo and should not be confused with the "sand cushion" or "bonded-to-concrete" methods mentioned above.

Thin terrazzo toppings, ⅜ inch or more thick, can be installed directly on a concrete slab by using an adhesive, e.g., polysulfide liquid polymer, as a bonding agent. This technique makes it possible to install poured-in-place terrazzo directly onto a concrete subfloor. It does not require an intermediate scratch coat or underbedding.

Terrazzo-over-wood floors is possible provided that the wood floor (new or old) is rigid, sound, and tight. After cleaning the structural floor, a waterproof membrane is laid (i.e., 15-pound roofing felt) and reinforcing wire mesh applied. The underbed, consisting of cement and sand, is spread to a minimum thickness of 2 inches over which a ⅝-inch terrazzo topping is applied.

There are several types of terrazzo toppings—standard, Venetian, rustic, Berliner, conductive, and abrasive. A brief description of each follows:

Standard: Minimum thickness (finished) of ⅝ inch; composed of marble chip sizes #1, #2, and sometimes #3.

Venetian: Minimum thickness of 1 inch; composed of marble chip sizes #1 through #8 (as desired); uses minimum 1½-inch deep divider strips.

Rustic (washed terrazzo): Any terrazzo topping that, after the rolling operation, is broom-finished or hosed with water, and, after curing, is treated with a solution of muriatic acid to etch the surface. The surface may or may not be ground.

Berliner (Palladiana): Minimum thickness of 1 inch; composed of broken marble in various sizes from 4 to 140 inches; a "standard terrazzo" joint, varying in width from ½ inch to 5 inches, is used.

Conductive (electrical): Same type as "standard," except that acetylene black is added to the topping and underbed in strict accordance with specifications for conductive terrazzo that meet National Fire Protection Association requirements.

Abrasive: Standard or Venetian terrazzo; used in areas where a smooth, yet highly slip-resistance surface is desired; incorporates abrasive aggregates sprinkled on the surface of the topping or distributed throughout the terrazzo mix. (Large proportions of abrasive aggregate added throughout the terrazzo topping will increase cost and should be specified only in extremely heavily trafficked and hazardous areas.)

The purpose of divider strips in a terrazzo installation is twofold. They control and localize setting shrinkage as well as flexure cracks, when these occur. They also permit the laying of different color mixtures in various patterns with ease and accuracy. The gauge and thickness of the divider does not affect the divider's purpose.

Fractures in terrazzo are caused by structural movement, expansion, contraction, or vibration. Correctly located dividers will eliminate fracturing. Crazing, i.e., cracks from shrinkage, does not occur in properly laid terrazzo. The shrinkage of terrazzo is largely governed by the installation technique and by the rate of evaporation of moisture from the surface. Thorough and sufficient rolling is necessary to minimize shrinkage and prevent crazing. Proper curing methods will control evaporation.

Dividers are made in a variety of sizes. Exposed face thicknesses range from a recommended minimum of 0.0403 inches (18 gauge) to heavy bars. Dividers of ⅛-inch face and wider are usually thick at the top and thin at the bottom. A 1¼-inch depth divider is recommended for the usual floor thickness. Divider strips at least 1½ inches deep are recommended for Venetian terrazzo floors.

Shallow strips are available for special shallow floors, borders, wainscots, etc. The standard length of dividers is 6 feet. Special lengths can be factory cut.

The most commonly used materials for dividers are half-hard brass, white alloy zinc (99 percent zinc), and plastic in various colors.

The anchorage features incorporated in the divider secure it to the terrazzo floor and create a line of cleavage in the terrazzo surface. A continuous lower edge cutting the sub-bed is a needed feature.

For long corridors and large areas, a special expansion strip is recommended to localize shrinkage cracks. It should be located not over 30 feet on center in long corridors and preferably should be placed over steel beams. This strip is a lamination of 1¼-inch by 14-gauge white alloy zinc, or 1¾-inch by 16-gauge brass, to both sides of 1¼-inch by ⅛-inch black neoprene. For monolithic terrazzo, a similar type of laminated expansion strip is recommended. This should be constructed of 16-gauge white alloy zinc angle, or 18-gauge brass angle with the proper depth to match the terrazzo and laminated to ⅛-inch black neoprene.

The portland cement used in the preparation of the terrazzo matrix is a product obtained by pulverizing clinker consisting essentially of hydraulic calcium silicates, to which no additions have been made subsequent to calcination other than water and/or untreated calcium sulfate. Special additives are sold for mixing with portland cement, which are claimed to improve its wetting, penetrating, and adhesive characteristics.

Liquid membrane-forming compounds are frequently used to prolong the curing period of the cement, thus increasing strength. They also protect the new floor from damage during construction.

Maintenance

New terrazzo often has a dull, grey appearance caused by efflorescence, i.e., the surfacing of mineral salts that are a by-product of the curing of the cement matrix. This chemical action continues at a decelerating rate over a period of months, unless the pores of the terrazzo are sealed. Efflorescence, also called "bloom," is a normal condition, and the deposit is removable by regular maintenance procedures.

New terrazzo should be scrubbed several times a week, and mopped on remaining days. The cleaning compounds used must be free from alkalies, acids, or other strong ingredients which can very easily do permanent damage to the floor. The floor must be carefully rinsed. All cleaning solution and rinse water must be picked up to prevent slipperiness. A wet-dry vacuum cleaner will do this job thoroughly and quickly. After a few months of maintenance in this manner, the new terrazzo will develop a beautiful, natural sheen.

A point sometimes overlooked in maintenance is that when dirty rinse water and cleaning solutions dry on terrazzo, they form a film that dulls the appearance and natural color. Cleaning solutions should be picked up completely, by squeegee, mop, or wet-dry vacuum, leaving no chance for film build-up. Rinsing should be as thorough as possible to minimize soil redeposition.

The cleaning solution selected must be neutral and free from harmful alkali or acid that may ruin the floor. The National Terrazzo & Mosaic Association specifically warns that soaps and scrubbing powders containing water soluble, inorganic salts, or crystallizing salts should never be used in the maintenance of terrazzo. Alkaline solutions will sink into the pores and, as they dry, they will expand and break the cells of the marble chips and matrix, causing spalling.

Place the solution on the floor with a wet mop, allowing several minutes for the grime-dissolving action to take place. Then squeegee, wet-vacuum, or mop up the dirt-laden solution. It is important that the floor be kept wet at all times during the cleaning operation to prevent dissolved soil from drying on the floor. Thorough rinsing is required, if a powdered compound is used. Also, if the solution is mopped up, it is important to change water frequently to ensure complete removal of soil and cleaning compound and to eliminate "moplines."

Since the surface of terrazzo is largely marble, which has a very low porosity, the flooring has very little absorption. The consistency of most staining materials is such as to make them too thick to be absorbed. Maintenance attention, therefore, should be directed to the cement matrix, which is porous and will absorb foreign matter that creates stains. Floor polishes will protect the surface but are not recommended for terrazzo, because they are easily "walked off" and might make the smooth surface slippery. Also, they do not allow the floor to take the natural sheen so long identified with terrazzo. Soft surface films only add to the maintenance budget, forcing the custodian to strip the floor to remove dirt embedded in the polish. To eliminate the problem of soil absorption by the cement matrix, a penetrating sealer should be used.

Following the original cleaning, the floor should be allowed to dry and then be sealed as soon as possible. A colorless, non-yellowing sealer should be used which will penetrate into the cement, sealing off its pores. Lacquer, shellac, or varnish should never be used. Proper protection of terrazzo is then accomplished internally, rather than on the surface, and only periodic resealing is necessary.

The cleaning cycle should be regulated by the amount of traffic. For general cleaning, a neutral cleaning compound diluted in accordance with the manufacturer's directions should be used. For extremely dirty areas, the amount of compound should be increased.

If a mop dressing is used for daily sweeping, it should be non-oily. Sweeping compounds containing oil will penetrate and permanently discolor terrazzo. Those compounds containing sand are difficult to sweep up and may abrade the surface if left on the floor. Wax-treated dust mops and wax-treated sweeping compounds may be used for this purpose.

Electric- or battery-powered scrubbing machines should be used periodically with a solution of neutral compound to loosen dirt that is difficult to remove during normal daily mop-cleaning. Steel wool should not be used on terrazzo, since steel-wool particles left on the floor may rust and cause stains. Floor machines should be equipped with fiber brushes, or with abrasive nylon pads. For badly soiled terrazzo, an open-mesh abrasive fabric may be used. Buffing the floor with a powered machine after each cleaning restores the luster to the surface, building a natural sheen.

Special care should be observed in the cleaning of conductive terrazzo floors. They must be kept completely free from deposits left by cleaning-solution residues that create an insulating film and destroy conductivity. A number of companies manufacture special liquid synthetic detergents. These compounds have a fine cleaning action, sufficient to remove dirt easily, leaving no scum. Special rinsing is not required other than to remove the loosened dirt, and, most important, residues which may alter the conductivity of the floor. Some companies manufacture products that also contain a deodorizer and sanitizer, which not only clean the floor but also control bacteria.

Terrazzo floors containing abrasive aggregates should never be sealed. They should be scrubbed regularly to keep them free of build-up of dirt and other foreign matter.

The cleaning program for terrazzo may be summarized as follows: (1) Daily sweeping with a cotton-wick floor brush, treated with a non-oily dressing, will control dust and make maintenance easier; (2) Regular damp-mopping keeps the surface free from dirt accumulations; (3) Machine buffing on a regular basis removes traffic marks and restores luster; (4) Touching up with sealer in traffic areas as needed protects the surface; (5) Periodic machine scrubbing removes heavy accumulations of dirt.

Stain removal

Ink stains: Different inks require different treatments. Ordinary writing inks may etch concrete because of acid content. To remove a stain of this type, one should make a strong solution of sodium perborate in hot water. This solution is mixed with whiting to a thick paste, applied in a ¼-inch layer, and left until dry. If some of the color is visible after the poultice is removed, the process should be repeated. Sodium perborate can be obtained from any druggist.

Many red, green, violet, and other bright-colored inks are water solutions of synthetic dyes. Stains made by this type of ink can usually be removed by the sodium perborate poultice described immediately above. Often, the stain can be removed by applying ammonia water on cotton batting. Javelle water (calcium or sodium hypochlorite) is also effective, when used in the same manner as ammonia water, or mixed as a paste with whiting and applied as a poultice. A mixture of equal parts of chlorinated lime and whiting reduced to a paste with water may also be used as a poulticing material.

Some blue inks contain Prussian blue, a ferrocyanide of iron, and cause stains that cannot be removed by the perborate poultice, Javelle water, or chlorinated lime poultice. Such stains yield to treatment of ammonia water applied with a layer of cotton batting. A strong soap solution applied in the same way may also be effective.

Indelible ink stains often consist entirely of synthetic dyes and may be treated as outlined above. Some indelible inks contain silver salts that cause a black stain, which may be removed with ammonia water applied by cotton gauze. Usually several applications are necessary.

Lubricating oil stains: Lubricating oil penetrates some concrete readily. It should be mopped off immediately, covering the spot with fuller's earth or dry powdered material, such as hydrated lime, whiting, or dry portland cement. If treated quickly, the stain will not persist, but removal of an old stain will require the following treatment. White flannel is saturated with a mixture of equal parts of acetone and amyl acetate and placed over the stain. The flannel is then covered with a slab of concrete or pane of glass. If the stain is on a vertical surface, means should be improvised to hold the cloth and its covering in place. The cloth is kept saturated until the stain is removed. If the solvent tends to spread the stain, a larger cloth should be used. Scrubbing with gasoline or benzine will often remove oil stains.

Tobacco stains: The following formula is generally effective. Two pounds of trisodium phosphate crystals, available from hardware and drug stores and chemical and laundry supply houses, are dissolved in one gallon of hot water. Twelve ounces of chlorinated lime are mixed to a paste in a shallow enameled pan by adding water slowly and mashing the lumps. This and the trisodium phosphate solution are poured into a two-gallon stoneware jar and water added to fill the jar. The mixture is stirred well, the jar covered, and the lime allowed to settle. For use, enough liquid is added to powdered talc to obtain a thick paste. This is applied with a trowel as a ¼-inch poultice. When applied with a brush, about one teaspoon of sugar is added to each pound of powdered talc.

When dry, the poultice is scraped off with a wooden paddle or trowel. The mixture is a strong bleaching agent and is corrosive to metals. Care should be taken not to drop it on colored fabrics or metal fixtures.

The method just described is useful in the treatment of other stains of unknown origin. If the stain is not bad, grit scrubbing powders, commonly used on marble, terrazzo, and tile floors, are often satisfactory as a poulticing material. The powder is stirred into hot water until mortar consistency is obtained. Then it is mixed thoroughly, applied to stained surface in a ½-inch layer, and left until dry. In most cases, two or more applications will be necessary.

Coffee stains: Coffee stains can be removed by applying a cloth saturated in glycerine diluted with four times its volume of water. Javelle water and the solutions used on blue ink stains containing Prussian blue are also effective.

Iodine stains: An iodine stain will gradually disappear without treatment. It may be removed quickly by applying alcohol and covering with whiting or talcum powder. If the stain occurs on a vertical surface, talcum should be mixed with alcohol to form a paste; then alcohol is applied to the stain, and it is covered with the paste.

Caution: These treatments should be used by trained and experienced personnel. Improper use may result in bleaching the terrazzo matrix, if a color dye was added at the time of installation.

Special problems

The correction of structural problems with terrazzo should be undertaken only on the advice of an expert; the actual repair work should be done by a terrazzo contractor.

Settling: The most common damage to terrazzo is cracking, due to settling of the underbed. There is no general remedy that can be suggested when cracks appear. However, under some conditions, which must be established by an expert, it is possible hydraulically to force an adhesive under the topping to fill in the underbed and raise the topping.

Cracks: These can be caulked with fresh portland cement or one of the special caulking compounds formulated for this application. In many cases, crack repair is a sanitary measure, since the caulked crack may be more conspicuous than the crack itself.

Holes: Holes in terrazzo can be repaired with fairly good results using a mix of matrix and 70 percent marble chips of matching colors.

Acid-damaged terrazzo: This can sometimes be restored to its original appearance by re-grinding the surface after the acid has been washed out of the topping. The area should be wetted and rubbed with No. 24 grit abrasive stones followed by No. 80 grit stones. The surface should be kept wet during the entire operation to keep dust down and to help lubricate the abrasive action. The grindings are squeegeed off and, if the floor is still rough, the operation is repeated. A larger area than the damaged spot should be treated in this way to feather out the grinding at the edges of the spot and avoid a noticeable depression.

Dusting terrazzo: This condition may be caused by improper installation or a worn surface seal. The area should be cleaned free of dust and fresh terrazzo sealer applied.

Yellowed terrazzo: This discoloration could occur for a number of reasons: (1) Use of an unsuitable sealer. In this case, the surface should be stripped or ground with abrasive pads and a water-white terrazzo sealer applied. (2) Build-up of soap films. Remove by machine scrubbing with synthetic detergent and an abrasive pad. (3) Build-up of polish. Scrub with stripping solution and abrasive pad; rinse thoroughly. Apply light-colored polish. Strip and refinish at regular intervals.

CERAMIC TILE

Description

Ceramic tile is made from clay or a mixture of clay and other organic materials that are fired in kilns at temperatures above red heat. In the manufacturing process, the clays are either compressed in steel dies or are extruded and cut to length by precision controlled wires. Most ceramic tile is available with either a glazed or unglazed surface although the unglazed variety is used more widely for floors; either type has a very hard, non-porous surface. Because ceramic tile can withstand freezing temperatures, it can be installed outdoors as well as indoors. Three varieties are widely used for floors: ceramic mosaic tile, quarry tile, and pavers.

Ceramic mosaic tile is manufactured in small sizes, various shapes and a wide variety of patterns. Unglazed ceramic mosaic tile comes in a wide range of earthy colors, while the glazed type is available in an even greater number of colors. Ceramic mosaic tile is very popular as a floor covering because of its durability, practically unlimited design possibilities, and the ease with which it can be maintained.

Quarry tile and pavers are made in larger sizes than ceramic mosaic tile. The most popular size, 6 by 6 inches square, ranges in thickness from ¾ inch to 1½ inches. Quarry tile and pavers give excellent service in the presence of oil, grease, and moisture. They come in a variety of colors and because the surface is slightly irregular, they have good slip resistance.

Installation

Ceramic tile can be successfully used on all grade levels and on almost any sound, rigid, clean surface.

Tile Council of America, Inc.

Ceramic mosaic tile in unusual pattern.

The conventional mortar installation is recommended for all heavy-duty-traffic floors and areas subject to wet conditions. It consists of a scratch coat of cement mortar, a setting bed of cement mortar, and a bond coat. This method usually requires that the ceramic tile be soaked in water prior to being set.

The more modern technique, called the "thin-bed method," makes use of mortars or adhesives that will bond or adhere dry ceramic tile to dry substrates. The technique requires no soaking of the ceramic tile—an important time-saving factor. The mortars and adhesives used in this method may be organic or inorganic, and the selection of the specific bonding agents will depend upon the environmental conditions to which the floor is subjected and to the composition of the subfloor. The most widely used types of thin-bed bonding materials are: dry-set mortar, organic adhesives, cement with latex additives, and epoxy mortar.

Dry-set mortars consist essentially of portland cement and relatively small amounts of additives that impart a high viscosity to the mortar mix. This viscosity retards the absorption of the water in the mix by porous substrates and dry ceramic tile. As a consequence, the water remains in the mortar to react chemically with the cement and to cause the mortar to harden. While dry-set mortar is relatively water retentive, it actually loses water at a very slow, controlled rate. It is this controlled loss of the water that makes possible the proper curing of the tile-setting bed.

Dry-set mortar is usually suitable for use over a variety of substrates including concrete block, brick, poured concrete, ceramic tile, and marble.

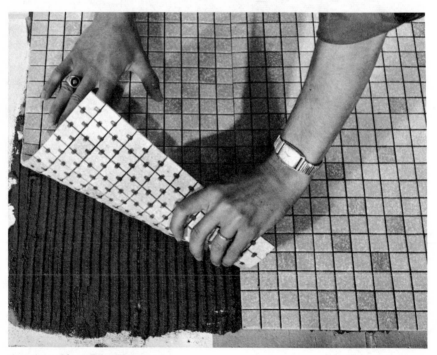

American Olean Tile Company

Installing back-mounted ceramic mosaic tile.

It is applied in one layer which may be as thin as 3/32 inch and provides bond strength up to 500 pounds per square inch. Dry-set mortar has excellent water and impact resistance, may be cleaned with water, is nonflammable, and is suitable for outside installations.

Organic adhesives are either solvent-base rubbers or resins that depend upon evaporation of the solvent to develop adequate adhesion. The rate of solvent evaporation must be slow enough to provide open time for setting the ceramic tile, yet rapid enough to permit the adhesive to gain strength within a reasonable time after the tile has been set. Because thick layers of the adhesive will be very slow to harden, it is important that the adhesive be applied in a uniformly thin layer. A notched trowel should be used.

The volume of an organic adhesive decreases about 30 percent as the solvent evaporates. This characteristic makes it essential that grouting of the tile (filling in the joints with a thin mortar) be delayed until practically all of the solvent has escaped and the volume of the adhesive has stabilized. Grout applied prematurely will crack as the adhesive dries and contracts.

Organic adhesives can be used over a wide variety of floor surfaces. Priming is recommended for porous surfaces to prevent extraction of essential plasticizers and oils from the adhesive, causing the adhesive to become brittle and to lose strength. Nonporous substrates do not need priming. Bond strengths vary greatly among the numerous brands available. Tests by the Tile Council of America, Inc. indicate that rubber solvent types develop bond strengths averaging 120 pounds per square inch.

A note of caution should be introduced here: Organic adhesives have low impact resistance, and ceramic tile installed with this bonding material is likely to crack under sharp impact, for example, that caused by women's stiletto heels. Consequently, organic adhesives are not recommended for use in public areas subject to heavy traffic.

Thin-bed bonding materials composed of cement with latex additives are commonly a mixture of portland cement with up to 10 percent additive of certain polymeric latices. This mix must be prepared on the job in exact ratio. It is applied to the substrate in one thin layer and may be used over a wide variety of surfaces. Bond strengths will vary from 80 to 200 pounds per square inch, depending on composition. No flammable or toxic solvents are required for clean-up. This type of thin-bed bonding material can also be a mixture of high-alumina or lumite cement with neoprene latex, yielding bond strengths above 450 pounds per square inch. This mix is especially recommended for ceramic tile installations over steel-plate substrates.

Epoxy mortar is another important advance in the field of thin-bed bonding materials. It is a two-part mortar system employing epoxy resin and hardener that was developed for installations where portland cement-

Tile Council of America, Inc.

Installing quarry tile in dry-set mortar.

based grouts were too porous and susceptible to corrosion for the intended use. Epoxy mortar, being acid- and alkali-resistant when set, is especially recommended whenever a stainproof, chemically resistant tile joint is desirable.

Suitable subfloors for epoxy mortar are concrete, wood (including plywood), steel plate, and ceramic tile. The mix can be applied in one thin layer to wet or dry surfaces and form bonds with strengths greater than 1,000 pounds per square inch.

Unlike conventional epoxy systems, excess material can be cleaned from the tile face with water. Tools and pails used during installation can also be cleaned with water. When used at a room temperature of 70° to 75° F., the pot life (i.e., working time) of the mixed epoxy is about 90 minutes from the time it is mixed. However, it will be 3 or 4 hours before the material becomes too stiff for touching up and finishing the tile joints.

The Tile Council of America, Inc., organized in 1945, consists of tile industry companies which jointly sponsor research studies to improve tiles and tile installation techniques. The Tile Council Licensing Program, whereby products are licensed to manufacturers for production and distribution, assures tile contractors that the products bearing the Tile Council seal meet established specifications. The Tile Council has also contributed to the promulgation of nationally recognized specifications for tilework.

Maintenance

Proper maintenance of ceramic tile begins with the tile setter. It is his responsibility to remove excess mortar and to free the tile surface of grout. Once properly installed, ceramic tile is quite easy to care for.

In cleaning ceramic tile, it is important to remember that there are two different surfaces, the tile and the grout. Cement grout is considerably more porous than ceramic tile and more susceptible to the accumulation of dirt and stains. Epoxy mortar grout is not so prone to soiling and staining. Because ceramic tile is usually set with cement mortar and grout, the same general precautions suggested in the maintenance of terrazzo should be followed in maintaining ceramic tile. Oily sweeping compounds, alkaline cleaning compounds, sealers, polishes, and nonslip coatings are not recommended. On tile set with acid- and alkali-resistant mortar, stronger cleaning compounds can be used.

Dry cleaning of a ceramic tile floor can be done by sweeping with a brush or dust mop or by vacuuming. Minor soils can be removed by going over the area with a mop moistened with water. When soiling becomes excessive, a general-purpose, synthetic detergent mixed with warm water should be used for washing the surface. Do not leave water or cleaning solution on the floor any longer than necessary. Rinse thoroughly and mop up rinse water, leaving the floor as dry as possible.

Fiber brushes and mechanical scrubbers are often used to accomplish routine cleaning of grouting. Dirty grouting can be scrubbed with a stiff brush and a mild abrasive powder. However, glazed tiles should not be subjected to harsh abrasives or other gritty materials.

Stain removal

The Tile Council of America has developed methods for removing stains most frequently encountered on tile surfaces. Although the methods have been thoroughly tested, the Tile Council suggests that each of the treatments should be tried out on a sample panel, or on a small inconspicuous area, of the ceramic tile to be cleaned. When the nature of the stain is known, use the treatment shown as suitable in the Guide to Stain Removal—Ceramic Tile, Table 18, and rinse carefully afterwards. Repetition of the treatment is suggested if the method does not remove the stain adequately in one application.

TABLE 18

GUIDE TO STAIN REMOVAL—CERAMIC TILE

Nature of Stain	Cleaning Compound	Procedure
Efflorescence (calcium or magnesium carbonates).	5% hydrochloric acid in water.*	Wash with acid, then rinse thoroughly with water.
Hard-water deposit.	10% "Versene-Na+" solution in water.	Wash with solution, allowing about 10 minutes contact time, followed by rinsing.
	Same as for efflorescence.	Same as for efflorescence.
Grease, fats.	10% sodium carbonate in water; 5% caustic soda, if required.	Wash with solution, allowing up to about one hour contact time; then rinse thoroughly.
Copper, silver, nickel compounds.	Household ammonia.	Wash with solution, and rinse immediately.
Iron metal (tool marks).	5% hydrochloric acid.*	Wash with acid; follow immediately with thorough water rinse.
Copper metal (tool marks).	10% nitric acid.*	Same as for iron metal.
Iron compounds (new).	10% hydrochloric acid.*	Same as for iron metal.
Iron compounds (old).	10% Versene Fe-3 specific.	Allow extended contact time, keeping wet 1 to 24 hours; rinse with water when stain no longer apparent.
Blood, coffee, mustard, food juices.	Household bleach.	Wash thoroughly for 5-10 minutes; rinse with water.
Ink.	Household bleach, or Versene Fe-3 specific (10% solution).	Wash thoroughly for 5-10 minutes; rinse with water.

* Acids should not be used for cleaning glazed tile.

SLATE TILE

Description

Slates to be used for tile floors are made from quarried blocks (of stratified, clayey, metamorphic rock) about 3 inches thick. A chisel, placed in position against the edge of the block, is lightly tapped with a mallet; a crack appears in the direction of cleavage, and slight leverage with the chisel serves to split the block into two pieces with smooth—but not uniformly flat—surfaces. This procedure is repeated until the original block is converted into 16 or 18 separate "slates," the thickness of which depends on many circumstances, such as the quality of the rock and the purpose for which the slates are to be used. The slates are then trimmed to size, usually by means of machine-driven rotating knives. In nature, slate occurs in several colors: it may be black, blue, purple, red, green, or gray. Slate tiles have great tensile strength and durability. Sizes of tiles for use in flooring (called dimension slate) typically range from 6 by 6 inches to 24 by 18 inches, in multiples of 3 inches.

Floors made of slate tile are suitable for areas subject to heavy traffic because of the durability and ease of maintenance of this material. Slate tends to be slippery when wet; for areas subject to wetness, the slipping hazard might be eliminated by the use of rubber mats or wooden grills laid over the surface.

Installation

Slate floors are usually laid over a concrete base in a setting bed of portland cement, approximately ¼ inch thinner than the thickness of the

Space Planning Services, A Division of Carson Pirie Scott & Co.

Slate tile floor.

slate. The setting bed is dusted with dry portland cement and the bottom side of the slate is spread with a mixture of pure portland cement and water. The slate is then placed firmly in position, and tamped with a wood block to ensure a good bond. The slate should be kept clean at all times with a damp sponge. The joints should be filled the same day the tile is set with a mix of half-and-half sifted silica sand and cement. The cement should not be allowed to dry on the face of the slate. After 48 hours, any residual cement still adhering to the slate's surface can be removed by use of a 10 percent solution of muriatic acid. Care should be taken to prevent the acid from seeping into the joints, and the hands should be protected with suitable gloves. After acid has been used, the surface should be hosed or rinsed thoroughly with water.

Maintenance

See maintenance of ceramic tile, page 237.

CONCRETE

Description

Concrete is made of a mixture of water, portland cement, and aggregate, which may be sand or gravel or a mixture of these. Significant advantages of concrete as a flooring material are its relatively low cost, durability, and inertness. However, it is impossible to maintain concrete at the high level of brilliance and uniformity of appearance associated with other hard-surface floors, especially if it is used outdoors or where there is considerable foot traffic. Thus, concrete is normally used where appearance is secondary to serviceability.

Installation

Concrete floor construction is a job best left to professionals because it requires specialized knowledge of subgrade preparation, careful selection of materials, special equipment, and skilled workmanship.

The subgrade for a concrete floor is brought to proper elevation with granular material and compacted with tampers or vibratory equipment. Columns are isolated from the floor slab by boxing them out with wood screeds (forms) or circular fiberboard forms while walls are isolated with asphalt-impregnated fiber sheets. Forms or screeds are set at proper elevation around the area to be concreted and grade stakes are installed within large areas to the proper height. The screeds are oiled to facilitate stripping, and the subgrade is dampened before concreting. A "concrete wet screed" is cast between the grade stakes, struck off (leveled) with a straight-edge, and the stakes removed. Concrete is deposited in the area and straight-edged to the elevation of the concrete screed. Spud vibrators are used to consolidate the concrete at corners and bulkheads created by the forms. After straight-edging, the concrete is smoothed with special equipment—bullfloat and darby—and the surface is finished by hand troweling. Immediately after finishing, the concrete is cured, i.e., kept moist, for several days by covering the entire surface with waterproofed curing paper, wet burlap, or an organic curing compound. Powered saws are used to cut control joints in the concrete which are later filled with sealers. After the floor has been cured for at least five days, it is allowed to air-dry a few days before opening it to traffic.

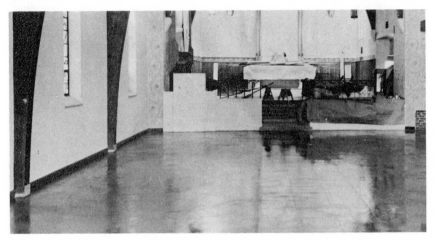

Portland Cement Association

Church installation using concrete as a finish floor.
The aisle is scored in large squares.

Maintenance

All unfinished concrete is porous, the degree depending to a large extent upon the original mix, its age, where it is installed, and the type of cleaning compounds used on it. Dry concrete will absorb alkaline salts, such as carbonates and trisodium phosphate. These absorbed salts will crystallize in the pores of the cement and increase in size as they pick up moisture. Eventually this process causes a surface powdering. Subsequent harsh washings cause additional damage and complicate the problem of maintenance. However, if the floor is thoroughly wet with plain water before alkaline compounds are used, the likelihood of damage is lessened. Prewetting, therefore, should be a standard maintenance procedure before using any cleaning solution on a concrete surface.

Washing uncoated or unpainted concrete should be done by scrubbing the wetted floor with a hot, synthetic detergent solution.

Soap should not be used because it will react with the lime in the concrete, forming a scum which will cause the floor to soil more rapidly. In washing heavy soils, such as grease or oil, it is best to use alkaline compounds. Sodium metasilicate powder (about 4 ounces per gallon of water) is good for this purpose, although the addition of a synthetic detergent is helpful. A stiff scrubbing brush should be used to remove well-embedded grease deposits. Poultice treatments are sometimes prescribed for very persistent oil stains. A typical poultice treatment consists of whiting and trisodium phosphate, mixed into a thick paste. This is left on the stained area until dry, then scraped off and the surface thoroughly rinsed with hot water. Rinsing should, of course, immediately follow any washing or poulticing. Volatile, flammable solvents such as gasoline should not be used to clean oil or grease stains, as they generally cause the soil to penetrate further into the concrete.

Well-sealed, dense concrete is easy to maintain and is less subject to injury from routine washing and scrubbing. Painting such floors with a good grade of concrete paint based on epoxy ester varnish, or tung oil-phenolics, or cement sealers based on chlorinated rubber extends their life, reduces dust, and results in easier maintenance.

MAGNESITE (OXYCHLORIDE)

Description

Like other masonry flooring materials, magnesite (sometimes called "oxychloride") affords an extremely durable surface. It has an especially high resistance to grease and oil but has poor resistance to water. Magnesite installations are seamless, and the material is available in a variety of colors.

Magnesite is composed of fillers, e.g., sawdust, and aggregates, e.g., stone chips, bound together with magnesium oxychloride cement, which produces a smooth, dense surface that is relatively flexible for a masonry floor. Inasmuch as magnesite can be composed of different fillers and aggregates, the finished floor can vary in density and appearance. This product can be formulated with marble chips to give an appearance resembling terrazzo and with special abrasive materials for areas in which slipperiness may be a hazard. It may also be mixed with heavy aggregates for heavy-traffic areas.

Installation

The main prerequisite is that the installation be made by magnesite flooring contractors, who are familiar with the various specifications required for the many types of magnesite installations.

After the floor has been laid, it should be allowed to set for at least 8 hours. It should then be rubbed with steel wool to smooth out any trowel marks and immediately sealed with a tung-oil-base sealer. Following this, the floor should be covered with a material permeable to water vapor, such as sawdust or absorbent paper. Sawdust is preferred. This material will facilitate curing of the magnesite and will prevent the floor from becoming unnecessarily soiled before it has had a chance to cure thoroughly. Once the floor has been sealed and covered with the absorbent material, it should be closed to all traffic for at least 48 hours.

E. H. O'Neill Floors Co.

Magnesite terrazzo floor installation.

While it is desirable to leave the absorbent material on the floor as long as possible during the curing period, which may range from two weeks to thirty days, the floor may be swept or vacuumed, if necessary. However, under no circumstances should the finished floor be given any kind of wet treatment until the curing period is over and the floor is thoroughly dried out. After curing, the floor may be wet-cleaned to remove any soil accumulation and a coating of solvent-base wax should be applied to enhance the appearance of the floor.

Maintenance

Magnesite floors should be regularly maintained by daily vacuuming and sweeping. Oily dust mops, sprays, and sweeping compounds may be used. Periodic maintenance requires scrubbing the magnesite floor with a mildly alkaline cleaning compound or a neutral synthetic detergent. Trisodium phosphate, silicates, and soda ash should be avoided. The solution should be mopped onto, but not allowed to soak into, the surface. After cleaning, the floor should be thoroughly rinsed with clear water and left as dry as possible. Because magnesite is not harmed by solvents, stubborn soils—such as grease spots and hardened soil coatings—can be removed by using de-greasers containing nonflammable solvents. Areas cleaned with solvents should be re-sealed as soon as they are dry.

When the floor is dry, it can be coated with a solvent-base wax and polished. Pigmented waxes may be used to even out the tone of the floor surface.

Magnesite floors should be thoroughly cleaned, dried, sealed, and polished at regular intervals—say, every six months—depending upon local use conditions. If the floors are not kept adequately sealed, serious problems can develop.

First, an unsealed magnesite floor exposed to excessive amounts of water over extended periods will become soft and porous, as the water leaches salts from the material. Second, soil and stains will be absorbed more readily into the pores of the magnesite and detract from its appearance—both in use and during cleaning operations. Third, unsealed magnesite floors cannot be properly polished.

BRICK

Description

Brick floors are very desirable wearing surfaces for interior floors as well as exterior walkways and patios because of color, pattern, and resistance to abrasion. Brick can provide a colorful, durable surface over the ground or over a structural flooring system, or bricks can be incorporated within a floor system.

Brick floors are relatively economical. Their resistance to abrasion ensures long life and low maintenance costs. In some cases, brick floors have proved to be less costly than some types of resilient tile.

Resistance to wear is associated with dense, hard-burned (vitrified) brick. For floors not subjected to heavy wear—i.e., most non-industrial floors—a low-absorption, dense brick will usually prove satisfactory. In addition, the denser the brick and the lower its absorption, the more resistant it is to discoloring and staining. As a consequence, floors of this type are easily cleaned and maintained.

Final appearance depends largely upon color and size of bricks and the patterns in which they are laid. A number of patterns are possible permitting great variety in design. Further variations are afforded by the thickness of mortar joints, color of the mortar, or by omitting mortar joints altogether.

Space Planning Services, A Division of Carson Pirie Scott & Co.

Brick floor in conference lounge.

When bricks are placed flat, i.e., largest plane surface horizontal, non-cored bricks are normally used. However, if placed on edge, cored bricks can be used.

Installation

Interior brick floors may have mortar joints or they may be "mortarless" installations. In general, they are placed over concrete slabs. Although most interior brick floors are selected for appearance and economy, and thus are not reinforced, it is entirely practical to reinforce them where greater strength is required.

The principal elements in unreinforced brick floor construction are: (1) the base, which is the principal support; (2) the cushion, an intermediate layer which facilitates leveling and placement; (3) the wearing surface; and (4) the joints, consisting of the space or the material in the space between the bricks.

For some kinds of installations of brick floors, no finishing is required at all. In places where a smooth surface is desired, the brick floor can be ground to a uniform smoothness by using a grinding machine.

Maintenance

Whether a natural or surface-ground finish is employed, floors may either be polished or left in their natural state. Although polish will not solve all problems, polished floor surfaces are preferred by many people. Once a floor is polished, it will require periodic maintenance. The maintenance procedures for ceramic tile described earlier in this chapter are recommended for brick floors.

Because some polishes discolor with age, turning yellow or gray, it is best to seal the floor before applying polish. Many commercial sealers are available for sealing brick floors. Once the sealer has dried, one should apply a suitable floor polish that is recommended for brick floors by a reputable polish manufacturer. A polished surface may have less tendency to stain.

The Structural Clay Products Institute does not recommend varnish or shellac as finishes for brick floors because these products do not stay in place and, after a short time, present a poor appearance.

6   WOOD FLOORS

Wood possesses a variety of properties that make it a highly desirable flooring material. In addition, one can choose from a variety of woods having distinctive grain characteristics, and from a number of flooring forms and patterns.

PROPERTIES OF WOOD FLOORING

Wood possesses in high degree the properties that are desirable for finish flooring. These include distinctive and attractive appearance adaptable to various styles of decor; good hardness and wearing qualities; a degree of resilience that provides foot comfort; low thermal conductivity; simplicity and facility of installation; relative freedom from slipperiness, depending on the finish used; and ease of maintenance when properly installed and finished.

Many species of wood are used and various grades are manufactured to meet practically any appearance requirement. Surface finishes that vary from polished brilliance to attractive natural finish can be applied to adapt a wood floor to almost any desired scheme of interior decoration.

Hedrich-Blessing

Random-width plank floor.

According to information published by the Maple Flooring Manufacturers Association, the kinds of wood used in flooring, under practically the same conditions, demonstrate wearing qualities in the following order: (1) hard maple; (2) beech and birch; (3) oak, quartersawed; (4) yellow pine, edge-grain; (5) fir, edge-grain; (6) oak, plainsawed; (7) yellow pine, flatsawed; (8) fir, flatsawed; (9) Norway pine; (10) white pine.

KINDS OF WOOD FLOORING

Early flooring was mostly of softwood, because of its availability and the relative ease of working it with handtools. Usually it was in the form of random-width planks as they came from the mill. The production of hardwoods that afforded better wear soon followed improvements in manufacturing equipment and seasoning methods. As a result, the use of hardwoods as flooring expanded to where they now comprise by far the greater proportion of total production.

More than one hundred species of American hardwoods are used commercially, each possessing qualities making it adaptable to specific purposes. Among these species, five are commonly used for floors, namely, oak (including species of both red and white oak), maple, beech, birch,

Harris Manufacturing Company

Study hall with parquet floor.

and pecan. Oak and maple are the hardwoods used most frequently for flooring. The term "hardwood" actually is a misnomer, because poplar, cottonwood, and several other species included in that classification are relatively soft-textured. These are known in the trade as "light hardwoods," while the hard species are called "heavy hardwoods."

Oak

Although oak is grouped into white or red varieties, there is little difference in quality or utility between the groups. Orders for most grades are placed specifically for either white or red oak. However, in one grade white and red oak may be mixed.

Oak is regularly manufactured into plainsawed and quartersawed flooring. Quartersawed oak is characterized by a rather striking figure and by a minimum of shrinking and swelling in width. The term rift-sawed has come into common use in recent years. In practice, this refers to a type intermediate between true plainsawed and true quartersawed; it has a less striking figure than quartersawed.

The distinctive appearance of oak stems from its cellular construction. It is one of the few heavy hardwoods that are ring-porous. This description arises from the appearance of the larger springwood growth in which the pores are more prominent than in the summerwood growth. The effect is particularly noticeable in plainsawed oak. Oak is also marked by strips of cells extending radially in the tree. These strips or wood rays appear as flake patterns when the log is quartersawed. White oak has a prominence of large rays.

Maple

Maple flooring is made from sugar maple (Acer Saccharum). It is known in different localities by various names, including sugar tree and rock maple. The trade name is "hard maple" or "northern hard maple."

Maple's exceptional hardness, strength, resistance to abrasion, and ability to take an excellent finish make it particularly desirable as flooring for areas subject to extremely heavy wear.

Maple is designated as a diffuse-porous wood because it has no springwood pores. Instead, its pores are very small and evenly distributed, yielding a close grain. Having no wood rays, it is not manufactured into quartersawed flooring. However, edge-grain maple flooring is available.

The heartwood of maple is light reddish brown; the sapwood is white with a slight brownish tinge. In the standard grading rules for maple flooring, the varying natural color is allowed, although a special grade provides for selected light stock.

Beech and birch

In contrast to maple, beech and more particularly birch are used only sparingly as flooring. Only 2 of the 15 to 20 species of birch native to the United States are manufactured into flooring. They are yellow birch and sweet birch with the former being more abundant and widely used. Only one species of beech grows in this country. The heartwood of all three of these woods is reddish brown, with a slight variation in color for each individual species. Certain color variations occur frequently, but these are not considered in grading. Special grades are manufactured from all red-faced stock.

Pecan

Pecan belongs to the hickory family, the hardest of all hardwoods. It is close-grained and has fine or invisible wood rays. Its heartwood is darker than that of most woods ordinarily used for flooring.

Other

The five hardwoods described above constitute the material for almost all hardwood flooring. Other kinds of wood used for flooring include walnut, cherry, ash, hickory, and East Indian teak. Some are extremely hard and durable while others offer striking grain patterns. Some flooring producers specialize in the use of these woods in the production of block flooring with geometric designs (parquetry) for pattern effects.

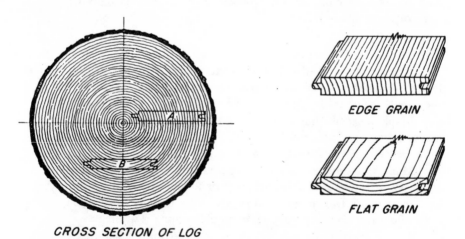

EDGE GRAIN

FLAT GRAIN

CROSS SECTION OF LOG

U. S. Forest Products Laboratory

Cross-section of log showing annual growth rings and position from which (A) edge-grain and (B) flat-grain flooring are obtained.

FORMS OF WOOD FLOORING

Wood flooring is manufactured in a variety of forms. Broadly, the various shapes may be classified as strip, plank, and block. One type of construction, called "parquet flooring," is sometimes given a separate classification although, strictly speaking, it is a variety of block flooring.

Strip

For a long time, strip flooring was the only type of hardwood flooring available. Due to improved quality through advances in mill practices and seasoning techniques, it still dominates the wood floor market despite the introduction of new types of wood flooring.

The most widely used strip flooring is $2\frac{5}{32}$ inch thick and $2\frac{1}{4}$ inches wide, but other thicknesses and widths are available. Most hardwood strip flooring today is tongued, grooved, and end-matched, so that each piece joins its neighbor snugly when being laid. Square-edge strips are also available.

Plank

This is one of the oldest types of wood floors. It is, in effect, strip flooring but is distinguished by greater widths. While it is usually the same thickness as strip flooring, it is generally available in random widths. Plank flooring is designed to simulate the appearance of the random-width planks commonly used in colonial times. To heighten this appearance further, wood plugs of contrasting color are sometimes inserted in the flooring to simulate the wood pins once used for fastening. Oak is customarily used for production of plank floors.

Block

Square block flooring has become a standard form of wood flooring. Regardless of the size or number of pieces that make up each block, certain basic types of construction are used in its manufacture. The most common constructions are unit, laminated, and parquet. In addition, there are a variety of other constructions too numerous to describe here. Perhaps the most common block size is nine inches square. Oak is by far the predominant kind of wood used in block flooring. Sometimes a mixture of hardwoods may be used at random in a single block.

Unit block (or solid unit block) is a square of wood composed of short lengths of standard strip flooring, edge-joined to form a unit. The unit block may generally be purchased in the same grades as standard strip flooring, some manufacturers having, in addition, special grades. A wide choice of pattern is available in unit block flooring.

Laminated (or plywood) block is made of layers of wood veneer, crossbanded and bonded. If the proper kind of glue is used at the time of manufacture to secure satisfactory bonding of the veneer layers, laminated block will not only remain intact during the life of the flooring but will shrink and swell less when its moisture content changes than will other types of wood flooring.

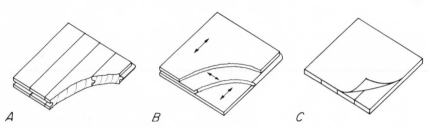

U. S. Forest Products Laboratory

Three types of block flooring—(A) unit block,
(B) laminated block, and (C) parquet.

Parquet, available in many styles, is a variety of wood block flooring; it is distinguished by geometric patterns that cannot be achieved as well in other varieties of wood block flooring. In parquet, individual pieces of wood are assembled into squares of a desired pattern and are fastened together by metal splines or held together by bonding the upper face of the block to a flexible membrane, usually paper. In the latter kind of assembly, the face membrane is peeled off the surface of the parquet after the block has been laid. Most parquet flooring is of oak, although it is produced in maple, birch, walnut, mahogany, teak, and ebonized wood.

RECENT DEVELOPMENTS

Many attempts have been made to develop wood floorings which have special properties or which use less of the high-grade woods that are in wide demand because of their good appearance. The U.S. Forest Products Laboratory has been especially active in this field.

Veneer flooring using strips of ½-inch veneer, 3 inches wide and from 20 to 40 inches long, has given good results when laid on a concrete slab with rubber-type adhesive.

Veneer-lumber flooring, developed for use on a concrete slab base, consists of a ⅛-inch layer of high-grade hardwood veneer glued to a ⅝-inch lumber backing, with the grain of the two at right angles. The backing lumber may be of any species denser than 25 pounds per cubic foot and may contain knots, checks, splits, and other defects, so long as there is an essentially sound surface adjacent to the face veneer. After the two components are glued together, the backing is grooved parallel to its grain at 1-inch intervals with the grooves extending almost through the backing. The cross-laminated construction provides considerable dimensional stability, and the grooving provides flexibility, permitting installation with a mastic adhesive over somewhat uneven surfaces.

U. S. Forest Products Laboratory

Laying veneer strip flooring in
rubber-base mastic on concrete.

Resin-impregnated paper has been glued to the surface of wood and plywood to impart improved properties. Some high-density types of overlays have been used experimentally on plywood for flooring. The major improvement attained with them has been to impart a hard, abrasion-resistant, highly decorative wearing surface to softwood plywood, which would otherwise not be suitable for finish flooring.

Particleboard is a combination of wood chips, wood particles, and a resin binder formed under pressure. The result is a high-density material that is used as floor underlayment and could be suitable for a floor wear surface. At least one company is producing a particleboard flooring tile. While this tile does not have the appearance of wood, it provides a low-cost, long-wearing floor.

GRADES OF WOOD FLOORING

To ensure uniformity and maintain high standards of manufacture, two trade associations have established grading rules for the common hardwoods used in flooring. Oak, beech, birch, hard maple, and pecan flooring are graded under the rules of the National Oak Flooring Manufacturers' Association (NOFMA). Hard maple, beech, and birch flooring are also graded under the rules of the Maple Flooring Manufacturers Association (MFMA). These rules have been so widely accepted by architects and builders that they are industry standards.

Standard flooring grades are based almost wholly on appearance. That is, they exclude or severely limit such defects as knots, wormholes, and the like in the higher grades and permit increasing sizes and numbers of these characteristics in the lower grades. Natural variations in color are generally not limited except that, in certain grades, the amount of the lighter colored sapwood is restricted. Special grades, selected for color, may be obtained in maple, beech, and birch. This is generally limited to the highest grade (clear) in which all-sap or all-heart maple and all-heart beech or birch may be obtained. The extra selection for color increases the cost of these special grades as compared with the standard grades.

MOISTURE CONTENT

A property of wood flooring that requires special attention is its tendency to shrink and swell as its moisture content changes. Modern methods of selection, seasoning, and installation have contributed greatly to the control of this characteristic. Other control factors include the choice of edge-grain over flat-grain material; the use of special flooring patterns; the development of dimensionally stable crossbanded types; the maintenance of proper moisture content at time of installation; and, when necessary, consideration of finishes that retard moisture change. Protection from moisture during delivery to and storage at the installation site will also help to prevent excessive shrinkage or expansion after the floor has been laid.

The following precautions for handling hardwood flooring prior to installation are prescribed by MFMA and NOFMA.

(1) Do not transport hardwood flooring in rain, snow, or excessively humid conditions. If the atmosphere is foggy or damp, cover the flooring with tarpaulin.

(2) Do not store flooring without shelter or in damp or wet enclosures.

(3) Do not store flooring on storage floors that are less than 18 inches from the ground and that do not have good air circulation underneath.

(4) Do not install flooring in a building that is cold and damp. New plaster and cement should be thoroughly dry and all but the final woodwork and trim should be installed.

(5) Do not lay flooring immediately after delivery. Pile the flooring loosely in the building for 3 to 5 days so that it may come to equilibrium with conditions within the building before being laid. In winter construction, the building should be heated to 70° F.

INSTALLATION

The once-common use of wood supporting frameworks for buildings made nail attachment of wooden floors fairly simple. As building construction went to other types of supporting materials, notably concrete, new types of finished floors began to take the place of wood. To counteract this trend, the wood flooring industry developed new methods for installing wood flooring over all types of supporting structures. For example, one technique for installing wood flooring over concrete entails the use of wood sleepers (usually 2- by 4-inch material) that serve as a nailing base for strip flooring. The sleepers are fastened to the concrete by anchors or mastic adhesives. Block flooring may be laid on a wood subfloor either by nailing or by laying in mastic, and on concrete by laying in mastic.

General comments about installation of wood flooring are given below. (Details of the various procedures of installation are available from the following organizations: Maple Flooring Manufacturers Association; National Oak Flooring Manufacturers' Association; U.S. Forest Products Laboratory; National Forest Products Association; American Parquet Association, Inc.; American Plywood Association; and Wood Flooring Institute of America.)

(1) Subfloors must be sound and properly laid and prepared.

(2) Sleepers or nailers used under a subfloor should be preserved with pentachlorophenol or its equivalent.

(3) Anchors for wood sleepers over concrete should be zinc-coated and so designed that they cannot pull out after the concrete has set.

(4) Floors laid on- or below-grade should be waterproofed with a vapor barrier before installation.

(5) Subfloors over joist construction are commonly covered with an insulation paper to deaden sound and prevent squeaks.

(6) Concrete slabs over which wood floors are to be laid in direct contact must be true and level without ridges or high spots.

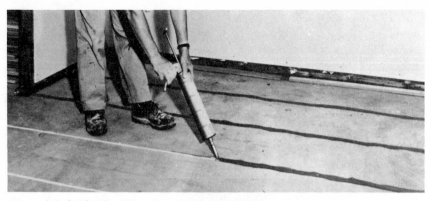

National Oak Flooring Manufacturers' Association

1. Sealing edges of bottom moisture-proof barrier.

National Oak Flooring Manufacturers' Association

2. Installing bottom sleepers.

National Oak Flooring Manufacturers' Association

3. Spreading polyethylene moisture-proof barrier.

National Oak Flooring Manufacturers' Association

4. Installing top sleepers.

National Oak Flooring Manufacturers' Association

5. Installing strip flooring.

Installing hardwood strip floor
directly over concrete subfloor.

FINISHING

After laying a wood floor, five steps may be needed to complete the finishing process, namely (1) sanding of the surface, (2) application of a stain to unify the color, (3) application of a filler to porous woods, (4) application of a final finish, and (5) application of a polish. Some of these steps are optional. For example, one may prefer to polish the surface following the application of filler, or one may wish to omit polishing following the application of shellac, varnish, or lacquer.

Sanding

All finishing operations require the surface of wood flooring to be made smooth by sanding or scraping just before the first coat of finishing material is applied. Just as the finish brings out the beauty of the wood, it also reveals any defects or roughness left in the surface. Even irregularities that can scarcely be seen before finishing become conspicuous afterwards. Unless prefinished, flooring usually has not been sanded by the manufacturer and bears slight ridges left by the planer which will mar the appearance when the finish has been applied. Moreover, if much time elapses between the final sanding and the finishing operation, changing moisture content may cause the grain of the wood to rise. Floors should be sanded immediately before finishing is begun—if possible, the day when the first coat of finish is to be applied.

Sanding or scraping can be done by hand, but that is a laborious method for large areas. Nevertheless, some handwork may be necessary in places that are inaccessible to powered machines. Most floor sanding is done with electrically driven sanding machines. The machine should be well designed, ruggedly built, with its bearings well aligned and kept in good condition. A machine with badly worn bearings may do more harm than good.

Floor sanding machines can often be rented at retail paint and hardware stores or from concerns that specialize in the renting of powered equipment. It should be pointed out, however, that sanding is by far the most exacting step in floor finishing. Nothing can be done later that will make up for defects of a poor sanding job. It is therefore advisable, whenever possible, to have floors sanded by a specialist.

Sanding procedure. The floor should be swept clean before beginning the sanding. No water should be used.

Newly laid hardwood floors should be traversed with the sanding machine at least three times, first with coarse sandpaper of grade No. 2½-30 or No. 2-36, then with medium paper of grade No. 1-50 or No. ½-60, and finally with fine paper of grade No. 0-80 or No. 2/0-100.

Although acceptable results are sometimes obtained with only two passes, three are recommended. For an especially smooth finish, the third pass should be made with No. 0-80 paper, followed by a fourth pass with No. 2/0-100 paper, and even a fifth pass with No. 3/0-120 paper.

Another method is to buff the hardwood floor with steel wool of No. 1 coarseness after the third pass with No. 0-80 sandpaper. Such buffing can be done by machine, because there are available rolls of steel wool that can be substituted for the drum in drum sanders. Steel wool, however, should not be used on oak floors unprotected by finish, because minute particles of steel left in the pores of the wood may later cause iron stains under certain conditions.

On strip flooring or other patterns in which all pieces lie with the grain in the same direction, drum sanders are operated with and across the grain of the wood. It is helpful to make one of the earlier passes with the coarse or medium sandpaper either across the grain or at an angle of 45° to the wood grain. Some authorities recommend that the pass across the grain be made with the coarse paper, whereas others prefer to make it with the medium paper. All other passes should be made with the grain, alternately from opposite directions. Some floor men prefer a disk sander for the last traverse, even when a drum sander is used for the earlier passes.

On parquet or unit block flooring, it is necessary to cross the grain of many pieces at each traverse. Each pass may be made in a different direction: two at right angles to each other and the third at 45° to the first two. Disk sanders necessarily cross the wood grain at each pass. Extra care should be taken to see that each traverse after the first is deep enough to remove all scratches left by the previous pass, and the last pass should be made with No. 2/0-100 or, if necessary, with No. 3/0-120 paper. Disk sanders are sometimes preferred over drum sanders for block floors.

After each pass with a drum sander, an edger should be used for the parts of the floor not reached by the drum sander. With a large disk sander, there will be places at the corners where an edger must be used to sand such areas. If there are places inaccessible even to an edger, such as near radiator pipes, they must be sanded or scraped by hand.

Before the sanding is considered complete, the floor should be inspected carefully to see that all blemishes and visible scratches have been removed and a smooth surface produced. Defects can be seen most readily if the floor is viewed against light at a low angle of incidence so that any ridges will cast shadows. Defects left at this time will show much more prominently after finishing materials have been applied.

When sanding is completed, the floor should be swept free from dust and wiped with a painter's tack-rag. The walls, windows, and doors also should be dusted to keep dust motes from dropping into wet finishing materials to mar their appearance. Application of finishing materials should begin promptly so that there will be no time for changing moisture conditions to raise the grain of the wood.

Sanding machines. Sanding machines are of two types, drum and disk. In drum sanders the sandpaper is mounted on a cylindrical drum that rotates on an axis parallel to the plane of the floor and at right angles to the direction in which the machine is moved. Thus the sandpaper makes its scratches in straight lines in the direction of the movement of the machine. In disk sanders the sandpaper is mounted on a disk that rotates in a circle in the plane of the floor. As a disk sander is moved over the floor, the grits make spiral scratches that necessarily cross the grain of the wood. The final sandpaper used with a disk sander therefore may need to be a grade or two finer than is necessary with a drum sander on a floor in which all pieces run in the same direction. A drum sander, however, cannot reach the last few inches of floor nearest the baseboard. Electric edgers, which are small disk sanders, can sand those edges of a floor not reached by a drum sander.

Varying the speed of rotation of floor-sanding machines is useful. If the speed is too great, enough heat may be generated by friction to heat the wood to incipient charring temperatures and thereby produce dark marks called burns, which can be removed only by sanding away more wood than is otherwise necessary. On the other hand, the operator wants to use the highest speed practicable to get the work done as rapidly as possible. Burns can also be produced if the machine is allowed to stand at one place while the drum or disk is rotating.

Sandpaper. The abrasive grits in sandpaper may be flint, garnet, or emery, which are natural minerals, or manufactured products such as aluminum oxide or silicon carbide. Flint is the cheapest, but wears most rapidly and is seldom recommended for sanding machines. Garnet and aluminum oxide are most widely used for woodworking. Aluminum oxide is generally preferred for high-speed machines such as floor sanders. A few professional floor men use silicon carbide. The sandpaper backing paper may be paper, cloth, or a combination of paper and cloth. Paper backing is satisfactory for floor sanding machines, although combination paper and cloth backing may be desirable for very coarse grits.

Sandpaper is sold in sheets 9 by 11 inches in size for handwork, in pieces precut to sizes to fit any one of the various models of drum sanders, and in circular disks to fit the disk sanders. In ordering, the make and model of the sanding machine should be specified. Sandpaper is also sold in rolls 50 yards long and of various widths from which the user may cut pieces with a suitable template to fit his sanding machine. There are also "thrift rolls" long enough to make ten pieces for drum sanders.

U. S. Forest Products Laboratory

Drum sanding machine.

U. S. Forest Products Laboratory

Disk sanding machine.

Staining

The next step in finishing is staining, although if the color of the floor is satisfactory, staining is omitted. The color of a hardwood floor may be altered without obscuring the grain of the wood by applying a stain of suitable color. Floors laid with wood of lower grades in which there may be conspicuous variation of natural color can be made more uniform in appearance by the use of a fairly dark stain. All clear finishes, even colorless ones, will darken the floor slightly; this fact should be considered when selecting a stain.

The color of wood stains is often indicated by naming them for the wood on which they are to be used or whose color they are to imitate, with further qualification for the shade or character of color, e.g., light oak, dark oak, walnut, red mahogany, brown mahogany, etc. Penetration of stains is especially shallow in very hard woods of close texture, such as maple. It may be slightly deeper in birch and beech and still deeper in open-textured hardwoods, such as oak, walnut, and teak.

A brush or rag is used to apply the stain. It should be applied evenly. With a dark-colored stain, the surplus remaining on the floor after about five minutes should be wiped off with waste or rags. Wiping also helps distribute the color. If the stain becomes gummy and hard to wipe, a rag wet with a little fresh stain or mineral spirits will remove the surplus. Light-colored stain should not be wiped. It must be brushed evenly in a very thin coat and left alone. All stains should be allowed to dry overnight before the next finishing operation is started.

Filling

Some hardwoods, mainly oak, walnut and teak, have pores which show as small voids in the wood. To achieve a perfectly smooth surface, these pores should be filled. On hardwoods with small pores, such as maple or beech, filler is useless. Colored filler is used when it is desired to accentuate the grain of birchwood by making the pores dark in color, but the pores are small enough to go without filler if darkening is not required.

Wood sealers are commonly used as a final finish for a wood floor. However, some manufacturers of wood sealers recommend that the application of filler be deferred until a coat of sealer has been applied and has dried. Others recommend that the usual practice of filling before sealing be followed. Sometimes filler may be omitted entirely even on hardwoods with large pores when sealers are used. In general, it is practicable to dispense with filling if the sealer is buffed with steel wool before it has hardened. But when shellac, varnish, or lacquer is used for the final finish, hardwoods with large pores should always be filled.

Fillers for wood are of two kinds: natural fillers that are transparent and without color and colored fillers that are opaque and usually dark brown to black in color. Colored fillers are commonly named for the wood on which they are considered especially appropriate, for example, oak, walnut, cherry, mahogany, etc. Fillers may be liquid, ready for application, or paste, which must be thinned with mineral spirits or turpentine (paint thinners) before application. The directions given by the manufacturer should be followed.

Filler is applied best with a 4-inch flat brush. The first strokes should be across the grain of the wood, then a light stroke with the grain. Care should be taken not to cover too large an area at once, because there is further work to be done before the filler has had time to dry. Soon after the initial glossy "wet" appearance gives way to a dull "dry" appearance, the excess filler must be wiped off with burlap, excelsior, or other suitable material. Wipe first across the grain to pack the filler into the pores and then finish with a few lighter strokes with the grain. In wiping, care should be taken to see that all excess filler is removed, otherwise the filler may appear uneven and smeared. Filler usually should be allowed to dry for 24 hours before further finish is applied. However, there are fast-drying fillers for which the manufacturer may indicate less drying time.

Final finishing

There are five basic types of final-finishing materials: sealers, varnishes, shellacs, lacquers, and paints. A final finish that leaves the wood in a condition as close to its natural appearance as possible is usually preferred. All finishing materials, however, even though entirely without color themselves, apparently deepen the natural color of wood, for the same reason that wood always appears more richly colored when wet than when dry. Deeply penetrating finishes, such as linseed oil and the "floor oils" that were often used in former times, deepen the wood color more than less penetrating finishes, such as wood sealers, varnish, shellac, and lacquers. If the finishing material itself has considerable color, this color will be added to the over-all effect.

A further enrichment of the color of wood floors comes with age. Light, even subdued indoor light, slowly deepens and browns the very thin superficial layer of wood into which the light penetrates, producing the patina so much prized on old wood pieces. In addition, light and oxygen gradually act on varnishes and wood sealers to form colored decomposition products. The extent to which wood floors change in color with age from these two processes depends both on the kind of wood and the properties of the finishing materials. Fortunately, the color changes are usually of a pleasing nature.

Wood floors can be maintained in good condition with any one of the available floor finishes if good materials are applied properly and if maintenance methods appropriate for each kind of finish and for the degree of wear to which the floor is subjected are used. No type of finish can be said to be superior in all respects, and none will long continue to give good service unless suitably maintained. The secret of good floors lies in the thorough understanding of the nature and limitations of the particular kind of finish chosen and in carefully following the appropriate maintenance program. Choice of finish should be dictated primarily by the appearance desired and the methods of maintenance considered most convenient.

If a highly glossy, lustrous finish is desired, the choice may well be shellac, varnish, or lacquer. Such materials form coatings over the wood surface a few thousandths of an inch thick. A more natural appearance with less gloss and resinous luster is obtained from the wood sealer finish.

Only varnishes, lacquers, and wood sealers made specifically for finishing floors should be used. Spar varnish made for surfaces exposed to the weather may be too soft to withstand the abrasion of traffic, and cabinet finishing varnish made for furniture may lack the toughness required for floors. It is best to use floor varnish that is clearly so labeled by its manufacturer. So-called all-purpose varnish should be used only if the label says specifically that it is suitable for floor finishing. Similar caution applies to lacquers and wood sealers.

Sealing. Although they require more frequent attention than other finishes, floor sealers are widely used as protective finishes for hardwood

U. S. Forest Products Laboratory

Applying sealer to hardwood floor.

floors. They penetrate the fibers of the wood and form a wear-resistant surface which does not extend above the surface of the wood, making it possible to refinish or touch up worn areas without resealing the entire floor.

Color may be imparted to wood during application of a wood sealer by mixing a suitable oil stain with the first coat of sealer. Wood sealers that already contain color may be purchased.

For maple floors, especially where heavy traffic is anticipated, sealer is the only recommended finish. The heavy traffic will wear away the wood and sealer together, so there is little indication of wear. Worn spots in heavy-traffic lanes can be touched up so that the floor will present a uniform appearance.

Floor sealers may be brushed on with a wide brush or mopped on with a squeegee or lamb's wool applicator, working first across the grain of the wood, then in the direction of the grain. After an interval of from 15 minutes to an hour, according to the characteristics of the sealer, the excess is wiped off with clean rags or a rubber squeegee. (Rags soaked in sealer are liable to ignite spontaneously; they must be picked up at the end of a day's work and stored where they will not cause a fire, or better, they should be destroyed by burning. Another safety precaution is to put them in a bucket of water.)

The floor is then buffed with No. 2 steel wool, although buffing may be omitted by those willing to sacrifice something in appearance and service. (On oak floors, presence of the sealer makes it unlikely that any particles of steel wool will become embedded in the surface as previously mentioned for bare floors.)

If possible, the buffing should be done by a power-driven machine designed for buffing with steel wool. The next best procedure is buffing with pads of steel wool attached to the bottom of a sanding machine. Buffing may be done by hand if no machine is available. One coat of sealer may suffice if it is applied very carefully, but a thin, second coat, applied in the direction of the wood grain, is recommended for floors that have just been sanded.

Before application of the second coat, any steel wool particles or dust left on the floor should be picked up with a vacuum cleaner. If a greater gloss is desired, the sealed floor makes an excellent base for varnish, or a coating of polish can be applied over the sealer.

A correct interval of time between application of sealer and buffing is very important. If the interval is too short, the sealer may still be too fluid to buff properly. If it is too long, the excess sealer "gums" the steel wool badly, is removed from the floor with difficulty, and where not removed becomes blackened with debris from the steel wool. If the manufacturer of the sealer does not specify the correct interval clearly, the user should determine it by trial on samples of flooring or in some inconspicuous places where imperfect results will not prove too obvious. Once the user has learned how to work successfully with one brand of sealer, he will do well to continue using that brand, since he might have to learn the technique all over again with another brand.

Oil-modified polyurethane sealers, after a long trial period, have been fully accepted as a wood sealer and heavy duty finish for hardwood floors by the Maple Flooring Manufacturers Association. These materials have proved to be extremely abrasive-resistant and to offer a long wear life. They now compete with older forms of final finishes. (For a more detailed discussion of polyurethanes and their application, see pages 298-300 in the chapter, "Formed-in-Place Floors.")

Varnishing. A good floor varnish presents a lustrous appearance and adds to the floor's service life. It is tough as well as scratch- and water-resistant. Varnishes are available that dry with a high gloss, a medium gloss, or a low gloss. The selection is a matter of preference, but the high-gloss varnishes are more wear-resistant. It should be noted that most gradually darken with age. The kind of service expected of the floor also determines the type of varnish to be selected. There are varnishes especially designed for use in public buildings.

The floor and room should be clean and as free from dust as possible before varnishing begins. Dust particles falling into wet varnish impair the smoothness and appearance of the finish. The room should be at 70° F. or somewhat warmer, with plenty of fresh air. Varnish requires oxygen from the air for its drying, and there should be good circulation to carry off the fumes of the volatile thinners in the varnish. Damp weather may create a problem, since varnish dries slowly when the air is very humid. It is well to test the drying power of the varnish a day ahead of time by applying it on a nonabsorptive surface such as glass, metal, or well-primed wood.

Some varnishes lose their ability to dry promptly after long storage on a dealer's shelf. Poorly drying varnish can be exchanged for fresher stock, or its drying properties may be restored by adding about a teaspoon of paint drier to a quart of varnish.

Varnish is applied with a wide brush. The brush should be cleaned well before using. Particles of old varnish or paint left in the brush may work their way into the fresh varnish to mar the finish. Even a new brush may well be washed with soap and water, shaken out, and dried before using. First spread a brushful of varnish with the grain of the wood, then stroke it across the grain, and finally brush it lightly with the grain again. Then go to the next area with a fresh brushful. Do not go back to restroke areas that have been covered previously.

Air bubbles are sometimes created in varnish films by the bristles of the brush, but they can be minimized by avoiding excessive brushing. When they do appear, they can be removed by brushing back into the area with light feathering strokes before the varnish begins to set.

At least 16 hours should elapse before the second coat of varnish is applied. Three coats will be needed as a rule if the floor was not filled. If filler was applied, two coats of varnish may suffice. Varnishes, even those that are quick-drying, require fairly long drying intervals between coats. After the last coat, at least 24 hours or even 48 hours should elapse before traffic is allowed on the floor. Varnish does not acquire its full resistance to wear for several days.

Shellacking. Shellac has the merit of drying so rapidly that a floor may be finished or refinished and put back into service overnight. Shellac also has the advantage of not darkening with age. However, shellac is less tough and more easily scratched than varnish, and it will turn white when exposed to water or long periods of high humidity.

Shellac for floors should be purchased in the form of 5-pound cut shellac, that is, 5 pounds of shellac resin in 1 gallon of alcohol. It should be pure shellac, unadulterated with cheaper resins. Bleached shellac, commonly called white shellac, is preferred for its pale color. Orange shellac imparts considerable color to a wood floor surface. Always test shellac varnish to see that it dries promptly without tackiness before applying it on a floor. When stored too long, white shellac loses its ability to dry hard as a result of chemical reaction between the resin and the alcohol.

Shellac should be sold either in glass containers or in metal containers that are lined with lead or other coating to keep the shellac away from iron. Shellac contaminated with iron may produce black stains on woods that contain tannins, such as oak.

The correct thinner for shellac varnish is 188-proof No. 1 denatured alcohol. For application, 5-pound cut shellac should be thinned with 1 quart of alcohol per gallon. It should be applied in long, even strokes with a wide brush that will cover three boards of strip flooring at a time. Care should be taken to joint the laps quickly and smoothly.

The first coat on bare wood requires 15 to 20 minutes to dry. It should then be rubbed lightly with fine steel wool or sandpaper and the floor swept clean. A second coat should be applied, allowed to dry 2 to 3 hours, then treated with steel wool or sandpaper, swept, and a third coat applied. The floor should not be put back into service until the next morning, although it may be walked on carefully about 3 hours after finishing.

If polish is to be used, it should be applied at least 8 hours after the last coat of shellac. Solvent-base paste wax is suitable. Water-base emulsion polishes should be avoided because water may turn shellac white.

Lacquering. Lacquer dries as rapidly as shellac, is as resistant to water as varnish, and seldom darkens with age. Lacquers made for brushing on, as opposed to spray gun application, are more expensive and rather difficult to apply evenly on large surfaces such as floors. Moreover, lacquers contain much more volatile material than varnish, so that more coats are required to make a finish comparable in luster to that obtained with varnish. For these reasons, lacquers are used much less than the other finishes.

Lacquer is applied much like varnish except that the work must be done more rapidly because lacquer dries so fast. The initial spreading, cross brushing, and final stroking must be done very quickly. Lacquer, if brushed too long, will not level out with a smooth surface. Lacquer holds its "wet edge" for a very limited time only. As far as possible, the edges of brush strokes, therefore, should coincide with the edges of boards in the floor, and the beginning of a second brushful must be joined to the end of the previous one very promptly. With lacquer, an hour or two between coats may be enough drying time. The manufacturer's directions should state the required time.

Painting. Opaque paint or enamel for use on wood floors should be hard enough to withstand abrasion and yet tough enough to withstand impact. Paints or enamels made for other purposes may not have such properties in sufficient degree. The manufacturer's label should say clearly that the product is intended for use on wood floors.

Paint or enamel can be used to finish wood floors when it is desired to hide the grain of the wood entirely and perhaps to provide colors that are not satisfactorily attainable in transparent finishes. Hardwood floors inside buildings, however, are seldom painted, because most users prefer to take advantage of the natural beauty of the wood.

Floors exposed to the weather are usually painted. None of the transparent finishes resists weather well enough to last very long outdoors. Good floor paint or enamel proves much more durable.

On new floors, or those just sanded, at least two coats of floor paint or enamel are necessary. The first coat should be thinned moderately with paint thinner in accordance with the manufacturer's directions. Subsequent coats usually should be applied unthinned. Each coat should dry for at least 16 hours before the next coat is applied or before the floor is opened to traffic.

Polishing

Wax should not be applied to unfinished wood, because it penetrates the wood and is difficult to remove. Wax by itself is not a durable finish. However, the finish on a floor can be protected against wear by keeping it waxed with a liquid or paste solvent-base wax. A newly finished floor should have at least two coats of paste solvent-base wax, and, if a liquid solvent-base wax is used, additional coats may be necessary to get an adequate film. Such liquid wax contains solvent that evaporates. The film formed, therefore, is thinner than that obtained with the paste wax. As noted above, some water-base emulsion polishes may react unfavorably with shellac; hence, caution should be used in applying such polishes to shellacked floors. A small area should be tested first to determine if a particular polish and shellac are compatible.

Polishes are not recommended for heavily used maple floors. The amount of wear for which maple flooring is most frequently employed destroys the polish coating.

Paste wax generally gives the best appearance and durability, particularly if polished by machine. It should be mopped on the floor and allowed to stand until the volatile thinner evaporates, which may take 15 to 30 minutes. The floor is then machine polished.

Water-base emulsion polish requires no buffing. It is mopped on the floor and allowed to dry. While commonly used, it gives a somewhat less attractive and less durable finish than does a buffed solvent-base wax.

A new development in solvent-soluble polymers permits the application of a bright-drying renewable coating which requires no buffing. These products can be used simultaneously to clean the floor and deposit a glossy film. Because the polymer coatings are not compatible with all polishes, a wise precaution is to test them on a small portion of the floor before large-scale application. Failure of the polymers to dry to a high gloss indicates that the floor must be stripped of old polish before they are used.

The polish coating on a properly maintained floor can be renewed several times without completely stripping and recoating. If it is in good condition, a new coat of polish, especially in traffic lanes, may be sufficient. Remove the old polish with rags moistened in turpentine, mineral spirits, or other paint thinner. Good ventilation is necessary. It is important to wipe up all solvent before it dries; otherwise the old polish will be redeposited. Steel wool can be used to loosen thick spots of polish.

Remaining polish should be washed off with soap and warm water, working as rapidly as possible to prevent water reaching the wood or turning a shellac finish white. After the surface has dried, a new coat of polish may be applied.

Refinishing

Varnish coatings and other finishes are not effective in preventing long-term moisture content changes in wood such as occur seasonally. They do, however, retard the entrance and exit of water and thus may be expected to moderate the effects of short-term changes, such as water

U. S. Forest Products Laboratory

1. Spreading mastic.

Harris Manufacturing Company

2. Peeling away face membrane.

U. S. Forest Products Laboratory

3. Tapping blocks firmly into place.

Laying block flooring directly in rubber-base
mastic on plywood subfloor.

spillage or short periods of extremely high humidity. It is desirable, therefore, to refinish worn areas as promptly as possible to reduce the possibility of excessive swelling, and perhaps buckling, from such short-term
effects as those mentioned.

Before applying a new coat of varnish or shellac, the floor should
be cleaned to remove dirt and stains. Then it should be sanded using fine
to medium sandpaper, moving with the grain to remove rough spots and
glossy areas on the old finish. Next, the dust is removed, preferably with
a vacuum cleaner, and the floor wiped with a dust rag or tack cloth. (The
latter is a cloth impregnated with a tacky substance.) It is now ready
for the new coat of varnish or other finish.

Small worn spots usually can be successfully retouched. If this can be done without leaving lap marks, complete removal of the finish is avoided. Sometimes the wood is roughened from wear after the finish has worn away. When this has occurred, a penetrating sealer should be applied to the spot before varnishing. Otherwise, the color in the varnish will make the spot darker than the balance of the floor.

With a sealer finish, no more work may be necessary than to mop fresh sealer on the worn areas of the traffic channels, wipe up any excess, and buff the surface as has already been described for the last coat on new floors. With varnish, lacquer, or shellac, two coats, advisable on the worn areas, would be too much on the areas of little wear. It may therefore be practicable to apply a first coat in the worn areas only, ending all brush strokes at joints between boards, and then to apply a second coat over the entire floor. A similar procedure can be used for paint, but once paint begins to crack and scale badly, it becomes necessary to remove it all by sanding or with paint remover. Painting can be started over again with a coating of even thickness.

After varnish, lacquer, or shellac finish has been renewed several times, it may no longer be possible to refinish the worn areas to match the appearance of the unworn areas where too much old finish, discolored by age, remains. It is then time to remove the old finish entirely.

The best way to remove old finish is by power sanding, which is necessary if the wood has become badly scuffed or marred. But there is a limit to the number of times a floor may be sanded because each sanding removes a substantial amount of wood as dust. Other methods of removing old finish therefore may be needed at times.

Oil-finished floors. An old linseed-oil finish embedded in the wood may cause some difficulty. If a steel-wool buffing machine is available, an attempt should first be made to clean the floor sufficiently merely by buffing with No. 3 steel wool. If this is not feasible or proves ineffective, a chemical treatment will be necessary. Mild alkalies change oil and many sealers and varnishes into soap that can be scrubbed off with water. The alkali used may be a water solution of trisodium phosphate, washing soda, or a commercial compound. Lye is inadvisable because it is strong enough to discolor some woods or even to swell and soften them. Because alkaline solutions are hard on the hands, rubber gloves should be worn.

In applying the alkali, flush a small area of the floor at a time with the solution and allow it to stand for a few minutes, then scrub with stiff brush or No. 1 steel wool. Next flush the area with clean water and scrub to remove the soap that has been formed, and finally remove all the water possible by mopping and let the floor dry thoroughly. If the floor turns gray in color as a result of the action of the alkali and water, bleach it with a saturated solution of oxalic acid in water. (*Caution:* Oxalic acid is poisonous and must be handled with care. Rubber gloves should be worn.) Rinse off the oxalic acid thoroughly with clean water, mop, and let the floor dry completely. Any raised grain or roughening of the surface of the boards should be smoothed with sandpaper or steel wool before new finish is applied.

Varnish- and lacquer-finished floors. Old varnish or lacquer can be removed with liquid varnish remover. The remover should be an organic liquid and should contain no water. The directions for using the liquid remover should be followed closely.

If the first coat of the original varnish was thinned too much and penetrated into the wood too far, some of it may still remain embedded. It will not interfere with the new finish except for the darker color it produces. If the color is unacceptable, it may be possible to remove the embedded varnish by the treatment with alkali described for floors originally finished with oil.

Shellac-finished floors. Old shellac finish can be removed by scouring the floor with No. 3 steel wool and denatured alcohol diluted with an equal amount of water. If the floor boards are level and not warped or cupped, the scouring can be done to advantage with a floor-polishing machine fitted with a wire brush to which a pad of No. 3 steel wool is attached. After scouring, the floor should be rinsed with a minimum amount of clean water and allowed to dry thoroughly before refinishing with shellac.

When white spots have developed in shellac finish from accidental contact with water, they may often be taken out by rubbing lightly with a soft cloth moistened with denatured alcohol diluted with an equal amount of water. Alcohol must be used with care to avoid cutting the shellac coating.

MAINTENANCE

Sweeping, dry mopping, or vacuuming are usually all that is necessary for routine daily cleaning of wood floors. Polishing should be necessary no more frequently than twice a month, and no less frequently than twice a year. Water is most damaging and continued exposure can cause dimensional changes which result in warping, shrinking, or splintering of the wood. For these reasons, water should never unnecessarily be brought into contact with a wood floor, except in a refinishing operation.

Here is the recommended system for maintenance of hardwood floors:

(1) The floor should be swept daily, using a floor brush or, preferably, chemically treated dust cloths or mops. A soft cotton floor mop kept barely dampened with a mixture of 3 parts of kerosene and 1 part of paraffin oil is excellent for dry mopping. Commercial preparations are

available for the purpose also. When the mop becomes dirty, it should be washed in hot water and soap, dried, and again dampened with the mixture of kerosene and paraffin oil.

(2) The floor should be re-buffed without applying any additional polish at intervals as required. It is desirable to re-buff at least every two weeks.

(3) The floor should be spot-cleaned, using a damp mop moistened with dilute solution of a liquid synthetic detergent and thoroughly wrung out. All areas which are spot-cleaned are re-buffed and, if necessary, a light coating of solvent-base wax is reapplied to the area.

Buffing can be omitted if a bright-drying, solvent-soluble polymer coating is used.

Polish over varnish, lacquer, shellac, and paint tends to make floors slippery unless the layer is kept very thin. Over sealer finishes, polish is usually less slippery. Some polishes are made with special ingredients to improve their resistance to slipping.

Sealer finishes applied and maintained adequately with electric buffing machines have proved especially satisfactory for floors subject to heavy use.

Patches of dirt that cannot be removed by dry mopping, or rubber burns from friction between rubber footwear and the floor, may be removed by rubbing lightly with fine steel wool moistened with turpentine or paint thinner.

For floors which have become very dirty and stained, a very heavy layer of liquid solvent-base wax or polymer coating is applied to a small area. It is allowed to soak for five minutes, then is rubbed thoroughly with No. 00 steel wool and wiped dry to remove all dirt. This treatment may have to be repeated before the original color is restored. If the floor cannot be cleaned by this method, it must be scraped and sanded.

SPECIAL MAINTENANCE PROBLEMS

Heel marks, caster marks

The marks should be rubbed with fine steel wool and solvent-base polish, working with the grain of the wood. The area is wiped dry and then polished.

Dark spots

The spot and the nearby area should be cleaned with No. 1 steel wool and solvent-base polish or mineral spirits. If the spot persists, it can be sanded with fine sandpaper, feathering at three to four inches into the surrounding area. If this treatment fails to remove the spot, a bleach such as oxalic acid solution—one ounce of oxalic acid per quart of water—

should be applied. The solution should be allowed to stand on the spot one hour; then the floor should be rinsed with clear water. A second treatment may be helpful if the spot does not fade. Even if the second application appears to have failed, the spot should be dried and refinished and then re-examined. If the spot appears to be too offensive, then the affected flooring strip should be replaced.

Light spots

These may be due to several causes: excess cleaning solution, milk or food dried on the floor, or standing water. If there is doubt about the origin of the spot, it should first be rubbed with a damp cloth and then dried. If this fails to remove the spot, it should be rubbed with fine sand-paper and then cleaned with No. 1 steel wool and mineral spirits. The floor should be allowed to dry and a matching finish applied to the spot, with the finish feathered out into the surrounding area. The floor may be polished after the finish dries thoroughly.

Streaks and smears

Too heavy an application of polish or insufficient buffing can leave the floor streaked and smeared. Additional polishing should eliminate this con-dition. If the streaks and smears are not removed by polishing, they are probably caused by dirt ground into the polish. First, an attempt should be made at cleaning with liquid polish and drying the surface. If this does not help, the instructions given for removing old polish, page 269, should be followed.

Ink stains

The same procedure as for "Dark spots" should be followed.

Scratches

The use of a finish-restoring compound sold for furniture is helpful in hiding scratches.

Cracks

When floors are laid originally with insufficient regard for control of moisture content, they may develop cracks or gaps between boards by the time they need refinishing. There is no satisfactory way of eliminating such cracks short of taking up the floor and relaying it.

Cracks open wider in winter when the wood reaches a minimum moisture content and become narrower in summer when the wood is more moist. If the cracks are filled with a soft putty or crack filler in winter, some of the filler may be squeezed out during the following summer to be tracked over the floor. If a hard filler is used, the wood may be further compressed during the summer. In either situation the cracks will open again during the next winter and become worse than they were before the filler was applied. Filler applied in the summer will be insufficient to fill the gaps when they become wider again in the winter. On the whole, when cracks develop it is best to put up with them unless they are bad enough to justify relaying the floor.

Wide cracks tend to collect dust and dirt. Regular use of a vacuum cleaner should serve to keep the cracks clean. Compacted dirt may be pried loose with a blunt instrument. Floors with wide cracks, into which some finishing material is bound to flow, are best refinished when the cracks are at their narrowest. When oak floors with wide cracks are buffed with steel wool in refinishing, it is well to use a vacuum cleaner a few days later to remove any particles of steel wool from the cracks.

Warped or buckled floors

This condition is usually caused by water or moisture vapor reaching the floor from below. First, the source should be found and eliminated. After the floor has returned to a flat condition, it should be sanded and refinished. A very bad condition may require driving screws from the subfloor up into the finish wood.

Raised grain

This effect is usually due to the use of water on improperly sealed floors. The area should be buffed with No. 2 steel wool, if the grain is slightly raised. More severe cases should be resanded. Matching finish is applied and allowed to dry thoroughly; then the floor may be polished.

Squeaks

Floor squeaks are caused by relative movement of the tongue of one flooring strip in the groove of its neighbor. Such movement may occur for any one of a number of reasons. For example, if the floor joists are not strong enough, they may deflect sufficiently to permit movement in the flooring. Similarly, if sleepers are not held down tightly to a concrete slab, or if they come loose in service, enough movement may be possible to cause squeaks. Poorly manufactured flooring in which the tongues are undersize and thus do not fit tightly in the grooves may also lead to squeaks. Warped flooring or subflooring may permit the boards to rock under traffic; this is unlikely to be a factor with hollow-back flooring. An unusual case, which might occur occasionally, is one where the joists change direction in adjoining rooms while the flooring direction is constant. Where this occurs, the flooring in one room would be parallel to the joists and deflection of the subfloor might permit sufficient movement to cause squeaks. Finally, and perhaps most commonly, squeaks may result from inadequate nailing.

Obviously, the best method of eliminating flooring squeaks is to install well-made flooring on a sound floor system, taking particular care in installation, especially with the nailing. If squeaks do occur in a finished floor, a number of steps may be taken.

First, determine the cause of movement so that proper steps may be taken for correction. Regardless of cause, one expedient is to lubricate the tongue with mineral oil introduced into the opening between adjacent boards. The oil must be used sparingly; too much may result in stains in the flooring.

A fairly common and effective procedure is to drive a nail through the face of the flooring into the subfloor—preferably also into a joist. The nail should be driven near the tongue edge of the flooring strip, then set and the hole filled.

Where flooring is warped and the under surface of the floor is exposed, screws through the subfloor and into the finish floor will be effective in reducing movement. From the standpoint of appearances, this procedure is less objectionable than face nailing.

7 FORMED-IN-PLACE FLOORS

GENERAL CHARACTERISTICS

The concept of forming floors in place is not new; concrete, terrazzo, magnesite, and mastic floors have a long history. However, since the late 1950's, many synthetic organic materials have been introduced into the flooring industry and these have had a revolutionary impact on the field. A side effect of this innovation has been the development of a wide variety of names associated with these new products and confusion has been generated by their use as interchangeable terms. Examples of the most popular labels for these floors are: poured floors, monolithic surfaces, toppings, troweled composition floors, resinous floors, and seamless floors.

These floors are all prepared at the time of installation by mixing the matrix, i.e., binding material, with fillers and/or decorative additives. The flooring material, after application, forms a seamless coating. Floors discussed in this category include one material, mastic, that has been in use for many years, and a group of new products called resinous flooring that includes epoxies, polyesters, polyurethanes, silicones, and polychloroprenes.

Part of the rapid growth of this segment of the flooring industry can be attributed to the fact that several varieties of seamless floors are possible. For example, utility floors are generally made with sand fillers; decorative floors contain marble chips (terrazzo style) or selected fillers yielding interesting designs. The recent development of flexible flooring using epoxy materials is expected to extend further the use of these materials in the industry.

Matrices

Although formed-in-place floors can be prepared by a combination of techniques, ordinarily the surface will be finished by one of three processes: self-leveling, trowel-finishing, or surface-grinding. The next few paragraphs will discuss the characteristics of and typical matrix materials used in each of these techniques.

Self-leveling mixes (1) require little or no surface work; (2) harden to a smooth surface; (3) are generally applied in thin films; (4) are fairly fluid; (5) give low build; (6) may or may not have fillers present; (7) are such that, if fillers are used, they are fine particles or thin flakes; (8) are such that the coating follows the general contour of the subfloor; (9) will not hide foundation cracks; and (10) can be decorative and/or functional.

279

Poraflor Inc.

Formed-in-place floor installation.

For self-leveling mixes, typical matrix materials are epoxy, polyester, and polyurethane.

Some mixes require trowel-finishing to develop a smooth surface and densify the top layer. These (1) are characterized by heavy viscosity; (2) are used in thicknesses ranging from ⅛ inch to over 2 inches; (3) require fillers; (4) are such that surface smoothness depends largely on the particle size of the filler; (5) can be used to level the foundation, subfloor, or base; (6) may hide future foundation cracks, depending on thickness and type of matrix; and (7) can be decorative and/or functional. For mixes that must be troweled, typical matrix materials are epoxy, polyester, polyurethane, asphalt emulsion, portland cement, latex-modified portland cement, and magnesium oxychloride cement.

Formed-in-place mixes that must be surface-ground to develop a smooth finish (1) contain marble or granite chips; (2) look like terrazzo; (3) have heavy viscosity; (4) are used in thicknesses ranging from ⅛ inch to over 2 inches; (5) may hide future foundation cracks, depending on thickness and type of matrix; and (6) can be decorative and/or functional. For mixes that must be surface ground, typical matrix materials are epoxy, polyester, portland cement, latex-modified portland cement, and magnesium oxychloride cement.

Solidification mechanisms

There are three general mechanisms by which the flooring matrix achieves a solid state: evaporation of solvent leaving a continuous film; a chemical reaction that converts the binder from a liquid to a solid state; and a combination of evaporation and chemical reaction.

Evaporation. In the first mechanism, the fundamental chemical properties of the matrix material are the same before and after application on the floor. The binding agent that will eventually form the continuous matrix can be (1) dissolved in a solvent (organic or water) to form a solution; (2) dispersed in water as a latex; and (3) dispersed in water as an emulsion.

For purposes of this discussion, we can regard latex and emulsion dispersions as having the same evaporative properties, because water is the basis of the solvent or liquid phase in both cases.

Film-forming floor materials cast from solution are normally continuous, self-leveling, thin films. Typical examples of solution floor coatings based on organic solvents are varnishes and lacquers.

Latex and emulsion dispersions used in floor applications consist of solid particles surrounded by a liquid water phase. As the water component evaporates, the remaining solid particles are drawn closer together by various physical phenomena including capillary action, surface tension, interfacial tension, etc. The tiny particles, which may be only microns in diameter, are subjected to very high pressures causing them to coalesce into a continuous matrix.

A typical characteristic of all floors containing volatile solvents is that dry-film and wet-film thickness is substantially different and depends on the volume ratio of solids-to-volatile liquids in the floor coating.

The inherent chemical and physical characteristics of the binder are attained only after all the solvent has evaporated from the applied coating. However, it is possible to open a floor area to light traffic before the ultimate strength and hardness of the matrix material have developed. Further treatment of the floors or the movement of heavy equipment over them usually require that all solvent be completely evaporated from the matrix.

The behavior of this category of matrix materials can be summarized as follows:

(1) The inherent physical and chemical properties of the matrix material are fixed before application to the floor.

(2) The dry-film thickness (build) is less than the wet or applied thickness.

(3) Attainment of the matrix material's final physical properties depends on the complete evaporation of the carrier solvent.

Chemical reaction. Within this category, it is helpful to distinguish between inorganic and organic matrix materials.

Inorganics, such as portland cement and magnesium oxychloride cement, must be mixed with sufficient water to convert the dry powder to a pastelike consistency. Water, in addition to reducing the powders to a flowable mass, plays an essential part in the chemical reaction that results in the curing of the inorganic binder. In fact, it is not uncommon to use evaporation retarders (curing compounds) to prevent premature loss of water which would result in reduced strength.

Organic binders—such as the epoxies, polyesters, and polyurethanes, often referred to by the trade as resins—are cured by the separate addition of cross-linking agents, polymerization catalysts, or oxidizing agents. These additives, called curing agents, hardeners, or catalysts, must be added to the resin in exact quantities to initiate the reaction and promote thorough curing.

The recent development of polyurethane resins, which are cured by absorption of moisture from the atmosphere, makes possible the single-can product and eliminates the need for careful measurement of a curing agent.

The products in this general category vary widely in their physical and chemical properties, practical film thickness, applicability, etc. However, they do share the following characteristics: (1) limited open or working time, (2) the development of chemical and physical properties after the addition or absorption of an additive, and (3) equivalence between dry film thickness and applied thickness.

Evaporation and chemical reaction. The most common floor products in this category are the latex-modified portland cement mixtures. In these products, the portland cement contributes compressive strength while the latex (neoprene or vinyl) adds resilience and waterproofness to the finished floor.

There are also available many solvent-thinned, thermosetting resins which are used as surface coatings for floors, walls, equipment, and so forth. They range in appearance from clear, varnish-like films to pigmented enamels. Matrix materials in this class, such as polyurethane, epoxy, and polyester, depend on solvent evaporation as well as chemical reaction to cure completely.

Installation precautions

In many cases failures of chemically-cured resinous floors have been traced to faulty installation techniques.

Resinous floors manufactured at the job site require highly qualified supervisors and well-trained workmen. Also, it is not readily appreciated by novices in the field or by operators previously adjusted to working with

Poraflor Inc.

1. Pouring base coat.

Poraflor Inc.

3. Scattering flake mix.

Poraflor Inc.

2. Spreading base coat.

Poraflor Inc.

4. Applying first top coat.

Installing a formed-in-place floor.

water systems that the new resinous materials cannot be cut with water or removed from tools and equipment with water. Special solvents must be used, which are, in many instances, flammable and quite strong in odor.

As with all the resinous materials, the conditions of the subfloor and its preparation is of extreme importance, since a good, strong bond is essential for a successful installation.

Special tools and equipment are required for the installation of various types of resinous flooring systems. These fall into four general categories: (1) trowels and hand tools, (2) power tools and mixers, (3) spray units and compressors, and (4) protective devices.

Because almost all resinous systems require spreading by trowel, an operator's dexterity with these instruments can play an important part in finishing the surface. Some systems are best spread with a vinyl squeegee applicator tool; others are most easily applied by a roll-on technique.

Another important factor in the preparation of decorative floorings is the need to measure precisely the amount of decorative plastic or marble chips to be added to the resin to attain a uniform design.

Careful selection of mixing equipment is necessary to avoid air entrapment which might create pinhole defects in the floor.

Large areas are sometimes formed by spray-on techniques. Again, the choice of equipment is important and its selection can be done only by an expert.

MASTIC

Description

Because mastic floors have been in use for some fifty years, many people are inclined to regard them as old-fashioned, without realizing that modern technology has greatly improved this type of flooring. The early mastic floors used crude emulsified asphalt as the binder for inert fillers. Today, refined asphalts are available with superior performance properties.

Mastic floors consist of asphalt emulsion (which serves as a binder), portland cement, and stone filler, ranging from sand to coarse aggregates, depending on the purpose of the floor.

Typical compositions for light-duty and heavy-duty mastic floors are shown in Table 19.

Mastic floors, being thermoplastic, have a tendency to soften under heat. They should not be exposed to temperatures over 125° F.

Today's high-quality mastics not only have a compressive strength of 3,000 to 3,500 pounds per square inch, but they will stand up under greater pressures than other floorings with higher p.s.i. ratings because of inherent flexibility and self-repairing capabilities.

burlap or other curing aids to permit proper hydration of the cement (this will increase the strength of the finished floor and will prevent shrinkage). (4) Allow time for proper curing of the floor.

Maintenance

Mastic floors are maintained by the same general methods described for asphalt tile in the section on resilient floor coverings, page 130. Because these floors are used predominantly in work areas which are functional rather than decorative, less effort is given to maintaining a highly polished surface and more to sweeping operations.

The most important point to remember in selecting maintenance products for use on mastic floors is the harmful effect of solvents, oils, and fatty materials on the binder. Therefore, oil-treated sweeping tools, oil-based sweeping compounds, solvent cleaning agents, pine-oil scrubbers, and solvent-base polishes are to be avoided.

Sharp edges on furniture and equipment can cut into mastic floors. Furniture supports will help prevent such damage.

Areas subject to spillage of oils, petroleum solvents, and hydrocarbon-type products can be protected by the use of recently developed epoxy coatings that adhere tenaciously to asphalt surfaces. Their high build of 10 mils (when cured) eliminates any surface roughness in the mastic floor and provides a heavy-duty wearing surface.

Excessive wear on mastic surfaces can sometimes be corrected by use of an epoxy overlay.

If the mastic is wearing because of frictional drag, e.g., at turning points, the condition might be helped by an epoxy overlay or the use of steel shot in the surface. An experienced person is needed to broadcast shot; it must be distributed evenly and the correct amount must be used.

EPOXY

Description

Epoxy resins are *thermosetting* materials. This term is used to describe products, made by chemical reaction, that cannot be melted and rehardened without destroying their properties. The term can be contrasted with *thermoplastic,* which is applied to materials which soften when heated and harden when cooled. Polyethylene, polystyrene, and polyvinyl are examples of thermoplastic resins. Polyester, polyurethane, and epoxies are examples of thermosetting resins.

The two basic constituents of an epoxy system are the epoxy resin and the hardener. Once they are mixed together, a chemical reaction is started which is irreversible. This reaction supplies its own heat, which causes the mix to cure. The mixture is cured when it solidifies and the reaction of the resin and the hardener stops. The time required for a mix to gel, that is, when it begins to harden, is known as the "pot life." This is measured from the instant the hardener is added to the resin and depends on the volume or mass of the mixed materials. Unlike products which depend on air for their cure, a large mass of epoxy will harden much faster than a smaller mass, because of the greater amount of heat generated and the difficulty of dissipating the heat.

When we think of epoxy resins, we associate the term chemically with the epoxy triangle. This triangle within the molecule is formed by two atoms of carbon and one atom of oxygen. The triangle opens when certain other chemicals called curing agents are present. The oxygen atom, through a chemical reaction with a curing agent, attaches itself to a nearby epoxy molecule. When this happens, the resin changes from a liquid to a solid and acquires the properties for which it is famous.

The chemical change caused by the curing agent is called "cross-linking." This means that the molecule in the epoxy compound, which can be pictured as long chains lying side by side, are linked so that they are no longer free to move independently. The links are composed of molecules of the curing agent, which now become part of the epoxy molecule.

The curing agent plays a key part in tailoring epoxies to specific uses. Before the curing agent is added, epoxies can be stored indefinitely. The combination of resin and curing agent, however, has a certain pot life, the length of time before significant cross-linking takes place. This is why most epoxies are supplied in "two-can" packages. One exception to this arrangement is the use of a hardener which can be blended safely with the liquid resin at room temperature. In this system, the hardener becomes effective only when the entire system is heated sufficiently to activate the hardening agent, thus triggering the reaction.

A wide variety of properties can be achieved through the judicious addition of various constituents. For example, the choice of resin and hardener will be based on such considerations as the chemical resistance required, the flexibility desired, and the length of cure for a particular application. Addition of pigments, fillers, anti-sag agents, and flow-control agents can alter the properties of the system to give the characteristics required for a particular application.

Epoxies are versatile resins because they have a number of desirable characteristics, including toughness, high mechanical strength, low shrinkage during cure, good electrical insulation properties, superior adhesion, good resistance to weathering, and good resistance to chemicals.

Flooring based on epoxies can be applied in thin layers ($\frac{1}{16}$ inch to $\frac{1}{4}$ inch) to yield the high strength and resistance necessary to meet construction requirements. Compared to concrete, epoxies have four times higher tensile strength and more than two times higher compressive strength.

One expert holds that epoxy resins have the highest adhesive power of any known resin, and that, while the adhesion of polyester is considerably greater than that of cement, it falls far short of the adhesive capacity of the epoxies.

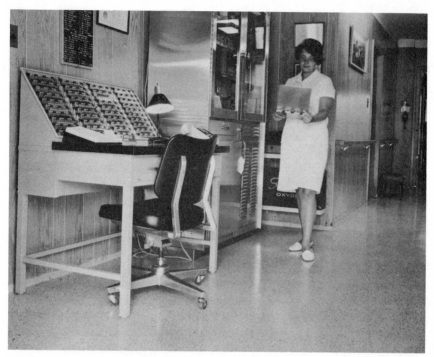

Poraflor Inc.

Formed-in-place floor installation.

Table 20 shows that an epoxy topping has excellent resistance to a great many chemicals. Where chemical resistance is an important requirement, the trowel-type compositions are preferred over resin-terrazzo mixtures because marble chips can deteriorate under the effects of some chemicals.

The setting times of the epoxy resins are predetermined or fixed by the manufacturer and cannot be varied on the job.

Epoxy resins usually will not set or harden at temperatures lower than 50° F. Therefore, during application, the temperature of the air and the concrete slab must be above 50° F.

The introduction of epoxy resins as a matrix for terrazzo floors has made possible the installation of thin terrazzo directly on concrete slabs without the customary two-inch cement/sand underbed. As a result, epoxy terrazzos offer the advantages of lightweight, speedier installation, simpler architectural design, and usually some cost savings.

Thin epoxy terrazzos will telegraph cracks or faults in the structural slab. To date, no method has been developed to install a seamless epoxy terrazzo floor and prevent the reflection of structural cracks.

TABLE 20

CHEMICAL RESISTANCE OF AN EPOXY TOPPING
(30-day Total Immersion)

Unaffected	Nitric acid, 20%
Acetic acid, 5%	Oil, petroleum
Alcohol, ethyl	Oil, vegetable
Alcohol, secondary butyl	Oleic acid
Ammonium hydroxide, 20%	Phosphoric acid, 50%
Ammonia vapor	Sodium hydroxide, 20% (lye)
Calcium hydrochlorite, 5%	Sodium hypochlorite, 5%
Carbon tetrachloride	Sulfuric acid, 10%
Citric acid, 10%	Toluene
Detergent solution	Urine
Fats, animal	Water
Fuel oil	Xylene
Gasoline	*Discolored; not attacked*
Glycerine	Sulfuric acid, 50%
Hydrochloric acid, 10%	*Failed within 30 days*
Hydrochloric acid concentrate	Acetic acid, glacial
Hydrochloric acid vapor	Acetone
Lactic acid, 10%	Cellosolve
Linseed fatty acid	Formaldehyde, 37%
Methyl isobutyl carbinol	Methyl ethyl ketone
Mineral spirits	Nitric acid, 30%
Muriatic acid	Sulfuric acid concentrate
Nitric acid, 10%	

Source: The Hallemite Manufacturing Co.

The high durability and chemical resistance of an epoxy floor coating make it an ideal material for heavy-duty areas. Application of the material does not require closing the floors for long periods, because it can be installed and ready to receive traffic within 24 hours. With aggregates added, the resinous material provides a safe non-skid surface.

Floor areas subjected to high impact such as on loading docks are suited to the use of an epoxy surface.

Epoxies are also suitable for a variety of floor uses because of their excellent resistance to effects of weather and their capacity for being pigmented any color. Only white tends to yellow. These properties make the product ideal for high-traffic areas where the choice of color is desirable.

Epoxy floorings and floor toppings increasingly are being used in places where a high level of cleanliness is essential. Their smooth, impermeable surface makes them easy to clean, and their non-dusting characteristics promote a dustless environment.

The main disadvantages in the use of epoxy floorings are (1) the relatively high cost of the resin, (2) the on-site labor costs entailed in troweling, and (3) the need for careful attention to subfloor preparation, mixing ratios, and application techniques. In addition, the curing agents must be handled with care because of their toxicity.

Epoxies are also used in the preparation of flexible, terrazzo-style tiles. Available in standard sizes, 9 by 9 inches by ⅛ inch and 12 by 12 inches by ⅛ inch, these tiles which contain marble chips are installed with the ease of resilient tiles.

Epoxies are suitable for application over any physically sound surface of concrete, brick, terrazzo, marble, slate, stone, metal, or wood. The surface should be thoroughly clean—free of oil, dirt, polish, loose paint, rust, scale—and completely dry.

Some surfaces over which epoxies should not be used are ceramic tile, asphalt tile, vinyl tile, and linoleum.

Preparation of the subfloor

New concrete. The surface of new concrete—even of good high-strength concrete—is always weak. This is because vibration and troweling movements, made when placing the concrete, encourage the lighter components, such as surplus portland cement and water, to rise to the surface. When this lighter material sets, it is called "laitance." It gives new concrete a typically smooth appearance and a deceptive impression of strength.

Laitance is present to a depth of about 0.05 inch and is weak in almost every respect. Unless it is removed, it will limit the performance and perhaps cause the failure of anything bonded to its surface.

Curing compounds are often sprayed onto wet concrete to act as a membrane for the purpose of retarding water evaporation while the concrete is curing. The membranes are almost invisible when the concrete has cured. The chemicals used for such compounds frequently are fatty oils or resinous materials of types that can act as "parting" agents for any subsequently applied topping. That is, they are likely to prevent good adhesion.

If possible, the use of such compounds should be prohibited in the specification for the concrete; if they have been used, they must be removed before any subsequent topping is applied. If there is doubt as to the condition of the concrete, a small patch of topping can be applied to test the bond.

Poraflor Inc.

Formed-in-place floor installation.

Because new concrete contains much water, some of which is surplus, the concrete must be permitted to cure, i.e., age, for as long as possible before a resinous topping is applied. There are three reasons for this: (1) to reduce the moisture content, (2) to permit the major part of slab shrinkage to take place, and (3) to allow the concrete to harden thoroughly.

The initial water content of the slab, its thickness, and the prevailing climatic conditions will all have great effect on the aging time. The aging time should be as long as possible, with 30 days regarded as the minimum.

Old concrete. Each floor should be considered separately and its condition analyzed before decisions are made with respect to placing a topping over it. Caution should be exercised regarding the surface of concrete that has been long exposed to penetrating substances such as soaps and oils.

All traces of oils, asphalt, and curing compounds act as parting agents and should be removed prior to thorough cleaning of the floor.

Old concrete is often deteriorated and has a weak surface for bonding purposes. Removal of this weak upper layer is always preferable and often essential.

Steel. Good results cannot be expected over a rusted surface. Any exposed steel over which a floor topping is to be placed must be sandblasted and vacuum-cleaned just prior to placing the topping. Where sandblasting is not possible, the steel surface should be de-greased and ground or mechanically abraded (by sanding or wire brushing) to reveal continuous bright metal.

Wood. This material is sometimes found as part of the subfloor. Sanding or sandblasting followed by vacuum-cleaning is recommended as a cleaning method. If the floor has been creosoted, an adhesion test should be made. Fresh creosote acts as a parting agent, but fair adhesion may be obtained with an old creosoted surface that has been well cleaned. Placing an epoxy topping over a subfloor made entirely of wood is not recommended because of the many problems that can be encountered.

Bituminous asphalt. This material should not be used as a subfloor. The reason is the same as that for rejecting the application of a hard paint over a weak surface.

Ceramic tile. The treatment of ceramic tile will vary according to type. Usually, an acid etch gives the best results; on some extremely acid-resistant tile, however, a sandblast and vacuum-cleaning technique may work better.

Old terrazzo. This should be treated in the same manner as old concrete with the preferred method being mechanical scarification by grinding, followed by vacuum-cleaning.

Installation

For a subsurface of wood, which shrinks and expands with varying humidity, the use of reinforcing overlay, e.g., open-mesh glass cloth or wire mesh, is advised prior to application of the epoxy floor compound. Another reason for using a layer of reinforcement over wood is avoidance of the possibility that the resin could pull off splinters of the wood, thus losing adhesion.

Moisture must not be allowed to come in contact with the floor coating during application and for at least 12 hours following. If the cement is not fully cured before application of an epoxy, the water used for cement crystallization will destroy the bond between the topping and the cement. Where it is known that the surface will be damp at the time of application, a polysulfide-modified mixture should be used.

Depending on the filler used, the epoxy resin can be applied by brush, roller, trowel, or spray. Brushing is the most practical means when small or hard-to-reach areas must be covered. Its major drawback is that only a comparatively thin formulation, one containing very little filler, can be applied by brush. Rolling presents the fastest method of covering large areas with a minimum of expense for equipment. Troweling is the preferred method of application for highly filled, viscous epoxy systems. Spraying with special equipment designed to handle the two-component nature of epoxy is ideal for quickly covering very large areas.

Maintenance

Rigorous rules for maintenance of epoxy resin floors have not yet been established because of the relative newness of these materials. In general, it is suggested that an epoxy floor be treated as if it were portland cement terrazzo. (See maintenance of terrazzo, pages 225-232.)

Floors should be swept daily, using treated sweeping tools. Damp-mopping with mild cleaning solutions should be done periodically to remove stubborn soils. The frequency of scrubbing will depend both on the amount of traffic and the nature of soiling.

The question of whether a coating of floor polish is required has not been finally resolved. If a high-gloss surface is desirable, then a slip-resistant, bright-drying polish should be applied. It should be remembered that, unlike portland cement terrazzo, epoxy terrazzo is non-absorptive and, therefore, requires little or no sealing of the pores. For this reason, polish should be applied in very thin films and only to the extent that surface gloss is desired.

In selecting any cleaning compound to be used on the epoxy surface, it would be well to avoid strong acids and such solvents as acetone, glycol-ether, formaldehyde, and methyl ethyl ketone.

Several proprietary products can be used to patch and repair cracks and surface faults that might develop in the epoxy floor. Since the decision as to which of these products should be selected depends on many factors including environment, type of epoxy used, nature of the subfloor, etc., the choice should be made by a flooring contractor or a flooring expert.

POLYESTER

Description

Polyester surface coatings are well established in Europe, particularly in Germany and Italy. Until recently, the big advance in the use of polyester in the United States has been in the field of fiber glass reinforced plastics. This development continues to increase the use of polyester resins as surface coatings, and their introduction to the flooring industry is expected to increase their utilization. Basically, they exhibit many of the same properties as epoxies when used as flooring, with the one big advantage being the lower cost of the resin. The polyester resins exhibit slightly more shrinkage than the epoxy resins. Their installation over wet or damp concrete slabs is questionable.

A few companies are offering specially compounded polyester resins together with bonding agents, which they claim make possible the application of polyester resins on concrete slabs that are on- or below-grade. Since most of these installations have been made within the past few years, there is no proof that installations of polyester resins can be made on concrete slabs that are damp or in contact with the earth.

Several companies are offering spray-applied polyester industrial floorings which incorporate fiber glass rovings (slightly twisted strands of fiber). This combination is reported to help polyester material overcome structural cracks.

Esters are the chemical-reaction products of acids and alcohols. When the acids and alcohols are difunctional, i.e., can react similarly at both ends of the molecule, the product formed grows to become a long chain called a "polyester." At first, this polymer is a quite viscous or perhaps solid thermoplastic material. It can be dissolved in a monomer, such as styrene, which acts as both a solvent and a potentially reactive intermediate.

Because of the chemical nature of one of the acids initially used in the manufacture of the polyester polymer, the whole system—polyester and the monomer solvent—is capable of reacting when properly catalyzed to form a hard, insolvent mass that cannot be melted.

The liquid resin as supplied may be stored for extended periods. During use, cure is accomplished through one of two basic methods, both of which require a peroxide-type catalyst.

The first method requires heat to activate the catalyst. The second method requires a promoter such as an organic derivative of cobalt or aniline, either of which will activate the catalyst at ambient temperatures. Through judicious use during manufacture of certain raw materials, such as the type of dibasic acids and alcohols, the type and amount of monomer, and the presence or absence of certain promoters and inhibitors, the physical properties of polyesters can be made to vary over a wide range. It is thereby possible actually to tailor-make resins to promote optimum working properties and maximum physical properties for particular fabricating methods and end uses.

Polyester resins all cure with considerable evolution of heat. This is known as the "exotherm" of the resin, and the highest temperature reached in the resin during cure is called the "peak exotherm." Fast liberation of exothermic heat during cure can cause cracking or warping, particularly in thick cross sections. An important feature of polyester resin technology is the control of the rate at which this heat is liberated.

Once started, the curing reaction of polyester resin is irreversible. Therefore, after being mixed and activated, the compound has a definite pot life.

Polyester floors, in the form intended for industrial use, are claimed to have the following desirable characteristics, and in the form for non-industrial uses—those that might be called both functional and decorative—have the added properties of attractiveness and variety of style. (1) They are readily installed over existing floors in thicknesses ranging from ⅛ inch to ¼ inch. (2) They bond monolithically and permanently to any floor surface that can be made clean, dry, and unglazed, e. g., concrete, brick, wood, metal. (3) They are non-porous, non-absorbent, greaseproof, stainproof, and completely sanitary. (4) They are inert and unaffected by most commonly used chemicals. (5) They will not crack, pit, or scratch even under severe usage. (6) They are not slippery. (7) Maintenance, other than routine washing with a cleaning solution, is eliminated.

Performance specifications. Following are the main properties of polyester flooring, each accompanied by a specific performance requirement. These were developed by the Terrazite Association of America.

Compressive strength: Shall exceed 8,500 p.s.i. within 11 days after pouring on a sound concrete slab.

Hardness: Indentation shall not exceed .075 inch diameter when a load of 200 pounds is transmitted to the surface by a 1-inch diameter steel ball and held for 30 minutes, the diameter of indentation measured at the contact point.

Moisture resistance: No moisture shall pass through the floor material when covered by a 2-inch head of water for 272 hours.

Absorption capacity: The floor material shall not increase more than 0.20 percent in weight when immersed for 24 hours in either water or gasoline.

Thermal shock resistance: No cracking or spalling shall occur when the floor material is placed in water of 32° F. for 2 minutes and immediately thereafter immersed in boiling water for 2 minutes, repeatedly for 50 continuous cycles.

Coefficient of expansion: 0.0000075 inch between 15° and 70° F.; 0.0000183 inch between 70° and 160° F.; 0.0000198 inch between 160° and 310° F.

Stain resistance: No permanent stain shall result from contact with water, urine, oil, grease, tobacco, coffee, any carbonated or alcoholic beverage.

Thermal conductivity: K-90 factor of approximately 3.69.

Electrical conductivity: Electrically nonconductive.

Chemical resistance: The floor material shall remain inert when subjected to concentrated and continuous contact with the following chemicals for 30 days at 20° C.: aliphatic hydrocarbon; aluminum sulphate; ammonium nitrate; benzene sulphonic acid; butyl alcohol; calcium chloride; carbon tetrachloride; chlorine (dry, gaseous); copper chloride; copper sulphate; diesel oil; engine oil; ethyl alcohol; ferric chloride; gasoline; hydraulic oils; hydrogen sulphide; iso-octane and iso-octane/Tol-7073; kerosene; lactic acid; lubrication oils; nickel chloride; nickel sulphate; potassium chloride; sodium bisulphate, tetrachloroethylene; toluene; urine; water; xylene; and zinc chloride.

Torginol of America, Inc.

Formed-in-place floor installation.

Chemicals that slightly affect polyester coatings, if permitted to remain in extended contact with the flooring, include acetic acid, benzene, chlorobenzene, sodium carbonate, and trichloroethylene. Constant subjection to these chemicals would probably require minor annual repairs to polyester floors.

Chemicals that significantly damage polyester floors include: acetone, aluminum fluoride, ammonium hydroxide, aniline, carbon bisulphide, chloroform, ether, ethyl acetate, ethylene dichloride, formic acid, lime, methyl acetate, methyl ethyl ketone, methylene chloride, nitrobenzene, phenol, potassium hydroxide, pyridine, and sodium hydroxide.

Polyester floors can be used in almost all of the applications previously described for epoxy floors. The biggest application for polyester floors is over concrete subfloors, although adequate precautions must be taken to avoid contact with moisture and to maintain the subfloor at a reasonable temperature during application and while the floor is curing. Those floor areas located below-grade and on-grade are potential trouble spots.

The use of polyester floors to renovate wooden surfaces requires the advice of a flooring expert.

Polyester terrazzo is well suited for areas of high traffic which also require a decorative surface. The same advantages previously noted for epoxy terrazzo also apply to polyester terrazzo.

Installation

One of the keys to the successful installation of polyester floors on any surface is the preparation of that surface prior to application of the coating. The same general instructions and precautions noted for epoxy floors apply also for polyester resin coatings (see page 291). (Specific instructions in application should be furnished by the flooring contractor and made part of any agreement for services.)

The use of a primer-coat material is very important in the application of polyester floor coatings. This material ensures penetration into the pores of the base, creates a completely monolithic bond, and becomes an integral part of the subsurface to which it is applied. The primer-coat material can be a thin application of the same polyester resins used in the binder or a thin coat of special polyurethane finish. In addition to serving as a bonding agent, the primer coat also serves as a moisture barrier between the subfloor and the topping.

Maintenance

See maintenance of epoxy floors, page 294.

POLYURETHANE

Description

Polyurethanes are synthetic polymers that may be either thermoplastic or thermosetting. These are usually made by the action of polylene di-isocyanate or other diamine with polyols, polyethers, polyesters, or other materials containing hydroxyl groups. Among the more recent developments in resinous flooring, the polyurethanes may be either single-component moisture-cured, single-component oil-modified, or two-component-catalyzed.

In the opinion of most research chemists at present, the polyurethanes are by far the most promising materials for the flooring industry. While each type of resinous coating has its place in the industry, most chemists agree that polyurethanes are capable of better abrasion resistance, impact resistance, flexibility, and chemical resistance—all in one package —than any other type of coating. Against the disadvantage of having to clean the installation equipment in the proper solvent immediately after use, there are the plus factors of very fast drying and high gloss without slipperiness.

Two general types of polyurethane systems are being used in flooring. "One-component" systems rely either upon oxidation or atmospheric moisture reaction for their cure, while the "two-component" systems rely upon the reaction of isocyanates in one component with the hydroxyl groups of polyesters, polyethers, or castor oils in the other.

Most of the polyurethane systems marketed today are of the one-component type which can be applied in thicknesses up to ⅛ inch. There is no thickness limit, however, with the two-component system. This type of polyurethane coating will, reportedly, dry fully in two hours, while the present one-component systems require a few days to achieve maximum cure.

While the use of polyurethane is not new to the flooring industry (it has performed admirably as a clear or pigmented protective coating for wood, concrete, and resilient floors), its application as a decorative, seamless flooring is relatively recent. It is in this area that most manufacturers are concentrating their efforts.

Polyurethane can be made to yield flexible foams, clear films, or rigid solids, depending on the choice of cross-linking additive used. By the same procedure, chemical properties can be adjusted to yield a wide variety of coatings.

The most common coatings for use on floors—especially hardwood floors—are the oil-modified polyurethanes dissolved in solvents. They are formulated into clear finishes and pigmented enamels. There are also sand-filled formulations for utility areas that show excellent toughness, hardness, and load-bearing characteristics as well as an attractive appearance.

The flexibility possible with polyurethane supports the belief that cracks in concrete slabs will not show through the finished floor as readily as with epoxy or polyester coatings. This elastomeric quality is responsible for polyurethane's unsuitability for terrazzo-type floor installations that require surface grinding.

Some of the characteristics claimed for polyurethane floors are as follows: (1) They are seamless and resilient. (2) They are readily installed over existing floors. (3) They have excellent bonding characteristics to any sound substrate. (4) They are grease- and stain-resistant. (5) They are unaffected by most commonly used chemicals. (6) They are not slippery. (7) They are easy to maintain at low cost. (8) They are available in a wide range of color combinations and surface textures. (9) Their usable thickness range is $\frac{1}{16}$ to $\frac{1}{8}$ inch. (10) They are very tough and have excellent resistance to scuffing, scratching, and indentation. (11) The material is not marked by women's spiked heels. (12) They can be recoated periodically to extend service life.

Installation

Typical installation instructions for decorative polyurethane require that the subfloor, usually wood or concrete, be stable, sound, dry, and free of oil, grease, polish, paint, mastic, rust, and scale.

The general floor preparation techniques described for epoxy floors apply also for areas to be covered with polyurethane.

A primer coat is used which pentrates the substrate to seal it against moisture transmission and to provide a strong mechanical and chemical bond. The primer is allowed to dry to a tacky condition, which indicates that most of the solvent has evaporated. A glaze coat is then applied and color chips are broadcast on the wet field. Determining the correct amount and proper coverage of the floor with decorative fillers is a problem for experts and requires considerable installation experience. Finishing is done by troweling the surface and applying alternate coats of chips and resin. Additional coats of glaze are used to develop a high degree of smoothness.

Some installations get as many as eight coats, including the prime coat, multiple top coats of glaze, and multiple coats of chips. This type of application builds the surface up to at least $\frac{1}{16}$ inch; the coating can reach $\frac{1}{8}$-inch thickness.

Most commercial floors, especially corridors, receive three to six extra coats of glaze. However, the number of top coats necessary will depend upon the amount of traffic and the floor environment.

Special inlaid effects are possible with polyurethane floors by cutting out portions of the floor before the final cure has occurred and replacing the removed sections with decorative, pre-formed inserts. However, such installations require considerable skill and knowledge of the floor material.

So far as application techniques are concerned, most of the polyurethane products now on the market are trowel-applied. However, a great deal of progress is being made in spray application, and it is expected that this procedure will be in general use before long.

Maintenance

See maintenance of epoxy floors, page 294.

SILICONES

The newest addition to seamless flooring materials is a silicone rubber product which is a formulation of polymeric resins, a moisture-curing urethane, and specially treated aggregate. The compound provides a surface texture similar to concrete. It is prepared by mixing with a vulcanizing agent prior to application, then troweled into place like concrete.

The primary use of silicone has been as a protective coating over conventional concrete floors where such conditions as water penetration, acid attack, and structural movement have caused damage. It has also been employed as a flexible grout for ceramic tile and patio stone and as a waterproof protective layer for roof surfaces and garage floors.

In the future, this material may be used as a simulated concrete coating over plywood floors. Its ability to bend and elongate also suggests its use in the renovation of old wood floors.

The product displays excellent flexibility, resistance to weathering, outstanding temperature stability, and good resistance to wear and abrasion. Another interesting characteristic of silicone flooring is that it has good resistance to water absorption coupled with high water vapor permeability.

Silicones have only fair chemical resistance compared to other resinous binders, exhibit only fair adhesion unless a primer is used, and have a short pot life similar to most other resinous binders. Their resistance to cutting under impact is relatively poor.

POLYCHLOROPRENES

These materials are one-component, air-curing liquids. After application, volatile solvents evaporate to leave a film of cured polychloroprene. The binders provide excellent abrasion resistance, flexibility, and outstanding resistance to embrittlement by age and temperature. Polychloroprenes show only fair chemical resistance. Because of their volatile solvents, they must be applied under conditions of controlled ventilation.

SELECTED REFERENCES

American Bitumals & Asphalt Co. *Bulletins B-11* and *G-15*, San Francisco: The Company, 1963.

Architectural Specification Study on Ceramic Tile, Toronto: Specification Writers Association of Canada, 1967.

Armstrong Technical Data, 1965-66, Lancaster, Pennsylvania: Armstrong Cork Co., 1965.

Asphalt and Vinyl Asbestos Tile Institute. *Recommended Installation Specifications for Vinyl Asbestos Tile Flooring and Asphalt Tile Flooring,* New York: The Institute, 1962.

BARNOFF, R. M.; DEGELMAN, L. O.; ISENBERG, M. W.; and PASS, V. L. *Literature Review on the Strength and Stiffness of Wood-Frame Floor Construction,* University Park, Pennsylvania: College of Engineering and Architecture, The Pennsylvania State University, 1962.

Basic Facts About the Carpet and Rug Industry, New York: American Carpet Institute, Inc., 1961, 1962, 1963, 1964.

BATES, J. E. "It Takes Three for Progress and Success," *Proceedings of 50th Mid-Year Meeting, May 18-20, 1964,* New York: Chemical Specialties Manufacturers Association, Inc., pp. 141-52.

"Bonding Tile to Treated Concrete," *Flooring,* April, 1966, pp. 41-42.

BROWN, LAMAR H. "Ceramic Tile," *Contract,* March, 1966, pp. 70-77.

————. "Usable Life Held Key Factor in Figuring Maintenance Costs," *Flooring,* July, 1964, p. 18.

Building Maintenance Manual, Racine, Wisconsin: S. C. Johnson & Son, Inc., 1963.

Building Research Institute. *Installation and Maintenance of Resilient Smooth-Surface Flooring,* Washington: National Academy of Sciences —National Research Council, 1958.

"Can Carpet Take It?," *Buildings,* February, 1964, pp. 86, 88, 90.

Cargill Polyurethanes for Coatings, Minneapolis: Cargill, Inc. (undated).

Carpet and Rugs, North Canton, Ohio: The Hoover Home Institute and the Engineering Division, The Hoover Company, 1959.

"Carpet Care," *Building Maintenance and Modernization,* February, 1962, pp. 12-13, 25-27.

"Carpet Constructions," *NIRC Voice* (National Institute of Rug Cleaners, Inc.), September, 1963, pp. 17-29.

"Carpet Industry's Rise Helps Synthetic Fibers," *Chemical & Engineering News,* February, 1964, pp. 32-33.

Carpet Maintenance Manual, Bridgeport, Pennsylvania: James Lees & Sons Company (undated).

Carpet Maintenance Manual, Rome, New York: The Kent Co., Inc. (undated).

Carpet Manufacture (No. A 11), New York: Chemstrand Co., Div. of Monsanto Co., November, 1963.

Carpet Sales Sessions, New York: American Carpet Institute, Inc. 1960.

Carpet Technology (N7), New York: Chemstrand Co., Div. of Monsanto Co., 1965.

"Carpet vs. Resilient Tile," *Buildings,* October, 1965, pp. 78-81.

"Carpeting," *Contract,* July-August, 1961, pp. 23-27.

"Carpets Take Care," *Buildings,* May, 1963, pp. 66-67.

"Ceramic Tile—Brand New Beauty with Age-Old Toughness," *Buildings,* February, 1967, pp. 42-43.

"Ceramic Tile—Cost Saving Prescription for Hospitals," *Modern Sanitation and Building Maintenance,* August, 1965, pp. 16-18.

"Ceramic Tile Stain Removal," *Buildings,* February 1966, pp. 116-17.

"Checklist for Carpet Selection," *Tourist Court Journal,* February, 1962, pp. 45-46.

"Choose Resilient Flooring," *Buildings,* April, 1966, pp. 96-97.

The Cleaning and Maintenance of Marble, Washington: Marble Institute of America, Inc., 1958.

"Cleaning Estimates," *Contract Cleaning,* January, 1965, pp. 9-11, 28.

"Cleaning Tricks for '66," *Buildings,* February, 1966, pp. 88-90, 128.

CLOYES, P. W. "Trowelled Composition Flooring," *Building Maintenance and Modernization,* July, 1964, pp. 23, 58-61.

———. "What Is the Right Floor for You?" *Modern Sanitation and Building Maintenance,* May, 1964, pp. 32, 55-57.

"Cold Welding—New Seaming Technique," *Flooring,* April, 1966, pp. 44-45.

Commercial Carpet Maintenance, New York: Firth Industries, Inc., subsidiary of Firth Carpet Company (undated).

CONRAD, M. J. AND GIBBINS, NEIL L. *Carpeting and Learning,* Columbus, Ohio: Ohio State University, 1963.

Custodial Management and Methods, Huntington, Indiana: Huntington Laboratories, Inc., 1966.

Cutting Costs With Carpet, New York: American Carpet Institute, 1963.

Cutting Maintenance and Costs with Ceramic Tile, New York: Tile Council of America, Inc., 1964.

Densylon—a Breakthrough, New York: Commercial Carpet Corp. (undated).

DUFFIN, D. J. *Carpet Laying and Estimating Handbook,* Princeton, New Jersey: D. Van Nostrand Co., Inc., 1962.

Easy Does It, New York: A. & M. Karagheusian, Inc., 1958.

"Epoxy Resilient Tile," *Flooring,* September, 1962.

Facts About Chemical Textile Fibers, New York: Chemstrand Co., Div. of Monsanto Co., 1962.

FELDMAN, EDWIN B. "Housekeeping During Construction or Renovation," *Building Maintenance and Modernization,* October, 1966, pp. 48-52.

Finishing Hardwood Floors. Washington: National Paint, Varnish and Lacquer Association, Inc., March, 1960. (Prepared jointly with Maple Flooring Manufacturers Association and National Oak Flooring Manufacturers' Association.)

"Floor Maintenance," *Buildings,* November, 1966, pp. 50-54.

"Floor Repair," *Building Maintenance and Modernization,* February, 1963, pp. 16-17, 50-51.

"Floors," *Buildings,* November, 1965, pp. 82-84, 86, 122, 124.

"Floors and Floor Coverings," *Buildings,* November, 1963, pp. 60-66.

"Floors from Cans," *Flooring,* August, 1964.

Floors from Cans, Technical Service Bulletin 6551, Buffalo, New York: Spencer Kellogg Division of Textron, Inc., 1965.

"Floors from Cans—A Great Outpouring," *Flooring,* July, 1965, pp. 31+.

Floors: Technical Data 1966-1967, Lancaster, Pennsylvania: Floor Division, Armstrong Cork Co., 1966.

A Fresh Look at Flooring Costs, Lancaster, Pennsylvania: Armstrong Cork Co., 1965.

FURRY, MARGARET S. *How to Prevent and Remove Mildew,* Home and Garden Bulletin No. 68, Washington: U. S. Department of Agriculture, 1960.

GABRIEL, G. P. "Industrial Floors With A Long Life," *Materials Protection,* May, 1965, pp. 49-51.

GARDNER, JOHN C. (Ed.). *Programmed Cleaning and Sanitation,* New York: The Soap and Detergent Association, 1966.

A Guide to the Armstrong Commercial Floor System, Lancaster, Pennsylvania: Armstrong Cork Co., 1961.

1967 Handbook for Ceramic Tile Installation, New York: Tile Council of America, Inc., 1967.

The Hardwood Flooring Handbook, Memphis: National Oak Flooring Manufacturers' Association (undated).

HARPER, W. R. "Introduction to Floor Pads," *Proceedings of 49th Annual Meeting, December 3-5, 1962,* New York: Chemical Specialties Manufacturers Association, Inc., pp. 164-65.

HARRIS, M. "The Role of Floor Pads in Modern Floor Maintenance," *Proceedings of 49th Annual Meeting, December 3-5, 1962,* New York: Chemical Specialties Manufacturers Association, Inc., pp. 166-67.

"Heat on Tile Makers," *Chemical Week,* July 20, 1963, pp. 97-100.

HEPPES, JULIEN O. "The Resilient Tile Story," *Modern Sanitation and Building Maintenance,* July, 1965, pp. 12-14.

How to Have Beautiful Hardwood Floors with the Easiest of Care, Memphis: E. L. Bruce Co., Inc. (undated).

"How to Plan Custodial Supply Closets for More Efficient Use," *Buildings,* October, 1963.

"How to Set Marble Floor," *Flooring,* May, 1964, p. 64.

"Interim Federal Specification 00-P-0046: Pads, Floors (Floor Polishing, Buffing, and Scrubbing, and Pads, Driving, and Pad Holders)," Washington: U.S. General Services Administration, Federal Supply Service, 1963.

"Introducing Hercules Co. and Herculon Polypropylene Olefin Fiber to the Textile Industry," *Fiber Facts,* November, 1962, pp. 1-4.

"It's a Floor," *Buildings,* January, 1966, pp. 46-47.

It's Easy to Care for Your Carpets & Rugs, New York: American Carpet Institute, Inc., 1961.

Johns-Manville Flooring Specifications Handbook, New York: Johns-Manville Flooring, 1965.

JONES, PAUL. "The American Carpet Industry—Its Past, Present and Future," *NIRC Voice* (National Institute of Rug Cleaners, Inc.), October, 1963, pp. 32-35.

Keep It Clean! New York: A. & M. Karagheusian, Inc., 1957.

LAVENBERG, GEORGE. "Recommend Installation That Is Best for the Job," *Flooring,* April, 1966, pp. 68-72.

Let's Talk About the Care of Wood Floors, Racine, Wisconsin: S. C. Johnson & Son, Inc. (undated).

Maintenance Manual, Wilmington, Delaware: E. I. du Pont de Nemours & Co., Inc. (undated).

"Maintenance Reference Sheet," *Maintenance,* November, 1964.

Marble Institute of America. *Standard Specifications for Interior Marble,* Washington: The Institute, 1963.

"Marble Maintenance Made Easy," *Buildings,* January, 1966, pp. 50-51.

MASLAND, C. H. *The Fiber Story,* Philadelphia: C. H. Masland & Sons (undated).

"May We Pour You a Floor?" *Buildings,* September, 1966, pp. 88-90.

McLENDON, VERDA I. *Removing Stains from Fabrics,* Home and Garden Bulletin No. 62, Washington: U. S. Department of Agriculture, 1961.

McMILLAN, ALFRED E. "Remodeling with Ceramic Tile," *Modern Maintenance Management,* August, 1966.

"Modern Floorings from Test Tubes," *Building Maintenance and Modernization,* July, 1966, pp. 70-72.

National Terrazzo and Mosaic Association. *Specifications, Details, Technical Data,* Arlington, Virginia: The Association, 1966.

"New Ideas on Grand Old Marble," *Buildings,* December, 1966, pp. 44-46.

"New Methods of Carpet Cleaning," *Better Building Maintenance,* December, 1960, pp. 16-20.

"Nylon Du Pont Style," *NIRC Voice* (National Institute of Rug Cleaners, Inc.), March, 1964, pp. 24-28.

PARKS, GEORGE M. *The Economics of Carpeting and Resilient Flooring,* Philadelphia: Wharton School of Finance and Commerce, University of Pennsylvania, 1966.

Physical Properties of Hercules Polypropylene Fiber, Bulletin FD-6, Wilmington, Delaware: Hercules Co., 1962.

Polyester Resin Selecter, Wayne, New Jersey: American Cyanamid Co., August, 1961.

"Polypropylene Fibers Set for Growth," *Chemical & Engineering News,* November, 1962, pp. 30-32.

"Problem Areas Undergo Probe," *Flooring,* April, 1964, and May, 1964.

"Resilient Flooring Eclipses Carpet in University of Pennsylvania Study," *Flooring,* July, 1966, pp. 40-44.

"Resilient Flooring Refresher," *Building Maintenance and Modernization,* November, 1966, pp. 20-28.

ROTHBERG, HENRY M. "Straight Talk on Latex Terrazzo," *Flooring,* January, 1964, pp. 78, 80.

————. "Thin Terrazzo Market Is Called Promising," *Flooring,* August, 1964, pp. 34-35.

"Rubber Floors and Rubber Heels Help to Prevent Falls," *Consumer Bulletin,* April, 1967, pp. 29-30.

Rubber Manufacturers Association. *Manual for the Preparation of Subfloors for the Installation of Solid Vinyl and Rubber Flooring,* New York: The Association, 1965.

Rusk, Thomas L. "How to Remove Stains from Acrilan and Cumuloft," *National Rug Cleaner,* January, 1962, pp. 6-9.

"Sanitary Surface for Bakeries with Strong, Scrubbable Epoxies," *Modern Sanitation and Building Maintenance,* September, 1959, pp. 28, 29, 86.

Sassano, J. M. *Modern Tools in Floor Maintenance,* Bronx, New York: General Floorcraft, Inc. (undated).

"Seamless Flooring," *Flooring,* June, 1966, pp. 41-71.

"Seamless Flooring Systems Extend Range of Market," *Flooring,* March, 1966, pp. 10, 13, 54.

"Seamless Poured Floors," *Contract,* July, 1966, pp. 70-72.

"Selecting A Floor," *Materials and Methods,* December, 1963, p. 146.

Sheppard, E. "Focus on Resilient Floor Finishes," *Buildings,* February, 1964.

Smalley, Dave E. (Ed.). *Floor Maintenance Manual,* Milwaukee: Trade Press Publishing Co., 1964.

Smongeski, Mary, "The Wide Wide World of Ceramic Tile," *Buildings,* 1965, pp. 42-44.

Specification Manual, Memphis: National Oak Flooring Manufacturers' Association, 1961.

Standard Specifications, Official Grading Rules. Northern Hard Maple, Beech, Birch Flooring, Oshkosh, Wisconsin: Maple Flooring Manufacturers' Association, 1964.

"Still More Monolithic Flooring," *Flooring,* September, 1965, p. 20.

"Substrate Keys Resin Terrazzo Performance," *Flooring,* July, 1965, p. 52.

"Sweeping and Dust Control," *Buildings,* November, 1966, p. 55.

"Synthetics Roll Up Rug Sales," *Chemical Week,* June, 1963, pp. 61-63.

"Take Care of That Floor Equipment," *Buildings,* February, 1966, p. 106.

"Terrazzo Market Broadens as Sidewalks Point Way," *Flooring,* September, 1965, pp. 83-86.

Textured Caprolan Nylon, Bulletin C-4, New York: Allied Chemical Corp., 1963.

"Tile vs. Carpet," *Western Floors,* May, 1964, pp. 38-39.

Tips on Cleaning Floor Coverings, Bethesda, Maryland: National Institute of Rug Cleaning, Inc., 1959.

"Tomorrow's Floors Today," *Building Research,* May-June, 1966, pp. 9-34.

"Trends in the Fast-Moving World of Synthetic Fibers," *Chemical & Engineering News,* August, 1962, pp. 86-96.

U. S. Forest Products Laboratory. *Wood Floors for Dwellings* (Agriculture Handbook No. 204), Washington: U. S. Govt. Print. Off., 1961.

VAN BUREN, MARTIN. "Is Carpet Practical?" *Library Journal,* December 1, 1965, pp. 5152-56.

"Vitreous Tile," *Buildings,* October, 1966.

WELCH, W. S. "When Not To Use Mastic Resurfacers," *Maintenance,* September, 1965, pp. 28-30.

WERTENBERGER, MORRIS D., JR., "Detergent Digest," *Building Maintenance and Modernization,* October, 1966, pp. 38-44.

"What's New In Floor Machines," *Building Maintenance and Modernization,* May, 1963, pp. 24+.

"Why Not Wood," *Buildings,* June, 1965, pp. 94-95.

Why Specify Carpets Made with Acrilan? New York: Chemstrand Co., Div. of Monsanto Co., 1962 (revised 1963).

Why Wood is Best for Floors, Washington: National Lumber Manufacturers' Association (undated).

"The Wide Quality Spread in Wet Mops," *Building Maintenance and Modernization,* June, 1967, pp. 42-46, 52-53.

WILLIAMS, DONALD R. "Chemical Clues to Cleanliness," *Modern Sanitation and Building Maintenance,* June, 1966, pp. 27-29.

INDEX

Correction: The credit for the picture on page 4 should read *E. L. Bruce Co.*

The text paper used in this book is "Permalife," a stable
and enduring paper produced by the Standard Paper Manufacturing
Company, Richmond, Virginia.